D1808332

MARITIME INFORMATION

A guide to libraries and
sources of information
in the United Kingdom

Fourth edition 2004

Roy Fenton Nuala Briody Mike Macdonald

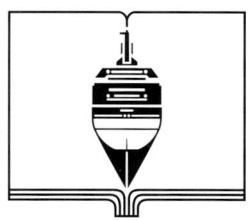

MARITIME INFORMATION

A guide to libraries and sources of information in the United Kingdom

Fourth edition 2004

Roy Fenton, Nuala Briody, Mike Macdonald

© Maritime Information Association, Roy Fenton, Nuala Briody, Mike Macdonald 2004

ISBN 1 901703 62 2

1st edition 1973
2nd edition 1983
3rd edition 1993

Cover: the flags spell out 'AZ'.

Designed by Hugh Smallwood and Roy Fenton

All rights reserved. No part of this publication may be reproduced, stored in a retrieval system or transmitted in any form or by any means, electronic, mechanical, photocopying, recording or otherwise, without the written permission of the publisher.

The right of Roy Fenton, Nuala Briody and Mike Macdonald to be identified as authors of this work has been asserted by them in accordance with the Copyright, Design and Patent Act 1998.

Address for correspondence: MIA Directory, 18 Durrington Avenue, London SW20 8NT
Distributed by: J. & M. Clarkson, 18 Franklands, Longton, Preston PR4 5PD

Typeset by Highlight Type Bureau, Bradford and printed by Amadeus Press Ltd., Cleckheaton.

FOREWORD

It gives me great pleasure to introduce the fourth edition of *Maritime Information, a guide to libraries and sources of information in the UK.*

Editor Roy Fenton and his team are to be congratulated on their efforts to incorporate the many changes that have taken place since the last edition was published ten years ago and to include new material that has come to light in the interim, all of which makes it even more comprehensive than before.

Whether it be for professional or personal reasons, those who require to look into specific areas of nautical history will find this handy well-indexed guide an invaluable tool. Moreover, despite the ever-increasing spread of computer-generated knowledge, a volume such as this that can be quickly plucked from a shelf is still hard to beat for speed and convenience.

No serious maritime researcher should be without it.

Ambrose Greenway
Deputy Chairman (House of Lords)
All Party Parliamentary Maritime Group.

INTRODUCTION

The object of this Guide is to list UK libraries, record offices, archives, museums, institutions, associations and other bodies that have, or can make available, information on maritime matters. The coverage is broad: for the purposes of the Guide maritime matters are considered as extending from the study of inland and oceanic waters, through the craft that navigate them, to the people who work on or serve those craft. Some organisations are listed which, although they do not hold information, may be of interest to shipping professionals, librarians and researchers. The entries use the descriptions supplied by the organisations themselves, lightly edited to achieve a degree of consistency.

Organisation of the Guide

Organisations are given their formal titles but are listed in alphabetical order of the name which users are most likely to look up. For instance, under the letter B are the London Borough of <u>B</u>arnet, the University of <u>B</u>ristol and the Centre for <u>B</u>uckinghamshire Studies. Cross references have been restricted to cases where a title may not be well known, for instance: 'Hull, University of,: see Brynmor Jones Library'. For organisations which had an entry in the previous edition of the Guide, but which are known to have changed their title, merged or moved their records elsewhere, a cross reference is given to a new organisation or location. If in any doubt, users should refer to the comprehensive index.

Updating the directory

The procedure adopted with organisations listed in the previous (1993) edition of the directory was to send to each a copy of their existing entry and a questionnaire with a request that amendments be notified or, if there were substantial changes, the questionnaire be completed. If no reply was received, the request was followed up by post, phone and e-mail. Efforts were made to contact the numerous organisations which had changed their address, title or phone number through directory enquiries, Internet searches or by personal enquiry. Thus, organisations were given several opportunities to amend or update their entry. Those for which no updated entry could be obtained, for whatever reason, are not included in this edition.

New candidates for inclusion were found in a variety of ways. Through articles in the MIA newsletter, members of the Association were encouraged to submit names. Guides to libraries were consulted, particularly useful being *Record Repositories in Great Britain* (11th edition) published by the National Archives. Respondents to questionnaires also provided information about new, or reconstituted, organisations with relevant records. Inevitably, this process of finding new sources is imperfect, and anyone knowing of an organisation deserving inclusion is asked to contact the MIA at the address given on the publishing data page.

The degree to which the entries had changed since the last edition was surprising. Well over half of the respondents found it simpler to fill in a new questionnaire than to amend their existing entry. This is encouraging, as it not only makes the work of producing a new edition of the Guide worthwhile, but also indicates that the world of maritime records is an evolving one, and belies the view that the UK is turning its back on its maritime past. The slight decrease in the total number of entries since the last edition reflects a reduction in the bodies serving the needs of a declining British shipping industry. This reduction has been largely compensated for by new entries for organisations concerned with recording the history of this industry.

Entries are generally corrected to mid-summer 2003. Whilst efforts have been made to ensure accuracy, users should note that neither the Maritime Information Association nor the editors can take responsibility for any problems arising from possible errors in this Guide.

Those involved

The process of updating this Guide has been a prolonged but very absorbing one, considerably eased and made enjoyable by the willing efforts of fellow compilers and by the support and assistance of the MIA committee members.

Nuala Briody took on the immense task of mailing all organisations listed in the 1993 edition, of reminding those who did not reply, and of keeping records of the entries as they came in. And just when she thought it was all over, Nuala was presented with typed-up entries to be submitted to respondents for verification.

Mike Macdonald became involved through his interest in shipbuilding, and kindly offered to contact record holders who were listed in Ritchies' *The Shipbuilding Industry: A Guide to Historical Records*. Once involved, Mike then undertook a formidable amount of compiling of new and revised entries.

As project manager, Roy Fenton had the most pleasant tasks of all, managing to get other people to do much of the work, and of writing about it all in the MIA Newsletter. If at times his predictions of a completion date were a trifle optimistic, his justification is that the timescale of maritime record keeping is one that goes back centuries, so what's a few months among archivists and librarians?

Others to be thanked are Elizabeth Wiggans for once again compiling the index, Debbie Beavis for Appendix 4, Gill Birchall whose background as a historian was immensely useful to the editorial team in her work of preparing the new entries, and Barbara Jones, Desma Goddard, Stephen Grace, Michael Naxton and Jenny Wraight who chased up recalcitrant libraries, suggested a number of new entrants, and – greatly appreciated by the editors – assisted with proof checking.

It is also appropriate to mention our predecessors as compilers, Rita and Terence Bryon. Their legacy to us was a Guide that was so complete that it has been almost impossible to find relevant organisations which existed at the time of the previous edition which were not listed. With modest additions, essentially websites and e-mail addresses, their format for entries has also served us very well.

This guide could not have been produced without the willing help of librarians, archivists and others who responded to our requests for updated or new entries. Almost without exception, their response to our pleas was willing and helpful, although perhaps none more than that from the lady from a major public archive who diverted whilst cycling home to deliver a vital document to one of the editors.

The way ahead

This Guide is restricted to the United Kingdom, although archivists in the Channel Isles and the Isle of Man have politely chided us to remember that they are *not* part of the United Kingdom! A logical extension would be to produce a guide to European sources of maritime information, an undertaking that would introduce some interesting linguistic challenges, but would undoubtedly benefit maritime researchers in a field which is almost by definition international.

Finally, perhaps a prediction might be in order. The next edition of this Guide will almost certainly be web based, possibly without a printed copy. At a stroke this would remove the substantial costs of printing and the labour of distribution, but would introduce problems of its own, notably how to recover the expenses incurred in updating entries. A web-based Guide would mean that entries could be kept up to date, but this would require frequent maintenance of the database, and a system by which organisations' entries were sent for review on a rolling basis, of say 20% each year.

Until such an electronic resource can be built up and - most importantly - maintained, we offer researchers and fellow librarians and archivists this 2004 directory, which we believe is the best guide available to sources of maritime information in the United Kingdom.

Roy Fenton   Nuala Briody   Mike Macdonald

December 2003

CONTENTS

Aberdeen Art Gallery
Records transferred to Aberdeen Maritime Museum

A1
ABERDEEN CITY ARCHIVES
Old Aberdeen House office
(previously Grampian Regional Archives)

Old Aberdeen House	Tel: 01224 481775
Dunbar Street	Fax: 01224 495830
Aberdeen AB24 3UJ	

e-mail: archives@legal.aberdeen.net.uk
Website: www. aberdeencity.gov.uk/acc/archivists.htm

Local government organisation

Facilities
Enquiries to Duty Archivist
Open to the public: Monday to Wednesday 0930-1300
1400-1630, appointment advisable
Information provided by phone, post, e-mail and fax
Photocopying facilities
Research service available: thirty minutes free,
thereafter £30 per hour

Subject coverage
Local government records of Aberdeenshire Council

Special collections
Harbour records for ports in Aberdeenshire, notably
Peterhead and Stonehaven in 19th and 20th centuries

A2
ABERDEEN CITY ARCHIVES
Town House office

Town House	Tel: 01224 522513
Aberdeen AB10 1AQ	Fax: 01224 638556

e-mail: archives@legal.Aberdeen.net.uk
Website: www. aberdeencity.gov.uk

Local government organisation

Facilities
Enquiries to Duty Archivist
Open to the public: Wednesday to Friday 0930-1630
Information provided by phone, post, e-mail and fax
Microfilm reader
Photocopying at the City Archivist's discretion

Subject coverage
City and port records

Special collections
Business records of A Hall and Co./Hall, Russell Ltd.
Aberdeen shipbuilders, 19th and 20th centuries
Aberdeen shipping registers 1824-1927
Aberdeen outport Customs and Excise records, 19th
and 20th centuries
Aberdeen harbour records, 1808-1935

Publications
Free general information sheet 'Aberdeen City
Archives'

A3
ABERDEEN CITY COUNCIL
CENTRAL LIBRARY - BUSINESS
AND TECHNOLOGY DEPARTMENT

Rosemount Viaduct	Tel: 01224 652500
Aberdeen	Fax: 01224 636811
Scotland	

e-mail: bustech@arts-rec.aberdeen.net.uk
Website: www.aberdeencity.gov.uk

Local government organisation

Facilities
Enquiries to the Librarian
Information provided by phone, fax and e-mail
Open to the public: Monday 0900-2000 and
Friday-Saturday 0900-1700
Photocopying facilities
Research service available - first 30 minutes free,
thereafter £15 per 20 minutes

Subject coverage
Computing; economics; law (business); intellectual
property; management; directories; statistics; market
research; engineering; fishing industry; oil and gas;
company and product; aviation; automotive and
construction; technical standards and maritime

Special collections
Oil and gas - Aberdeen
Aberdeen company information
European and community information
Business
Fishing News Vol. 1, 1913 onwards
Lloyd's Registers of Shipping
British Standards

Specific databases:
ESPACE - patents
MARQUESA - trade marks
Key British Enterprises 200
Key Scottish Enterprises
Applied New Technology and Engineering
Institute of Management International Database
Offshore Europe

Publications
See website

A4
ABERDEEN MARITIME MUSEUM
City of Aberdeen, Arts and Recreation Department

Shiprow	Tel: 01224 337700
Aberdeen AB11 5BY	Fax: 01224 213066

Website: www.aberdeencity.gov.uk

Museum (North Sea Museums Network, UK Maritime Collections Initiative)

Facilities
Enquiries to the Keeper or Assistant Keeper
Information provided by phone, post, fax and e-mail
Open to the public
Appointment necessary for library
Photocopying facilities

Subject coverage
North Sea oil and gas industries; Aberdeen harbour; fishing; shipbuilding

Special collections
Shipyard plans and records
North Sea oil and gas collections

Specific companies and groups
Shipyard drawings: Hall Russell and Co. (12,500 plans)
John Lewis & Son (2,000 plans)

Specific databases
Shipbuilders' database covering all Aberdeen yards

Publications
See: www.aagm.co.uk
Maritime leaflet (free)

A5
ABERDEEN UNIVERSITY LIBRARY - HISTORIC COLLECTIONS

King's College   Tel: 01224 272598
Aberdeen AB24 3SW   Fax: 01224 273891
e-mail: speclib@abdn.ac.uk
Website: www.abdn.ac.uk/diss/historic/

University department

Facilities
Enquiries to the Reading Room Manager
Information provided by phone, post, fax and e-mail
Open to the public; loans to members only
Photocopying facilities
Microfilm and microfiche readers; microcopies and fullsize copies can be provided
CD-ROM available; on-line information retrieval; library's catalogue is on DYNIX and accessible through JANET
Research service not provided

Subject coverage
Shipbuilding; passenger services; maritime labour; trawling; maritime associations

Special collections
David Cardno diary, Arctic ocean whaler 1866-1917

Walker Henderson diary, ship's surgeon, Greenland 1853
George Kerr diary, surgeon northern whale fishery 1791
Davis Straits diary, unidentified surgeon 1831
Aberdeen Steam Navigation Co. 1836-1925
Crew lists and indentures of Aberdeen trawlers 1891-1971
Records of Aberdeen trawlers 1891-1913
Aberdeen Shipmasters' Society 1630-1965
National Union of Dock Labourers 1912-27
National Union of Seamen 1926-59 *
Ship Constructors and Shipwrights Association 1916-65
Steamfishing Vessels, Engineers' and Firemen's Union 1906-57
Aberdeen Fish Curers' & Merchants' Association 1888-1947
United Society of Boilermakers, Shipbuilders and Structural Workers 1936, 1955-8 *
* Aberdeen Branches

Publications
See website

A6
ABERDEEN UNIVERSITY LIBRARY - QUEEN MOTHER LIBRARY

Meston Walk   Tel: 01224 273330
Aberdeen AB24 3UE   Fax: 01224 487048
e-mail: library@abdn.ac.uk
Website: www.abdn.ac.uk/diss/library

University department

Facilities
Enquiries to Director's Secretary
Information provided by phone, post, fax and e-mail
Open to the public; borrowing by registered members only
Opening hours: Monday-Saturday 0900-2200; Sunday 1300-2200 in termtime and Easter vacation; for opening during Christmas and summer vacations, check with library
Photocopying facilities; microcopies and fullsize copies provided
Microfilm, microfiche and microcard/microprint readers available; CD-ROM; on-line information retrieval service
Research service not provided, but will accept queries on a chargeable basis; individual charging depends on time taken

Subject coverage
Naval history of Britain and USA; fishing industry and aquaculture; North Sea oil industry, engineering and safety aspects; shipping history; naval architecture

Special collections
G W Wilson collection of early photographs 1856-

1910, covering England, Scotland, Australia, South Africa, Gibraltar, Spain and Morocco

Publications
Website: www.abdn.ac.uk/diss/library gives access to library catalogue
www.abdn.ac.uk/diss/historic/ gives access to G W Wilson Collection

---

A7
ABP MARINE ENVIRONMENTAL RESEARCH LTD

Pathfinder House   Tel: 023 8033 8100
Maritime Way   Fax: 023 8033 8040
Southampton
Hampshire SO14 3AE
e-mail: enquiries@abpmer.co.uk
Website: abpmer.co.uk

Commercial company

Facilities
Enquiries to the Librarian
Information provided by phone, post, fax and e-mail; loans on request
Open to public by prior arrangement
Photocopying facilities
Research service not provided

Subject coverage
Port development; dredging studies and licencing; navigation and mooring studies; marina projects; lock design and operation; hydraulic structures; sea defences and bank protection; wave studies; flood studies and water resource management; environmental impact assessment; estuary morphology studies; habitat creation; waterways; numerical modelling and computer applications; hydrographic surveys and field investigations; general research; library and navigational advisory services; GIS applications

---

Admiral Blake Museum
Now Blake Museum

Admiralty Library
See Ministry of Defence

A8
ADVISORY COMMITTEE ON PROTECTION OF THE SEA (ACOPS)

11 Dartmouth Street   Tel: 020 7799 3033
London SW1H 9BN   Fax: 020 7799 2933
e-mail: info@acops.org
Website: www.acops.org

Registered charity

Facilities
Enquiries to the Programme Co-ordinator and Executive Director
Information provided by phone, post, fax and e-mail
Open to the public
Photocopying facilities
Research service available

Subject coverage
Protection of the marine environment from pollution; both legislation and scientific research

Publications
ACOPS Yearbook from 1990 (usually biennial)
Newsletters - 6-monthly

Albert Sloman Library
See University of Essex

A9
THE ALDERNEY SOCIETY MUSEUM

High Street   Tel: 01481 823222
Alderney   Fax: 01481 824979
Channel Islands GY9 3TG
e-mail: alderney.museum@alderney.net
Website: www.alderneysociety.org

Museum/voluntary organisation

Facilities
Enquiries to the Administrator
Information provided by phone (between 1000 and 1200), post, fax and e-mail
Open to the public: reference only from Easter to end of October and by appointment from October to Easter
Photocopying facilities
Limited research service available, according to availability of qualified volunteers

Subject coverage
Photographs, documents, maps and charts of Alderney

Special collections
Iron Age pottery-making site (cinerary urns) and pots
19th century harbour and fortifications plans and pictures
Loan exhibition of late 16th century wreck objects

Specific databases
Alderney Museum object records database
Alderney objects in Guernsey database (restricted by States of Guernsey copyright) e.g. works of art

Publications
Planned to be available through Guernsey Museum website

A10
AMATEUR YACHT RESEARCH SOCIETY

BCM AYRS   Tel: 01727 862268
London WC1N 3XX
e-mail: ayrs@fishwick.demon.co.uk
Website: www.ayrs.org

Voluntary organisation

Facilities
Enquiries to the Honorary Secretary
Information provided by e-mail
Open to the public

Subject coverage
Papers on yacht science and technology

Publications
List on website

A11
AMLWCH INDUSTRIAL HERITAGE TRUST (AIHT)

Friends of the Amlwch Industrial Heritage Trust
The Old Sail Loft
Amlwch Port
Anglesey LL68 9DB
e-mail: neil@parysmountain.co.uk
website: www.parysmountain.co.uk

Voluntary organisation. The Sail Loft is a small museum containing shipping artefacts, models and items recovered from shipwrecks.

Facilities
Enquiries to the Chairman or Archivist
Information provided by e-mail and post
Open to the public 1000-1700 Easter to October

Computer database
Limited research service on local history

Subject coverage
The history of the copper mines of Amlwch, at one time the largest in the world; the port of Amlwch; local shipyards and ship owners.

Special collections
Local ship-builders Treweek, Cox, Payrter, and William Thomas; ship owners; mine owners and workers; breweries; tobacco companies

Publications
'A Curious Place - The Industrial History of Amlwch (1850-1950)', Brian Hope

---

A12
ANGLESEY COUNTY RECORD OFFICE

Shirehall   Tel: 01248 752080
Glanhwfa Road   Fax: 01248 751289
Llangefni
Ynys Môn
LL77 7TW
e-mail: archives@anglesey.gov.uk
Website: www.anglesey.gov.uk (via Libraries or Education)

Local government organisation

Facilities
Enquiries to the Archivist
Information provided by: phone, post, fax and e-mail
Open to the public (CARN readers ticket available on day of visit on production of suitable proof of identity):
Monday-Friday 0900-1300 and 1400-1700
Closed first full week of November, Bank Holidays and St. David's Day
Photocopying facilities
Research service available - £10 for first half hour, £15 per hour thereafter

Subject coverage
Records of the maritime history of Anglesey and its inhabitants

Special collections
Crew lists, port of Beaumaris, Register General of Shipping and Seamen
Board of Trade Marine maps and plans
Records of ports and harbours (no good series)
Records of seafaring careers of individual seafarers
Records of ships
Anglesey RNLI
N.B. There is a shipping section in the index - all documents are catalogued and many indexed

Specific companies and groups
William Thomas and Sons, Amlwch Port
W.H. Owen (1825-1896), Plas Penrhyn, owners of many Liverpool-based ships

Publications
'Anglesey Bibliography' (1977) has a guide to the Record Office as an appendix

---

A13
ARBROATH MUSEUM

The Signal Tower   Tel: 01241 875598
Ladyloan
Arbroath DD11 1PU
e-mail: signal.tower@angus.gov.uk
Website: www.angus.gov.uk/history

Museum, local government organisation

Facilities
Enquiries to the Curator
Information provided by phone, post, fax and e-mail
Open to the public
Photocopying facilities

Subject coverage
Fishing in Angus; Arbroath Harbour; Arbroath shipping; Arbroath/Angus trade; fish-processing

Special collections
Arbroath shipping
Photographic collections
Fisher costume and social history
Bell Rock Lighthouse archives, including visitor albums

A14
ARGYLL AND BUTE COUNCIL ARCHIVES

Kilmory	Tel: 01546 604120
Lochgilphead	Fax: 01546 606897
Argyll PA31 8RT	

e-mail: murdo.macdonald@argyll-bute.gov.uk

Local government organisation

Facilities
Enquiries to the Archivist
Information provided by: phone, post, fax and e-mail
Open to the public by appointment: Tuesday-Friday
1000-1300 and 1400-1630
Photocopying facilities

Subject coverage
Local authority records relating to piers and harbours, ferry services and shipping services, c.1700 to present, including harbours of Campbeltown, Dunoon, Helensburgh, Inveraray, Oban and Rothesay, and islands such as Coll, Gigha, Islay, Jura, Luing, Mull and Tiree

Special collections
David Boyd, naval architect - plans, 1953-1972

Specific companies and groups
Campbeltown and Glasgow Steam Packet Co. Ltd.
Alex. Robertson and Sons Ltd., (yacht builders) Sandbank
Campbeltown Shipbuilding Company

A15
ASSOCIATED BRITISH PORTS

150 Holborn	Tel: 0207 4301177
London EC1N 2LR	Fax: 0207 4301384

e-mail: pr@abports.co.uk
Website: www. abports.co.uk

Commercial port-operating company

Enquiries to Corporate Communications Department

Subject coverage
ABP port operations

Publications
Ports Handbook

A16
ASSOCIATED BRITISH PORTS, IPSWICH

Old Custom House	Tel: 01473 231010
Key Street	Fax: 01473 230914
Ipswich IP4 1BY	

e-mail: Ipswich@abports.co.uk
Website: www.abports.co.uk

Port operator

Facilities
Enquiries to the Port Manager
Information provided by post, phone, visit and e-mail

Subject coverage
Port history

Publications
Port brochure
ABP Handbook

A17
ASSOCIATION OF BRITISH SAILMAKERS (ABS)

2 Orchard Road	Tel: 01489 601517
Lock's Heath	Fax: 01489 601518
Southampton SO31 6PR	

e-mail: secretariat@uk-sailmakers.org

An organisation to provide technical information and support for sailmakers, to improve standards in all aspects of the trade.

Facilities
Enquiries to the Joint Secretary
Information given by phone, post, fax and email to members only
Technical arbitration service

Subject coverage
Sailcloth and sailmaking

Publications
'Mainsheet' produced 6 to 10 times a year for members and advertising suppliers

Association of Brokers and Yacht Agents
See Yacht Designers and Surveyors Association

A18
ASSOCIATION OF INLAND NAVIGATION AUTHORITIES

42 Falcon Walk   Tel: 01642 590257
Hilton   Fax: 01642 590527
Yarm
Stockton-on-Tees TS15 9JB
e-mail: pburgess.aina@virgin.net
Website: www.aina.gov.uk

Representative body for UK inland navigation authorities

A19
THE ASSOCIATION OF LIGHTHOUSE KEEPERS

The Secretary   Tel: 020 8293 9813
Flat B, 7 Glenluce Road
Westcombe Park
London SE3 7SD
e-mail: nosliwkj@aol.com
Website: www.lighthouse.fsnet.co.uk

Registered charity

Facilities
Enquiries to the Secretary
Open to the public, with concessionary facilities for members
Archive access by appointment or written enquiry
Photocopying facilities
Research service available - costs determined on an individual basis

Subject coverage
All aspects of pharology - lighthouses, light vessels, support vessels, administration - from ancient history to developing aids to navigation

Special collections
Original service documents: service circulars, letter and station books, sound recordings, interviews, videos, cine film, uniforms and items of station equipment
Authors' research material
Donated private collections (mainly photographs and documents)

Specific companies and groups
Some records from Trinity House, London

Specific databases
Archive register database currently being compiled

Publications
Information leaflets
'Lamp' quarterly journal.

Association of Old Worcesters

Association has been wound up

A20
ASSOCIATION OF SEA TRAINING ORGANISATIONS (ASTO)

c/o Royal Yachting Association   Tel: 023 8060 4100
RYA House   Fax: 023 8060 4299
Ensign Way
Hamble
Southampton SO31 4YA
Website: www.asto.org.uk

Voluntary organisation

Facilities
Enquiries to the Secretary
Information provided by phone, post and fax

Subject coverage
Sail training opportunities, primarily for young people

Publications
Brochure 'Sail to Adventure' lists sail training opportunities and is published every two years

---

A21
ASTRONOMICAL SOCIETY OF EDINBURGH

City Observatory   Tel: 0131 5564365
Calton Hill   (answer phone only)
Edinburgh EH7 5AA
e-mail secretary@astronomyedinburgh.org
Website: www.astronomyedinburgh.org

Amateur astronomical society

Facilities
Enquiries to the Secretary
Open to members only
Loans to members only

Publications
Monthly bulletin
Journal of the ASE - twice yearly

A22
AYRSHIRE ARCHIVES CENTRE

Craigie Estate   Tel: 01292 287584
Ayr KA8 0SS   Fax: 01292 284918
e-mail: archives@south-ayrshire.gov.uk
Website: www.ayrshirearchives.org.uk

Local government organisation

Facilities
Enquiries to the Archivist
Information provided by phone, post, fax, e-mail and visit
Open to the public preferably by appointment:
Tuesdays, Wednesdays, Thursdays: 1000-1300; 1400-1630
Photocopying facilities

Research service provided. Flat rate fee of £15.50.

Subject coverage
Customs and excise records for Irvine outport and district; Troon outport and district; Ayr outport and district; Ardrossan outport and district.
For all these, the archives hold records such as collector to board; board to collector; general letter books; collector to board of excise; board of excise to collector; excise general letter books; shipping registers; miscellaneous excise records

B1
THE BALLAST TRUST
Monarch Works   Tel: 01505 328488
18-20 Walkinshaw Street   Fax: 01505 328720
Johnstone
Renfrewshire PA5 8AE

Independent charitable trust

Facilities
The Trust is not open to the public but will handle limited enquiries which fall within its remit

Subject coverage
Identification, selection and cataloguing of technical plans and associated business records, prior to their deposit in local, institutional and national archives

Special collections
British Corporation for the Survey and Registry of Shipping: plans
Thomas McLaren and Co. (Glasgow) Ltd., Shipbrokers: plans
Dan McDonald Collection: photographic negatives of ships

B2
THE BALTIC EXCHANGE LTD
St Mary Axe   Tel: 020 7623 5501
London EC3 8BH   Fax: 020 7369 1639
e-mail: enquiries@balticexchange.com
Website: www.balticexchange.com

International shipping exchange

Facilities
Enquiries to the Record Clerk
Information provided by phone, post, fax and e-mail
Open to members only, with limited access for public
Photocopying facilities

Subject coverage
Mainly membership details - all archives up to 1950 at Guildhall Library

B3
BANGOR UNIVERSITY COLLEGE ARCHIFDY Y BRIFYSGOL/ARCHIVES DEPARTMENT
Coleg y Brifysgol/University College
Bangor   Tel: 01248 382966
Cymru/Wales LL7 2DG   Fax: 01248 370576
e-mail: e.w.thomas@bangor.ac.uk
Website: www.bangor.ac.uk

University department

Facilities
Enquiries to the Archifydd/Archivist
Information provided by phone, post, fax and e-mail
Open to the public: Monday-Friday 0900-1300, 1400-1700
Photocopying facilities
Research service available - limited to half hour searches

Subject coverage
Estate records (most of the major estates in North Wales); mine and quarrying papers; literary MSS in Welsh and English; records of the University

Special collections
Penrhyn estate documents, 13th-20th centuries
Charts from 17th-20th centuries

B4
LONDON BOROUGH OF BARNET ARCHIVES & LOCAL STUDIES CENTRE
c/o Hendon Library   Tel: 020 8359 2876
The Burroughs   Fax:020 8359 2883
London NW4 4BQ
e-mail: library.archives@barnet.gov.uk
Website: www.barnet.gov.uk

Local government organisation

Facilities
Enquiries to the Archivist
Information provided by phone, post and e-mail
Open to the public by appointment: Tuesday, Wednesday, Saturday 0930-1230 and 1330-1700 and Thursday 1230-1930
Photocopying facilities

Subject coverage
Local authority minutes and records, 1874 to present; deposited documents of local relevance: maps, photographs, pictures, ephemera, publications

Barrow Museum
See Dock Museum, Barrow

B5
BARTLETT LIBRARY
NATIONAL MARITIME MUSEUM
CORNWALL

Discovery Quay   Tel: 01326 214 579
Falmouth
Cornwall TR11 3QY
e-mail: library@nmmc.co.uk
Website: www.nmmc.co.uk

Museum

Facilities
Enquiries to the Head of Library
Information provided by: phone, post and e-mail
Open to the public: Tuesday-Saturday 1000-1700
Photocopying facilities
Research service available - first half-hour free, then
£10 per hour

Subject coverage
Over 6,000 volumes in the Bartlett library cover all
types of vessels, merchant and naval. The collection
includes runs of 'Lloyds Register of Ships', the
'Mercantile Navy List', 'Jane's Fighting Ships', and the
majority of published shipping company histories

Special collections
Falmouth Harbourmasters' day books
Falmouth Pilots' records

Specific companies and groups
Curnow Shipping

Specific databases
Cornish-built ships, 1786-1914

Publications
Brief guide on website
Book catalogue will be published on website

B6
THE BEACON

West Strand   Tel: 01946 592302
Whitehaven   Fax: 01946 598150
Cumbria CA28 7LY
e-mail: thebeacon@copelandbc.gov.uk
Website: www.copelandbc.gov.uk/tourism

Museum

Facilities
Enquiries to the Collections Officer
Information provided by phone, post, fax, e-mail and
visit.
Open to the public
Appointment necessary for library
Photocopying facilities
Research service available - £10 per hour

Subject coverage
Maritime history of Whitehaven from 1600 to present
day; shipbuilding; harbour development; slavery; imports
and exports

Special collections
'Lloyd's Register of Ships' from 18th century
Local newspapers - 18th century 'Cumberland Paquet'

Specific companies and groups
Brocklebank/Cunard
Shepherd

B7
BEDFORDSHIRE AND LUTON
ARCHIVES AND RECORDS
SERVICE

County Hall   Tel: 01234 228833
Cauldwell Street   Fax: 01234 228854
Bedford MKH2 9AP
e-mail: archive@csd.bedfordshire.gov.uk
Website: www.bedfordshire.gov.uk

Local government organisation

Facilities
Enquiries to the County Archivist
Information provided by phone, post, fax and e-mail
Open to the public: Monday-Friday 0900-1700 except
1st Thursday in month (1000-1700). No documents
produced between 1245 and 1400 or after 1630
Photocopying facilities
Research service available - advice and very short
specific first-time searches given free, otherwise £25
per hour

Subject coverage
Parish archives, records of local authority, maps, picture
collection, personal and estate records, business
archives, quarter sessions archives

Special collections
Admiral Bayntun: log books, muster books and letter
books
Captain Richard Bastard: personal papers regarding
certificates of service, commissions and training, also
his logbooks of the Lord Wellington on microfilm
Quarter sessions papers on recruitment, impressment
and taxation for the Navy
Photographs of steam turbines made by WH Allen of
Bedford
Details of HMS Bedford and HMS Oakley
Correspondence of Samuel Whitbread MP regarding
naval scandals and the Copenhagen expedition, 1797-
1815

Specific companies and groups
WH Allen of Bedford, now part of the Rolls Royce
Group, including some records and photos of naval

projects in the 20th century and a little information on the company's work on the *Titanic*

Publications
For Summary List of Archive Holdings please also see website above
For website of some 10% of our archive lists see: http://blars.adlibsoft.com

---

B8
BEKEN OF COWES LTD

16 Birmingham Road	Tel: 01983 297311
Cowes	Fax: 01983 201059
Isle of Wight P031 7BH	

e-mail: beken@beken.co.uk
Website: www.beken.co.uk

Commercial photographic company

Facilities
Enquiries to the General Manager
Information provided by phone, post, fax and e-mail
Photocopying facilities
Library of photographs open to the public; selections of photographs sent on approval
Opening hours: Mondays-Saturdays 0900-1730
Research service provided

Subject coverage
Maritime photographs, all types of sailing and powered craft, dating back to 1888

Special collections
The Beken Archive Collection

HMS Belfast
See Imperial War Museum

B9
BERKSHIRE RECORD OFFICE

9 Coley Avenue	Tel: 0118 901 5132
Reading	Fax: 0118 901 5131
Berks RG1 6AF	

e-mail: arch@reading.gov.uk
Website: www.berkshirerecordoffice.org.uk

Local authority archive and record office

Facilities
Enquiries to the County Archivist
Information provided by phone, post, fax and e-mail
Open to the public: Tuesdays & Wednesdays 0900-1700; Thursdays 0900-2100; Fridays 0900-1630
Photocopying facilities
Research service provided. Charge £15.00 per hour; 2 hours maximum at any one time

Special collections
Records of Plenty Ltd. of Newbury, marine engineers: corporate, financial and production records 19th-20th centuries. Restricted access

---

B10
BERWICK-UPON-TWEED RECORD OFFICE

Council Offices	Tel: 01289 301865 or
Wallace Green	01289 330044 Ext. 265
Berwick-upon-Tweed	Fax: 01289 330540
TD15 1ED	

e-mail: lb@berwick-upon-tweed.gov.uk

Local government organisation

Facilities
Enquiries to the Borough Archivist
Information provided by post and e-mail
Open to the public: Wednesday-Thursday 0930-1300 and 1400-1700
Photocopying facilities
Research service available - up to 3 hours per enquiry, minimum charge of £16, each half hour thereafter £8

Subject coverage
Naval history; seamanship and trade

Special collections
Port of Berwick shipping registers, 1824-1910
Port of Berwick crew lists, 1873-1913
Minutes of Berwick Shipping Co., 1820-1961 (in the 1850s the name changed to Berwick Salmon Fisheries Co.)
Register of Declarations by Masters arriving at Berwick for insurance purposes, 1864-1869
Berwick Harbour Account Books, 1804-1808, including names of ships and cargo

Specific databases
Ship sailings to and from Berwick, 1808-1837; 1870-1900
Ships registered in the port of Berwick, 1823-1987
Berwick built ships, 1856-1979
Owners of Berwick registered ships, 1824-1910

Publications
Some catalogues will eventually be on the A2A website: www.pro.a2a.gov.uk

---

B11
BIRMINGHAM CITY ARCHIVES

Birmingham Central Library	Tel: 0121 303 4217
Chamberlain Square	Fax: 0121 464 1176
Birmingham B3 3HQ	

e-mail: archives@birmingham.gov.uk
Website: www.birmingham.gov.uk/archives

Local government organisation

Facilities
Enquiries to the Senior Archivist
Information provided by phone, post, fax and e-mail
Open to the public (no appointment necessary):
Tuesday, Wednesday, Friday, Saturday 1000-1700;
Thursday 1000-2000
Photocopying facilities

Subject coverage
Anglican and non-conformist church records;
Birmingham City Council archives; other District
Council archives; court, hospital, probate and school
records; records of businesses and trades; solicitors'
collections

Special collections
Boulton and Watt Collection: engineering drawings,
order books and correspondence re. design of boat
engines, 1802-1900 (B and W); photos of *Great Eastern*,
1858 (B and W)
Belliss and Marcom, Ltd.: minutes, patents, notebooks
and photographs re. design and construction of steam,
gas and diesel turbines, c.1890-1950
Thomas Walker and Sons Ltd., ships' log
manufacturers: order books, 1888-1929; letterbooks,
1877-1901; stock book, 1868-c.1910

Specific companies and groups:
Boulton and Watt (B&W)
Bellis and Morcom (MS 1708)
Thomas Walker and Sons, Ltd. (MS 1233)

Publications
Short guide available on website or free on demand

B12
BLACKPOOL AND THE FYLDE COLLEGE

Nautical Campus	Tel: 01253 352352
Broadwater	Fax: 01253 773014
Fleetwood	
Lancashire FY7 8JZ	

Independent college

Facilities
Enquiries to Learning Resources Advisor
Information provided by phone and post
Library open to the public; loans to those on courses
CD-ROM, videos and Internet services
Photocopying and scanning services

Subject coverage
Navigation, seamanship, marine engineering, merchant
navy, pollution

Special collections
All nautical statutory instruments
Merchant shipping notices
Newspapers and periodicals

B13
BLAKE MUSEUM
(Formerly Admiral Blake Museum)

Blake Street	Tel: 01278 456127
Bridgwater	Fax: 01278 446412
Somerset TA6 3NB	

e-mail: museums@sedgemoor.gov.uk
Website: www.sedgemoor.gov.uk

Museum

Facilities
Enquiries to the Curator
Information provided by phone, post, fax and e-mail
Open to the public
Photocopying facilities

Subject coverage
Photographs, ephemera, models, paintings and
documents associated with local shipping; directories

Special collections
Letters written by Robert Blake (General-at-sea),
1598-1657
Local photographs

Publications
Museum Guide
Website - see above

BMT CORTEC Ltd.
Now British Maritime Technology

Boat Museum Trust
See Waterways Trust

B14
BOLTON ARCHIVE AND LOCAL STUDIES SERVICE

Central Library	Tel: 01204 332185
Civic Centre	Fax: 01204 332225
Le Mans Crescent	
Bolton BL1 1SE	

Local government organisation

Facilities
Enquiries to the Archivist
Information provided by phone, post and fax
Open to the public: Tuesday, Thursday 0930-1930,
Wednesday, Friday 0930-1730 and Saturday 0930-1700
Search room closed on Mondays
Microfilm and microfiche readers; microcopies
provided for a fee

Subject coverage
Marine engineering including records of local
engineering firms

B15
BP PLC
BP Archive   Tel: 024 7657 3929
University of Warwick   Fax: 024 7652 4523
Coventry CV4 7AL
e-mail: bparchive@bp.com
Website: www.bp.com

Corporate archive

Facilities
Enquiries to the Archivist
Information provided by phone, post, fax and e-mail
Open to the general public by prior arrangement

Subject coverage
Records of BP's shipping fleets, including the British
Tanker Company
Main classes - photographs, wartime casualty files and
some ships' plans

Specific databases
An electronic catalogue of the Archives' holdings is
available for consultation onsite

B16
BRISTOL CITY MUSEUMS SERVICE
Consisting of
Bristol City Museum   Tel: 0117 9223571
Queens Road   Fax: 0117 9222047
Bristol BS8 1RL
e-mail: andy_king@bristol-city.gov.uk
Website: www.bristol-city.gov.uk/museums
and
Bristol Industrial Museum   Tel: 0117 9251470
Princes Wharf   Fax: 0117 9297318
City Docks
Bristol BS1 4RN

Local government museum service

Facilities
Enquiries to the Curator
Information provided by phone, post, fax and e-mail
Open to the public
Photocopying facilities - fullsize copies provided

Subject coverage
Photographic archive of maritime and port history,
c.1870-1970, primarily Bristol, Avonmouth and
Portishead

Special collections
York collection of photographs of ships in Bristol,
c.1870-1914, catalogued by ship name

B17
BRISTOL PORT COMPANY
St Andrews Road   Tel: 0117 920000
Avonmouth
Bristol BS11 9DQ

Port operator

B18
BRISTOL RECORD OFFICE
'B' Bond Warehouse   Tel: 0117 9224224
Smeaton Road   Fax: 0117-9224236
Bristol BS1 6XN
e-mail: bro@bristol-city.gov.uk
Website: www.bristol-city.gov.uk/recordoffice

Local government organisation

Facilities
Enquiries to the City Archivist
Information provided by phone, post, fax and e-mail
Microfilm and microfiche readers; microcopies can be
provided
Open to the public; appointments advisable, but not
essential: Mondays-Thursdays 0930-1645
Photocopying facilities
Research service provided; standard (per hour) £19;
priority (per hour) £38

Subject coverage
Ships registered at Bristol; merchant shipping crew
lists; seamen

Special collection
Illustrated logbook (1771-2) of Nicholas Pocock,
marine artist

Publications
Record Office general information leaflet
Record Office quarterly newsletter
Information leaflet: sources for ships, seamen and
emigrants

B19
THE BRISTOL SHIPLOVERS SOCIETY
Peter J. Stuckey (President)   Tel: 0117 9671307
8 Tweeney Lane
North Common
Warmley
Bristol BS30 5JT

Voluntary organisation

Facilities
Enquiries to the Secretary
Open to members only
Photocopying facilities

Subject coverage
Minute books and books published by Bristol Shiplovers; books on specific subjects written by individual members

Special collections
Logbook of talks delivered to the Society from 1931

B20
UNIVERSITY OF BRISTOL INFORMATION SERVICES, DEPARTMENT OF SPECIAL COLLECTIONS

Tyndall Avenue   Tel: 0117 9288014
Bristol BS8 1TJ   Fax: 0117 9255334
e-mail: special-collections@bris.ac.uk
Website: www.bris.ac.uk/is/services/specialcollections

University department

Facilities
Enquiries to the Special Collections Librarian or the Archivist, Special Collections Department
Information provided by: phone, post and fax
Loans to members only
Photocopying facilities
CD and online services available to members of the University only because of licence restrictions

Subject coverage
Maritime archaeology

Special collections
Brunel Collection, papers of Sir Marc Isambard Brunel, Isambard Kingdom Brunel and Henry Marc Brunel - includes journals, diaries, letterbooks, correspondence, notebooks, sketchbooks, calculations and accounts; especially rich in material on *Great Eastern* steamship, e.g. Eastern Steam Navigation and Great Ship Co. letterbooks, 1852-1859, contracts, accounts, legal documents, memoranda, minute books, draft history of *Great Western, Great Britain* and *Great Eastern,* 1835-1859; preliminary experiments, ships' trials; Thames Tunnel journal of transactions, 1824-1827; Thames Tunnel works, 1823-1827
Ledger of imports and exports of Port of London, 1715-16
Material relating to privateer *Tartar,* 1776-79
Rare books collection includes accounts of voyages, e.g. Harris's 'Navigantium; A collection of voyages and travels' compiled from the Earl of Oxford's library; Pinkerton's 'General collection of the best and most interesting voyages and travels'; Columbus's journal in facsimile; accounts of polar voyages
Early map and atlas material in original, copy and facsimile
Miscellaneous material on naval affairs, e.g. Lediard's 'Lives of the Admirals'; Boteler's 'Six dialogues about sea-services'

Publications:
'Special collections in the library of the University of Bristol', 1991
'The Brunel Collection', 1992

B21
BRITANNIA ROYAL NAVAL COLLEGE

Dartmouth   Tel 01803 677279
Devon TQ6 0HJ   Fax 01803 677015
Email r.kennell@brnc.ac.uk

Government institution

Facilities
Enquiries to the Librarian

Subject coverage
Foreign affairs and defence studies, naval history, sea systems, engineering science and ship technology.

Special collections
The Simons Collection: 3,000 books in English and French relating to British naval history and both world wars.

Publications
Accession lists and library guide

B22
BRITISH ANTARCTIC SURVEY

1 High Cross   Tel: 01223 221400
Madingley Road   Fax: 01223 362616
Cambridge CB3 0ET   Telex: 817725 BASCAM G
e-mail: information@bas.ac.uk
Website: www.antarctica.ac.uk

Research organisation

Enquiries to the Senior Information Officer
Information provided by phone, post, fax and e-mail; microfiche reader, CD-ROM available for images
Open to the public by appointment only: Mondays-Fridays 0900-1700

Subject coverage
Physical oceanography and marine biology, particularly of the polar regions; history of research in marine sciences in Antarctic region

Special collections
Archives relating to research vessels and their operations, sea ice and marine biological research in Antarctic waters, 1943 onwards
Maps, survey data and air photographs of coastline of British Antarctic Territory, South Georgia and South Sandwich Islands.
Archives usually only available when more than 30

years old.

Publications
Annual Report £8.00
General publications on seals, penguins, clothing and whales
Occasional scientific publications free.

British Boatbuilders Association
Association has been wound up.

B23
BRITISH CANOE UNION (BCU)

John Dudderidge House	Tel: 0115 9821100
Adbolton Lane	Fax: 0115 9821797
West Bridgford	
Nottingham NG2 5AS	
e-mail: info@bcu.org.uk	
Website: www.bcu.org.uk	

Governing body for the sport and recreation of canoeing and kayaking in the UK (affiliated to the Sports Council)

Facilities
Enquiries to the Information Officer
Information provided by phone, post and fax

Subject coverage
Canoeing and kayaking

B24
BRITISH AND INTERNATIONAL SAILORS' SOCIETY

3A Orchard Place	Tel: 02380 337333
Southampton	Fax: 02380 338333
Hampshire SO14 3AT	
e-mail: admin@biss.org.uk	
Website: www.biss.org.uk	

International Christian charity for seafarers

Facilities
Enquiries to the General Secretary
Information provided by phone, post, fax, e-mail, website and helpline
Open to seafarers and their families and retired seafarers
Photocopying facilities

Subject coverage
Welfare of seafarers

Special collections
Bound copies of magazines back to the Society's foundation in the early 19th century
Various Society records held at the National Maritime Museum

Publications
'Chart and Compass' four times yearly
Annual Review (free)

B25
BRITISH LIBRARY

96 Euston Road	Tel: 020 7412 7332
London NW1 2DB	Fax: 020 7412 7340
Website: www.bl.uk	

National Library

Facilities:
Enquiries to Reader Services Enquiries (020 7412 7676)
Information provided by phone, post, fax and e-mail
Reading rooms are only open to holders of a Reader's Pass, but exhibition galleries are open to the public. All applicants must provide proof of identity to apply for a pass
Access is available for the purposes of research and reference to material not readily available in other libraries (age limitation to over 18s)
Opening hours vary from one reading room to another
Photocopying facilities

Subject coverage
The UK's main legal deposit library; holdings cover books on ships and shipbuilding; periodicals; wide variety of other maritime-related subjects

Publications
See website for details of the British Library public catalogue, manuscripts and newspapers catalogues and India Office select materials
Numerous books and leaflets are published

B26
BRITISH LIBRARY - DEPARTMENT OF MANUSCRIPTS

96 Euston Road	Tel: 020 7412 7503
London NW1 2DB	Fax: 020 7412 7787
e-mail: mss@bl.uk	
Website: www.bl.uk/collection/manuscripts.html	

Part of the National Library

Facilities
Enquiries to the Head of Manuscripts
Information provided by phone, post, fax and e-mail
Open to those in possession of a Reader's Pass -
Manuscript reading room: Monday 1000-1700 and Tuesday-Saturday 0930-1700
Photographic facilities
Research service available - no general or lengthy research for readers but specific enquiries of up to 30 minutes research

Subject coverage
Naval history and navigation - maps, letters, personal papers

Special collections
Jellicoe papers
Nelson papers

Publications
Hard copy catalogues are available in the Reading Room
Manuscripts catalogue on website

B27
BRITISH LIBRARY - DOCUMENT SUPPLY CENTRE

Boston Spa   Tel: 01937 546060
Wetherby   Fax: 01937 546333
West Yorkshire
LS23 7BQ
e-mail: dsc-customer-services@bl.uk
website: www.bl.uk/dsc

Part of the National Library

Facilities
Enquiries to Customer Services
Information provided via the website or by phone, post and e-mail
Reading room, including National Sound Archive facilities, open to the general public
Photocopies available to the general public; loans available to registered organisations
Opening hours (Customer Services): 0830-1700
Reading Room: 0930-1630 standard retrieval times at 1045, 1330 and 1500; items can be reserved in advance for the Reading Room
Research service available: STM (Science, Technology & Medicine) SEARCH; telephone 020 7412 7477
The search covers science, technology and medicine and costs £21 per 15 minutes of staff time, plus VAT and online search fees. Enquirers are advised to call STM SEARCH to discuss requirements

Subject coverage
All subjects

Databases
Large parts of the collection can be browsed using the online catalogue http://blpc.bl.uk

---

B28
BRITISH LIBRARY - MAP LIBRARY

96 Euston Road   Tel: 020 7412 7702
London NW1 2DB   Fax: 020 7412 7780
e-mail: maps@bl.uk
Website: www.bl.uk

Part of the National Library

Facilities
Enquiries to the Map Librarian
Information provided by phone, fax, e-mail and visit
Open to those in possession of a Reader's Pass to the British Library: Monday 1000-1700, Tuesday-Saturday 0930-1700 closed Bank Holidays and for Christmas and New Year
Photocopying facilities

Subject coverage
British mapping up to present day (reserved on copyright deposit); antiquarian collections (cartographic, topographic material etc.); overseas mapping at smaller and larger scales; Ministry of Defence cartographic archive; Admiralty charts and other maritime material; cartographic/geographic ephemera; 4.5 million items and reference books

Special collections
King's Topographical Collections (50,000 items: manuscripts and printed, relating to areas of British influence, 17th and 18th centuries)
Crace Collection - London plans and maps, 16-19th centuries
King's Maritime Collection of charts

Specific companies and groups
Definitive collection of Ordnance Survey mapping from their earliest beginnings in the 1790s
Royal United Services Institution (RUSI) Collection - 18th century antiquarian material relating to British and North American history

Publications
Map Library catalogue on CD-ROM and online via COPAC

B29
BRITISH LIBRARY - NEWSPAPER LIBRARY

Colindale Avenue   Tel: 020 7412 7353
London NW9 5HE   Fax: 020 7412 7379
e-mail: newspaper@bl.uk
Website: www.bl.uk/collections/newspapers.html

Part of the National Library

Facilities
Enquiries to the Information Services Manager
Information provided by: phone, post, fax and e-mail
Open to holders of a British Library or Newspaper Library Pass: Monday-Saturday 1000-1645.
Photocopying service provided if full publication details are known; microfilm copies of items in collections can also be purchased
Research service available only via list of freelance research workers

Subject coverage

National archive collection of British and overseas newspapers - including full sets of main London editions of all national daily and Sunday papers from 1801 to present; regional local and overseas newspapers from early 18th century onwards; trade papers and popular periodicals from 1801 onwards

Special collections

'Lloyd's List', 1801 to date
'Mitchell's Maritime Register', 1856-1934
'Weekly Shipping Record', 1820-27
London Customs Bill of Entry Ship Reports, 1827-1939
London Customs Bill of Entry Ship Imports, Exports and Shipping, 1827-1934
London Customs Bill of Entry Ship Coal Tables, 1902-1939

Specific databases

Selection of British and overseas newspapers and indexes and related resources available for readers to consult via networked CD ROMS or online in the Colindale Reading Room

Publications

Catalogue on website:
www.bl.uk/catalogues/newspapers.html
Guide to collection -
www.bl.uk/collection/newspapers.html

B30
BRITISH LIBRARY - ORIENTAL AND INDIA OFFICE COLLECTIONS

96 Euston Road   Tel: 020 7412 7873
London NW1 2DB   Fax: 020 7412 7641
e-mail: oioc-enquiries@bl.uk
Website: www.bl.uk/collections/oriental

Part of the National Library

Facilities

Enquiries to the Duty Curator on Enquiry Desk in OIOC Reading Room
Information provided by phone, post, fax and e-mail
Open to public with British Library Reader's Pass
Reader admission for passes Monday-Thursday 0930-1800, Friday-Saturday 0930-1630
OIOC Reading Room: Monday 1000-1700 and Tuesday-Saturday 0930-1700 by appointment only
Photocopying facilities
Research service available - ecclesiastical search and certified copy service, 5-year search £25.85 (UK and Europe) £22 (Rest of the World), certified copies of certificates £13
Lists of research agents supplied on request

Special collections

East India Company, 1600-1858
Government of India, 1858-1947

Specific databases

In progress - listing of records online access

Publications

www.bl.uk/collections/oriental/

B31
BRITISH LIBRARY OF POLITICAL AND ECONOMIC SCIENCE, LONDON SCHOOL OF ECONOMICS

10 Portugal Street   Tel: 020 7955 7223
London WC2A 2HD   Fax: 020 7955 7475
e-mail: lse.ac.uk/archives
Website: www.document@lse.ac.uk

University department

Facilities

Enquiries to the archivist
Information provided by phone, post, fax, e-mail and visit.
Open to the public: Monday-Thursday 1000-2000; Friday 1000-1700; Saturday 1100-1800 (term and Easter vacation only)
Photocopying facilities
Detailed research cannot be undertaken.

Subject coverage

Political, social and labour history

Special collections

Papers of Charles Booth, Liverpool shipowner, relating to his social investigations in London
Shipping register of J Byrn, c. 1809
Ship account book of John S.P. Mills, master of steamers *Striver, Runnelstone,* and *Charlwood,* 1920-1926
Wage books A Collins, London docker, 1906-1949
Report on shipping control in First World War and subsequent correspondence of Sir K S Anderson, manager of Orient Steam Navigation Co.
Papers of the Inland Waterways Association, 1971-1983
Papers relating to political and foreign affairs interests of Edmund D Morel, 1873-1924, shipowner
Business documents of Robert Newman and Co. of Dartmouth, traders with Newfoundland, 1774-1955

Publications

On-line guide and searchable catalogues on website

British Marine Equipment Council

Now Society of Maritime Industries

B32
BRITISH MARINE FEDERATION

Marine House　　　　　Tel: 01784 473377
Thorpe Lea Road　　　Fax: 01784 439678
Egham
Surrey TW20 8BF
E-mail: info@britishmarine.co.uk
Website: www.britishmarine.co.uk

Trade association

Facilities
Enquiries to the Secretary General

Subject coverage
Government representation; statistics and market research; legal and commercial advice; environmental advice; technical support; export support; training and recruitment

Publications
List available on request

B33
BRITISH MARINE FEDERATION, SCOTLAND

Westgate　　　　　　Tel: 01369 870251
Toward　　　　　　　Fax: 01369 870251
Dunoon PA23 7UA
Website: www.britishmarine.co.uk

Trade association

Facilities
Enquiries to the Secretary
Access by appointment
Information provided by: phone, fax, post, or e-mail, usually to members but the public can be helped if appropriate.

B34
BRITISH MARITIME LAW ASSOCIATION

c/o Ince and Co.　　　　Tel: 020 7623 2011
Knollys House　　　　　Fax: 020 7623 3225
11 Byward Street
London EC3R 5EN
e-mail: patrick.griggs@ince.co.uk
Website: www.bmla@ince.org.uk

Association representing maritime lawyers and others involved in shipping law

Facilities
Enquiries to the Secretary
Information provided by phone, post, fax and e-mail
Open to the public by appointment during office hours
Photocopying facilities

Subject coverage
Reports, files, etc. on projects to promote uniformity of maritime law

Special collections
CMI Yearbooks going back to the early 1900s

Publications
For most recent material see website above

B35
BRITISH MARITIME TECHNOLOGY (BMT) – TEDDINGTON

Orlando House　　　　Tel: 020 8943 5544
1 Waldegrave Road　　Fax: 020 8943 5347
Teddington
Middlesex TW11 8LZ
e-mail: dgriffiths@bmtmail.com
Website: www.bmt.org

Consultancy/research organisation with many subsidiaries, member of AIRTO

Facilities
Enquiries to the Librarian
Information provided by phone, post and fax (may be charged)
Open to members only but loans to all via the British Library ILL scheme
Research service available - literature search (£25 for up to 20 references and £1 per additional reference), and more in-depth searches (fee by arrangement)

Subject coverage
Naval architecture; marine engineering; ocean engineering; wind engineering; industrial aerodynamics; marine traffic operations; port and harbour design and operation

Special collections
Archives of National Physical Laboratory Ship Division
Transactions of Royal Institution of Naval Architects (RINA) and Society of Naval Architects and Marine Engineers (SNAME)
Reports of Ship, Aero and Maritime Science Divisions of the National Physical Laboratory
National Maritime Institute Reports

Specific databases
BMT Abstracts available online (as Marine Science and Technology Abstracts) at: www.marinescienceandtechnology.com

Publications
'BMT News' approx. quarterly (free)
Technical reports - price list available
'BMT Abstracts' (published monthly, price p.a. £220)
Reports prepared by predecessor organisations (National Maritime Institute and National Physical Laboratory Ship and Aero Divisions) are still for sale

---

B36
BRITISH MARITIME TECHNOLOGY (BMT) - TYNESIDE

Ceres House   Tel: 0191 262 5242
Davy Bank   Fax: 0191 263 8754
Wallsend
Tyne and Wear NE28 6UY
e-mail: gs.bmtlib@britishlibrary.net
Website: www.bmt.org

Consultancy/research

Facilities
Enquiries to the Head of Information Services
Information provided by phone, post, fax and e-mail
Loans to members only
Restricted photocopying facilities (subject to copyright)
Research service available - literature (£25 for up to 20 references and £1 per additional reference), and more in-depth searches (fee by arrangement)

Subject coverage
Marine engineering; naval architecture; ocean engineering

Special collections
Transactions of Royal Institution of Naval Architects
Transactions of Society of Naval Architects and Marine Engineers
Transactions of North and East Coast Institution of Engineers and Shipbuilders
Transactions of Engineers and Shipbuilders in Scotland
Reports and Technical Memoranda of British Ship Research Association (BSRA)

Specific databases
BMT Abstracts available online at
www.marinescienceandtechnology.com

Publications
BMT Abstracts (published monthly) see above
Technical reports of BSRA
Miscellaneous publications

British Petroleum
See BP plc

B37
BRITISH PORTS ASSOCIATION

Africa House   Tel 020 7242 1200
Kingsway   Fax 020 7430 7474
London
WC2B 6AH
Email info@britishports.org.uk
Website: www.britishports.org.uk

Trade association; affiliated to the International Association of Ports and Harbours

Facilities
Enquiries to the Association Secretary

Subject coverage
Port industry and policy

British Sailors' Society
Now British and International Sailors' Society

British Shipbuilding Database
See under Newcastle-upon-Tyne University School of Marine Science and Technology

---

B38
BRITISH SUB AQUA CLUB (BSAC)

Telford's Quay   Tel: 0151 350 6200
South Pier Road   Fax: 0151 350 6215
Ellesmere Port
Cheshire CH65 4FL
e-mail: alistairr@bsac.com
Website: www.bsac.com

Non-profit-making organisation/governing body for sport

Facilities
Enquiries to the Technical Manager
Information provided by phone, post, fax and e-mail
Open to the public
Photocopying facilities

Subject coverage
All topics relating to recreational scuba diving and snorkelling, including technical diving

Specific databases
Diving incident reports
Diving membership growth
Membership/school/corporate members database

B39
BRITISH TITANIC SOCIETY

1 Mardon Close
Swaythling
Hampshire SO18 2HP

B40
BRITISH TUGOWNERS ASSOCIATION

Docklands Business Centre
10-16 Tiller Road
London E14 8PX

B41
BRITISH WATER SKI FEDERATION

390 City Road   Tel: 020 7833 2855
London EC1V 2Q4   Fax: 020 7837 5879
e-mail: info@bwsf.co.uk
Website: www.britishwaterski.co.uk

Sports governing body/member organisation

Facilities
Enquiries to the Executive Officer
Information provided by phone, fax, website and e-mail
Open to the public

Subject coverage
All aspects of waterskiing in the UK; waterskiing coaching qualifications and boat driving licences

Publications
Available on request

B42
BRITISH WATERWAYS

Willow Grange   Tel 01923 201120
Church Road   Fax
Watford
Herts WD17 4QA
Email enquiries.hq@britishwaterways.co.uk
Website: www.britishwaterways.co.uk

Publicly owned corporation

Facilities
Information provided by phone, post, fax and e-mail

Subject coverage
Inland navigation, canals, rivers, waterways

See also **Waterways Trust**

B43
BRIXHAM HERITAGE MUSEUM & HISTORY SOCIETY

Old Police Station   Tel: 01803 856267
Bolton Cross
Brixham
Devon TQ5 8LZ
e-mail: mail@brixhamheritage.org.uk
Website: www.brixhamheritage.org.uk

Museum

Facilities
Enquiries to the Curator
Information provided by phone, post and e-mail
Open to Society members, and the public by appointment
Photocopies can be provided by arrangement

Research/enquiry service available - £3 plus charge for any photocopies supplied

Subject coverage
Brixham maritime history, especially relating to local shipbuilding and fishing industries

Specific companies and groups
Simpson and Strickland, Ltd.: boatyard drawings and blueprints of steam launches, yachts and other vessels, 1887-1915

Specific databases
Vessels built, owned or registered in Brixham from 1784

Publications
Refer to website for details

Brunel Society

Society wound up, 1992

B44
BRUNEL UNIVERSITY

Uxbridge   Tel 01895 274000
Middlesex UB8 3PH   Fax 01895 232806
Email library@brunel.co.uk
Web www.brunel.ac.uk

University department

Facilities
Enquiries to the Archivist
Library open to the public
Information given by phone, post and email
Loans to members only
Microfilm and microfiche readers;
CD-ROM
On-line information retrieval
Current charges £60.00 per annum for external readers.

Special Collections
Isambard Kingdom Brunel, pictorial record of the *Great Eastern*.

B45
BRYNMOR JONES LIBRARY, THE UNIVERSITY OF HULL

Cottingham Road   Tel: 01482 465265
Hull HU6 7RX   Fax: 01482 466205
e-mail: archives@hull.ac.uk
Website: www.hull.ac.uk/lib

University department

Facilities

Enquiries to the University Archivist
Information provided by phone, post, fax and e-mail
Archives open to the public by appointment only; library open to members only
Photocopying facilities

Subject coverage

Hull and East Yorkshire marine/maritime history, including fishing

Special collections

Archives of Ellerman's Wilson Line
Archives of Earle's Shipbuilding and Engineering Company
Archives of John Good & Sons
Archives of the Humber Pilots Ltd.
Some archives of Hull Trinity House
Archives of George Buckton & Sons

Specific databases

HUMAD2 - the Hull University Manuscripts and Archives Database, available via the website

Publications

Introductory leaflet, 'Archives and Manuscripts' (please send s.a.e.)
Other publications available via website

B46
CENTRE FOR BUCKINGHAMSHIRE STUDIES (FORMERLY BUCKINGHAMSHIRE RECORD OFFICE)

County Hall   Tel: 01296 382587
Aylesbury
Bucks HP20 1UU
e-mail: archives@buckscc.gov.uk
Website: www.buckscc.gov.uk/archives

Local government organisation

Facilities

Enquiries to the County Archivist
Information provided by phone, post, fax and e-mail
Open to the public: Monday-Friday 0900-1715 and Saturday 0900-1545 (archive searchroom)
Readers are advised to reserve a seat in advance; admission by CARN readers' ticket (please bring identification with name, address and signature for issue of ticket)
Photocopying facilities - subject to copyright restrictions and only if in suitable format and condition

Subject coverage

Fremantle family MSS, including papers of Admiral Sir T F Fremantle, c.1793-1819, Admiral Sir Charles Fremantle, 1855-1856 and Captain S G Fremantle, 1833-1860

Official correspondence of the 12th Duke of Somerset as First Lord of the Admiralty, 1859-1866
Minutes of subscribers and managers' meetings organised to raise £1 million for insuring ships and merchandise, 1719 (papers of Charles Shales)
Papers relating to the *Denham*, East Indiaman burnt at Bencoolen in 1760-61, 1757-1779
Diary of Rev. Thomas Pocock, 1704, a naval chaplain which includes the taking of Gibraltar, 23-27th August, 1704

Publications

Many family and estate catalogues now on Access to Archives website on www.pro.a2a.gov.uk

---

B47
BUCKLER'S HARD MARITIME MUSEUM

Buckler's Hard   Tel: 01590 616203
Beaulieu   Fax: 01590 616283
Brockenhurst
Hampshire SO42 7XB
e-mail: info@bucklershard.co.uk
Website: www.beaulieu.co.uk

Independent museum

Facilities

Enquiries to the Archivist at John Montagu Building, Beaulieu SO42 7ZN
Information provided by phone, post, fax and e-mail
Open to the public (archives by appointment only); Monday-Friday 1000-1500
Photocopying facilities

Subject coverage

18th century shipbuilding and village life at Buckler's Hard only

Publications

General Visitor Guide to Buckler's Hard village and Maritime Museum

---

B48
BUDE-STRATTON MUSEUM

c/o The Castle   Tel: 01288 353576
Bude   Fax: 01288 353576
Cornwall EX23 8LG
e-mail: theclerk@bude-stratton.gov.uk
Website: www.budemuseum.org.uk

Museum

Facilities

Enquiries to the Town Clerk
Information supplied by post and e-mail
Museum open to the general public
Photocopying facilities

Subject coverage
Bude as a 19th century port; shipwrecks in the Bude area from the 17th century; Bude lifeboat from the 19th century; Sir Goldsworthy Gurney (local inventor)

Publications
Books and cards on local boats and shipwrecks

B49
BUREAU VERITAS

2nd Floor	Tel: 020 7550 8900
Tower Bridge Court	Fax: 020 7403 1590
224-226 Tower Bridge Road	
London SE1 2TX	
Website: www.bureauveritas.co.uk	

Classification society, parent company of the Bureau Veritas Group.

Facilities
Enquiries to the Information Officer
Information provided by phone, post or fax

Publications
Rules and regulations are charged for; guidance notes are free

---

B50
BURNHAM-ON-CROUCH AND DISTRICT MUSEUM

The Quay	Tel: 01621 783444
Burnham-on-Crouch	
Essex CM0 8DH.	
e-mail: histmus@aol.com	

Local authority organisation

Facilities
Enquiries to Hon. Curator.

Subject coverage
Many photographs of yachts designed and built in Burnham from early 20th century until c. 1970.
Classes include Crouch one-design, Royal Corinthian one-design, Royal Burnham one-design, Stella class, plus many 'one-offs'.
Collections of Burnham boatyard pictures, including construction of yachts. Yards include King's, Tucker-Browns', Prior's and Petticrow.
Photographs of 19th century and 20th century barges using Burnham
Oyster industry on the Crouch (including maps), from medieval period, including a major research study on medieval Crouch and Essex fisheries.
Research project on ferry crossings across the Crouch
Early sea trade from the port of Burnham
Artefact collection includes shipwrights' tools, sailmakers' tools, yacht test models. Very little of the maritime collection extends beyond Burnham.

B51
BURY ARCHIVE SERVICE

Edwin Street (off Crompton St.)	Tel: 0161 797 6697
Bury	Fax: 0161 797 6697
Greater Manchester BL9 0AS	(please ring first)
e-mail: archives@bury.gov.uk	
Website: www.bury.gov.uk	

Local government organisation

Facilities
Enquiries to the Archivist
Information by phone, post, e-mail and visit
Open to the public: weekdays 1000-1300, 1400-1700 by appointment, but none needed on Tuesdays
Fullsize copies available
Research service not provided

Special collections
Some family papers regarding foreign travel with voyage diaries, 19th century
Photos of liners and prints of US paddle steamers

Publications
Interim Guide £2-50 and see website: www.bury.gov.uk under 'A' for 'Archives'

Business Archives Council
The library of the Business Archives Council has been deposited at:
Centre for Business History in Scotland

University of Glasgow	Tel: 0141 339 8855
4 University Gardens	
Glasgow G12 8QQ	

B52
BUTE MUSEUM

7 Stuart Street	Tel: 01700 505067
Rothesay	
Isle of Bute PA20 0EP	
e-mail: Ivor@bute museum.fsnet.co.uk	

Voluntary organisation and museum (member of the Scottish Museums Council)

Facilities
Enquiries to the Museum Custodian
Information provided by phone and post
Open to the public: Summer: 1000-1630, (except Sunday 1430-1630); Winter: Tuesday-Saturday 1430-1630, with access by appointment at other times
Photocopying facilities
Research service available - £25 per hour after 1st hour, plus costs of photocopying and p&p

Subject coverage
Naval and local history, 1939-1946, including midget submarine research and development; Clyde steamers

from 1812 to present day; archive material from early 18th century, including vessels trading activities through Rothesay Customs

Special collections
Comprehensive model and photographic collection of Clyde steamers, pennants and name boards

---

C1
CAERNARFON HARBOUR TRUST

Harbour Office   Tel: 01286 672118
Slate Quay   Fax: 01286 678729
Caernarfon
Gwynedd LL55 2PB
e-mail: cht@caernarfon-hbr.demon.co.uk
Website: www.caernarfon-hbr.demon.co.uk

Small port authority

Facilities
Enquiries to the Harbour Master
Information provided by phone, post, fax and e-mail
Open to the public during normal office hours
Photocopying facilities

Subject coverage
Local maritime records

Special collections
Documents of maritime interest deposited with Gwynedd Archive Service, Caernarfon (q.v.)

C2
CAMBRIDGE COUNTY RECORD OFFICE - CAMBRIDGE

Box RES 1009   Tel: 01223 717281
Shire Hall   Fax: 01223 717201
Castle Hill
Cambridge CB3 0AP
e-mail:
county.records.cambridge@cambridgeshire.gov.uk
Website: www.cambridgeshire.gov.uk

Local government organisation

Facilities
Enquiries to the Deputy County Archivist
Information provided by phone, post, fax and e-mail
Open to the public: Tuesday-Thursday 0900-1245, 1345-1715, Friday 0900-1245, 1345-1615 (Tuesday evening strictly by appointment)
Photocopying facilities
Research service available - 2 hours maximum at any one time (£12 per half hour, £21 per hour)

Subject coverage
Wisbech shipping

Special collections
Registers of ships registered at port of Wisbech, 1836-1854; transactions register, 1855-1877; crew lists for 94 vessels registered at Wisbech, 1863-1913

C3
CAMBRIDGE COUNTY RECORD OFFICE - HUNTINGDON

Grammar School Walk   Tel: 01480 375842
Huntington   Fax: 01480 375842
Cambridge PE29 3LF
e-mail: county.records.hunts@cambridgeshire.gov.uk
Website: www.cambridgeshire.gov.uk

Local government organisation

Facilities
Enquiries to the Senior Archivist
Information provided by: phone, post, fax and e-mail
Open to the public - Tuesday-Thursday 0900-1245 and 1345-1715, Friday 0900-1245 and 1345-1615 and Saturday (2nd each month) 0900-1200
Photocopying facilities
Research service available - £12 for the first 30 minutes and £9 for each additional 30 minute block

Special collections
Compilations of 17th century Admiralty statutes and laws
Notebooks of Viscount Mandeville at Royal Naval College, Dartmouth and on training on HMS *Temeraire*, 1913-1930
Estate records only of 4th Earl of Sandwich

Publications
A-Z Guide on website

C4
CAMBRIDGE REFRIGERATION TECHNOLOGY

140 Newmarket Road   Tel: 01223 461352
Cambridge CB5 8HE   Fax: 01223 461522
e-mail: crt@crtech.demon.co.uk
Website: www.crtech.co.uk

Research associates

Facilities
Enquiries to Mrs GD Goddard
Information provided by phone, post, fax and e-mail
Open to members and the public by appointment: Monday-Friday 0900-1700
Search service available from the website (see above) - minimum charge for photocopying is £25

Subject coverage
Archives; abstracts; photographs; slides; fiche

Special collections
Early refrigeration transportation
Early transportation of perishables

Specific databases
Refrigerators
Refrigeration - FRIDOC, ASHRAE
Fruit and vegetables - air storage, controlled
atmosphere
Dry freight storage
Library

Publications
Hard copy or CD ROM version of databases
Guide to collection on website

C5
CAMBRIDGE UNIVERSITY
LIBRARY

West Road   Tel: 01223 333000
Cambridge CB3 9DR   Fax: 01223 333160
e-mail: library@lib.cam.ac.uk
Website: www.lib.cam.ac.uk

University and legal deposit library

Facilities
Enquiries to the Librarian
Information provided by phone, post, fax and e-mail
Open to members of the University; others on
application: Monday-Friday 0900-1900 (2200 in Easter
Full Term) and Saturday 0900-1700
Photocopying facilities
Research service available - reasonable research
enquiries answered free of charge, subject to
limitations of staff time and expertise

Subject coverage
Collections cover all subjects (approximately 6.8
million printed books, pamphlets and serial volumes,
including 4,800 incunabula); 60,000 current periodical
titles; 100,000 music scores; 1.1 million maps; 1.75
million microforms; electronic resources as below;
150,000 manuscripts from medieval illuminated to
modern scientific papers; archives including University
of Cambridge, several Cambridge colleges, diocese of
Ely, Dean and Chapter of Ely Cathedral, several
businesses

Special collections
Cruising Association Library (Hanson Collection)
Royal Greenwich Observatory Archive
Ships' logs associated with Commodore John Acton,
1714-44
Tuscan naval vessels, 1750-76
West Indiaman *Alarm*, 1782-83
HMS *Pompee*, 1806-07
HMS *Hannibal*, Crimea, 1855-56
Maritime atlases and charts

Specific companies and groups
Vickers plc archives (including Armstrong Whitworth)
mostly from the period 1870-1970

Specific databases
Collection of CD-ROMs networked in library
Subscriptions to many online databases and electronic
journals, but most accessible only by current staff and
students of the University

Publications
Online catalogue of books published 1978 onwards
(ongoing project to add earlier imprints) and of
manuscripts at collection level; some published
catalogues of specific collections; manual catalogues of
other material available in the library
List of the library's publications available on website

C6
CAMBRIDGE UNIVERSITY
DOWNING COLLEGE
THE MAITLAND ROBINSON
LIBRARY

Downing College   Tel: 01223 335352
Regent Street
Cambridge C82 1DQ
e-mail: library@dow.cam.ac.uk
Website: www.dow.cam.ac.uk

College library

Facilities
Enquiries to the Librarian
Information given by phone and e-mail
Material can be consulted and photocopied by prior
arrangement
Books lent only to college members
Open daily during university terms

Subject coverage
Naval history

Special collections
The Richmond Collection given by Admiral Sir Herbert
Richmond

Cammell Laird Shipbuilders Ltd.
Records with Wirral Museums and Williamson Art
Gallery, q.v.

C7
CANAL MUSEUM

Stoke Bruerne   Tel: 01604
Towcester   Fax: 01604
Northants NN12 7SE
e-mail: canal.museum@thewaterwaystrust.co.uk

Museum - part of the Waterways Trust

Facilities
Enquiries to the Site Manager
Information provided by: phone, in person, fax and e-mail
Open to the public by appointment
Photocopying facilities
Limited research service available

Special collections:
Wide range of artefacts relating to inland navigation (in particular the Midlands to London) - decoration of narrow boats a main feature

---

C8
CARMARTHENSHIRE ARCHIVE SERVICE

Parc Myrddin	Tel: 01267 2282232
Richmond Terrace	Fax: 01267 228237

Carmarthen SA31 1DS
e-mail: archives@carmarthenshire.gov.uk
Website: www.carmarthenshire.gov.uk

Local government organisation

Facilities
Enquiries to the County Archivist
Information provided by phone, post, fax, e-mail and visit
Open to the public
Digital images and photocopying facilities
Research service available - charge of £15 per hour

Subject coverage
Usual local authority archive holdings

Special collections:
Register of ships, Carmarthen, 1839-1849
Register of ships, Llanelli, 1824-1885
Register of fishing boats, Llanelli, 1902-1943
Register of transactions, Llanelli 1825-1931
Shipping lists 1863-1913
Crew agreements of Carmarthen and Llanelli registered ships

Publications
Summary of collections can be viewed online at County Council website

---

Centre for Marine Resource Economics (CEMARE)
See Portsmouth University

C9
CENTRE FOR ENVIRONMENT, FISHERIES AND AQUACULTURE SCIENCE (CEFAS)

Fisheries Laboratory	Tel: 01502 562244
Pakefield Road	Fax: 01502 524525

Lowestoft
Suffolk NR33 9BR
e-mail: lowlibrary@cefas.co.uk
Website: www.cefas.co.uk

Government agency

Facilities
Enquiries to Reception
Information provided by phone, post, fax and e-mail
Library open primarily to laboratory staff and for reference to other research workers and bona fide enquirers by prior arrangement: Monday-Thursday 0830-1700 and Friday 0830-1630
Photocopying facilities

Subject coverage
Books; pamphlets; reprints and translations; current periodicals and serials covering fish and shellfish research; marine biology; oceanography; aquatic pollution

Special collections:
Expedition reports
Food and Agriculture Organisation fisheries publications
International Council for the Exploration of the Sea publications

Publications
CEFAS Publications Catalogue (annually)
CEFAS Library Information Leaflet (quarterly)

C10
CENTRE FOR MIGRATION STUDIES AT THE ULSTER AMERICAN FOLK PARK

Mellon Road	Tel: 028 8225 6315
Castletown	Fax: 028 8224 2241

Omagh
County Tyrone
Northern Ireland BT78 5QY
e-mail: uafp@iol.ie
Website: www.qub.ac.uk/cms/
www.folkpark.com

Research centre attached to museum

Facilities
Enquiries to the Librarian and Director
Information provided by phone, post, fax and e-mail
Reference library open to the public, loans to staff members only: Monday-Friday 0930-1630 (closed weekends and public holidays)
No appointment necessary except for groups

Photocopying facilities, charged at 10p per copy
Internet and e-mail facilities for public use
Limited research service available - Irish Emigration
Database and compilation of subject booklists of
books in collection

Subject coverage
Irish migration history, 17th-20th century inclusive,
including information on ships and shipping, the Atlantic
voyage and some journals of voyages across the
Atlantic

Specific databases
Irish Emigration Database - containing 30,000 plus
documents dealing with Irish emigration to North
America - including emigrant letters, government
reports, shipping advertisements, shipping news,
passenger lists and newspaper articles/reports

C11
CEREDIGION ARCHIVES
Swyddfa'r Sir　　　　　　Tel: 01970 633697
Glan y Mor　　　　　　　Fax: 01970 633663
Aberystwyth
Ceredigion SY23 2DE
e-mail: archives@ceredigion.gov.uk
Website: www.llgc.org.uk/cac/cac0009.htm

Local government organisation

Facilities
Enquiries to the County Archivist
Information provided by phone, post, fax and e-mail
Open to the public: Monday 1000-1300 and 1400-1900
and Tuesday-Friday 1000-1300 and 1400-1600
Photocopying facilities
Limited research service available (free but donations
are welcomed) dependent on time available. Charge of
£10 an hour for more detailed searches

Subject coverage
Cardiganshire shipping

Special collections
Records of HM Customs and Excise; shipping registers
for Aberystwyth, 1824-1925; record of sailings from
Aberystwyth, 1794-1799; some crew agreements,
1863-1897; log books; Aberystwyth harbour records,
c.1900-1914; Marine Board of Trade maps, 19th-20th
century; shipping register for Cardigan, 1855-1869; port
book for Aberystwyth, 1854-1901 (with gaps)

Centre for Kentish Studies
See under Kent

C12
CHALLENGER SOCIETY FOR MARINE SCIENCE
Room 251/20　　　　　　Tel: 02380 596097
Southampton Oceanography　Fax: 02380 596149
Centre
Waterfront Campus
Southampton SO14 3ZH
e-mail: jxj@soc.soton.ac.uk
Website: www.challenger-society.org.uk

Learned society

Facilities
Enquiries to the Executive Secretary
Information provided by phone and e-mail
Open to the public
Photocopying facilities

C13
THE CHAMBER OF SHIPPING
Carthusian Court　　　　Tel: 020 7417 2800
12 Carthusian Street　　　Fax: 020 7726 2080
London EC1M 6EZ
e-mail: postmaster@british-shipping.org
Website: www.british-shipping.org

Trade association

Facilities
Enquiries to the Company Secretary
Information provided by phone, post, fax and e-mail
Facilities may be provided to the public at our
discretion and only by appointment
Photocopying facilities
Research service available by special arrangement

Subject coverage
Information on national and international law and
developments affecting ships and shipping information
about the UK fleet and its manpower

Special collections
Seafarer earnings data
National Maritime Board records

C14
CHARTERED INSTITUTE OF LOGISTICS
11/12 Buckingham Gate　　Tel: 01536 740100
London SW1 6LB　　　　　Fax: 020 7592 3111
Website: www.cilt-international.com

Professional institute

Facilities
Enquiries to the Librarian
Information provided by phone, post, e-mail, or fax

Library open to members - a charge is made to non-members
Loans to members only

Subject coverage
Business and management aspects of passenger transport, logistics and supply chains

Publications
Logistics and Transport Focus, supplied ten times annualy to members
'CILT World' supplied three times annually to members

C15
CHARTERED INSTITUTE OF LOSS ADJUSTERS (CILA)

Peninsular House   Tel: 020 7337 9960
36 Monument Street   Fax: 020 7929 3082
London EC3R 8LJ
e-mail: info@cila.co.uk
Website: www.cila.co.uk

Professional organisation

Facilities
Enquiries to the Executive Director

Subject coverage
Loss adjusting; insurance claims

C16
CHATHAM HISTORIC DOCKYARD TRUST

The Historic Dockyard   Tel: 01634 823800
Chatham   Fax: 01634 823801
Kent ME4 4TZ
Website: www.chdt.org.uk

Museum

Facilities
Enquiries to the Librarian
Information provided by phone, post, fax and e-mail
Open to the public by appointment
Photocopying facilities
Minor research service available

Subject coverage
Naval; dockyard; general maritime; architectural drawings; photographs

Special collections
Primary source material concerning operation of Chatham Dockyard, c.1900-1980

C17
CHELSEA REFERENCE LIBRARY

Old Town Hall   Tel: 0207 352 6056
King's Road
London SW3 5EZ
e-mail: information.services@rbkc.gov.uk
Website: www.rbkc.gov.uk

Public Library

Facilities
Enquiries to the Reference Librarian
Information provided by phone, post, or e-mail
Open to the general public: Mondays, Tuesdays & Thursdays 0930-2000; Wednesdays 0930-1300; Fridays & Saturdays 0930-1700
Photocopying facilities
Microfilm and microfiche readers available
Research facilities not provided, except for census records and ratebooks

Subject coverage
A huge Local History Department, stocking all available materials relating to Chelsea.

Special collections
Books on Chelsea history
Drawings and paintings, prints and engravings, photographs, cuttings, maps and plans
Newspapers and periodicals, directories for Chelsea electoral registers (1863-); census returns; ratebooks (1796-)

C18
CHESHIRE AND CHESTER ARCHIVES AND LOCAL STUDIES

Chester Record Office   Tel: 01244 602574
Duke Street   Fax: 01244 603812
Chester CH1 1RL
e-mail: recordoffice@cheshire.gov.uk
Website: www.cheshire.gov.uk/recoff/home

Local government organisation

Facilities
Enquiries to the Principal Archivist
Information provided by phone, post, fax or e-mail
Open to the public, preferably by appointment
Opening hours: see website
Fullsize copies provided on request
Microfilm and microfiche readers available
Research service provided; for conditions, see website

Special collections
Archives of local ship and boat builders:
Henry Gibson, Northwich
Isaac Pimblott, Northwich
W J Yarwood and Sons, Northwich
Port of Runcorn crew agreements

Publications
Cheshire Record Office Guide, 1991

C19
CHESTER HISTORY AND HERITAGE

St Michael's Church
Bridge Street Row East
Chester
Cheshire CH1 1NW
e-mail: s.oswald@chestercc.gov.uk
Website:
www.chestercc.gov.uk/heritage/archives/home.html

Tel: 01244 402110
Fax: 01244 312243

Local government organisation

Facilities
Enquiries to the Community Heritage Officer
Information provided by phone, fax, post, e-mail, talks and events
Open to the public: Monday to Thursday 1000-1600
Photocopying facilities (for staff use only)

Subject coverage
City of Chester history

Special collections
GRO Index 1837-1949; 1881 census - national; census for Chester; electoral registers for Chester; IGI for Cheshire and surrounding counties; Local History Library; trade directories
Chester Photographic survey
Chester City Council minutes
Overleigh Cemetery registers
Chester Archaeological Society Library

Specific databases
Image bank (over 4,000 images of Chester district)

C20
CLARKSON, JOHN & MARION (SHIPS IN FOCUS)

18 Franklands
Longton
Preston
Lanes PR4 5PD
e-mail: sales@shipsinfocus.co.uk
www.shipsinfocus.co.uk

Tel: 01772 612855
Fax: 01772 612855

Photographic collector, maritime publisher

Facilities
Enquiries to John Clarkson
Information given by post if accompanied by s.a.e.
Charges made for photographs
Book catalogue available on request

Subject coverage
Negatives of ships of all types, but stronger in ships of 10,000 tons gross or less, including tugs, trawlers, coasters.
Publishing on most aspects of merchant shipping history.

Special collections
Negative collections include those of:
Basil Feilden, Southport
Harry Stewart, Preston
Tom Rayner, Isle of Wight
John MacRoberts, Wallasey.

Publications
'Ships in Focus Record', a 64-page illustrated journal quarterly of shipping history.
Histories and fleet lists of shipping companies, illustrated histories, books of photographs and marine paintings, and the bi-annual 'Short Sea Shipping'.

Cleveland County Archives
See Teesside Archives

Clwyd Record Office
See Flintshire Record Office

C21
CLYDE YACHT CLUBS' ASSOCIATION

PO Box 5438
Helensburgh
Argyll and Bute G84 8WH
e-mail: cycaoffice@rya-online.net
Website: www.cyca-online.org.uk

Tel: 01436 821234
Fax: 01436 821234

Association of yacht clubs

Facilities
Enquiries to the Hon. Secretary
Information provided by phone, post, fax, e-mail and website
Open to the public
Photocopying facilities

Subject coverage
Repository of C-suffix sail numbers (CYCA is issuing body)
Repository of Clyde handicaps (CYCA handicapping system)

Specific databases
As above

Publications
'CYCA Yearbook' (March, annually) £2.50
'CYCA Handicap Manual' (annually, April), £25.00

Clydebank Library

See West Dunbartonshire Libraries - Clydebank

C22
CLYDEBANK MUSEUM

Town Hall	Tel: 01389 738702
Dumbarton Road	Fax: 0141 952 1243 or
Clydebank G81 6UB	0141 952 8260

e-mail: cbank.museum@west-dumbarton.gov.uk

Local government museum

Facilities
Enquiries to the Curator
Information provided by phone, post and e-mail
Open to the public
Opening hours: Mondays, Wednesdays, Thursdays,
Fridays 14.00-16.30; Tuesdays and Saturdays 10.00-16.30

Subject coverage
Marine engineering

Special collections
Gilbert Mann philatelic collection - first day covers -
Queen Mary, Queen Elizabeth 2
Small collection of ship models

Specific companies and groups
Small collection relating to John Brown (shipbuilders)
Main collection held at West Dunbartonshire Library,
Clydebank (contact Information Services Librarian)

Publications
'Making Ships Making Men', 1991

C23
CLYDEPORT LTD

16 Robertson Street	Tel: 0141 221 8733
Glasgow G2 8DS	Fax: 0141 248 3167

Website: www.clydeport.co.uk

Port operating company

C24
COASTAL FORCES VETERANS ASSOCIATION

15 Henning Street	Tel: 020 7228 6256
Battersea	
London SW11 3DR	

Ex-service association (Royal Navy)

Facilities
Enquiries to the National Secretary
Information provided by phone and post
Open to members but can answer general enquiries
Limited research service available via the Association's
Historian

For research, please contact Mr G Hudson, 25, The
Avenue, Halifax, W. Yorkshire HX3 8NP, tel. 01422
201234, sending an SAE

Subject coverage
Operation of light coastal forces, e.g., MTBs, MGBs,
MLs, in Second World War.
Boat types, numbers and flotillas; some crew names;
details of actions

Special collections
Heritage Trust holds books and artefacts, which will
eventually be added to the RN Museum at Portsmouth
Dockyard

Publications
Quarterly newsletter

C25
HMS COLLINGWOOD COMMUNICATIONS AND RADAR MUSEUM

HMS Collingwood Museum	Tel: 01329 332535
(Mondays only)	
Newgate Lane	
Fareham	
Hampshire PO14 1AS	

Museum

Facilities
Enquiries to the Museum Curator or Museum
Archivist
Information provided by phone and post
Open to the public by appointment
Photocopying facilities
Research service available - no fixed cost but
donations welcome

Subject coverage
Civilian and naval publications relating to naval
communications and radar equipment, 1885-1990

Special collections:
HMS *Vernon* dockets, 1880-1920

C26
COMITE INTERNATIONAL RADIO-MARITIME (CIRM)

South Bank House	Tel: 0207 587 1245
Black Prince Road	Fax: 0207 587 1436
London SE1 7SJ	

e-mail: secgen@cirm.org
Website: www.cirm.org

International non-governmental organisation for
maritime electronics

Facilities
Enquiries to the Secretary General
Open to members only

Subject coverage
Maritime radiocommunications including GMDS, EPIRBs, SART; navigational systems and equipment including GNSS, radar, ARPA, ECDIS, AIS and VDR

Publications
See website

C27
COMMONWEALTH WAR GRAVES COMMISSION

2 Marlow Road	Tel: 01628 507200
Maidenhead	Fax: 01628 771208
Berkshire SL6 7DX	

e-mail: casualty.enq@cwgc.org
Website: www.cwgc.org

Government organisation

Facilities
Enquiries to the Enquiries Section for casualty traces and Records Section for research
Information provided by phone for simple traces, otherwise written enquiries preferred
No personal callers - bona fide researchers by special arrangement only
Photocopying facilities

Subject coverage
Limited to Commonwealth casualties and burials of the two world wars, plus civilian war dead

Specific databases
First and Second World Wars Commonwealth casualty database, includes Second World War civilian war dead

Publications
'Debt of Honour' website (search via: www.cwgc.org)
Annual Report
Information sheets on some CWGC Memorials and Cemeteries

C28
CONFEDERATION OF SHIPBUILDING AND ENGINEERING UNIONS (CSEU)

140/142 Walworth Road
London
SE17 1JW

Trade union, affiliated to the Parliamentary Maritime Group

Enquiries to the General Secretary

Subject coverage
Shipbuilding; ship repair; marine engine manufacture

C29
THE CORACLE SOCIETY

Membership Secretary	Chairman
The Coracle Society	24 Watling Street
5 Cedar Close	Leintwardine
Teignmouth	Shropshire SY7 0LW
Devon TQ14 8UZ	

e-mail: (Ed. Officer) info@coracle-society.org
Website: www.coracle-society.org

Society for those interested or involved in coracles and allied craft

Facilities
Enquiries to the Chairman
Information provided by phone, post and (preferred) e-mail
Open to the public - some information available to members only
Research service not available - information provided free or posted at nominal charge

Subject coverage
The Society holds few records of its own but individual members hold information which can be made available on coracles, curraghs and allied craft, their use, distribution and construction
Archive at Museum of Welsh Folk Life, St. Fagan's, Cardiff

Special collections
Unique photographic collection of Irish curraghs
Cenarth Coracle Centre: Martin Fowler: www.coraclecentre.co.uk

Publications
See website for details of publications, including bibliography, safety guidelines, paddling guide

---

Cornish History Research Centre
See Courtney Library

C30
CORNWALL COUNTY RECORD OFFICE

County Hall	Tel: 01872 323127
Truro	Fax: 01872 270340
Cornwall TR1 3AY	

e-mail: cro@cornwall.gov.uk
Website: www.cornwall.gov.uk

Local government organisation

Facilities

Enquiries to the County Archivist
Information provided by phone, post and e-mail
Open to the public: Tuesdays-Thursdays 0930-1700;
Fridays 0900-1600; Saturdays 0900-1200; appointments
required
Photocopying facilities
Microfilm and microfiche readers; microcopies and
fullsize copies provided
Research service provided; £13 per hour, plus VAT

Subject coverage

Shipbuilding; registration ports; crew lists; fishing boat
agreements; Customs and Excise records; lifeboat
records; ships' logs

C31
CORPORATION OF LONDON RECORDS OFFICE (CLRO)

P.O. Box 270   Tel: 020 7332 1251
Guildhall   Fax: 020 7710 8682
London EC2P 2EJ
e-mail: CLRO@corpoflondon.gov.uk
Website: www.cityoflondon.gov.uk/archives/clro

Local government organisation

Facilities

Enquiries to the City Archivist
Information provided by phone, post, fax and e-mail
Open to the public: Monday-Friday 0930-1645
Photocopying facilities - photocopying policy applies
Very limited research service available in response to
enquiries, without charge

Subject coverage

Archives of the Corporation of London, including
Thames navigation; City Canal/Isle of Dogs Canal;
conservation of the River Thames to 1857; Port of
London; Admiralty suits (City of London Court, later
Mayor's and City of London Court); Coroner's records
(City of London and Southwark) including details of
accidental deaths (some maritime)

Special collections:

The City's medieval archives include an account of the
Battle of Sluys, 1340, with some details of ships, and
there are occasional references to ships and shipping
generally. A text of the medieval maritime laws known
as the laws of Oléron is contained within the 14th
century Liber Horn

Publications

'Greater London History Sources: Volume 1 City of
London' (Guildhall Library in association with the
Greater London Archives Network, 2000) covering
CLRO, Guildhall Library and St. Bartholomew's
Hospital Archives and Museum

C32
THE CORPORATION OF TRINITY HOUSE

Trinity House   Tel: 020 7481 6900
Tower Hill   Fax: 020 7480 7662
London EC3N 4DH
e-mail: Breda.Wall@thls.org ;
Howard.Cooper@thls.org
Website: www.trinityhouse.co.uk

National government organisation

Facilities

Enquiries to the Media & Communication Officer
Information provided by phone, post, fax or e-mail

Subject coverage

The history of the Corporation of Trinity House; the
history of lighthouses and pilotage; the present day
activities of the lighthouse service

Special collections

The archives of the Corporation of Trinity House have
recently been transferred to Guildhall Library where
they can be accessed by the public.
There is a private collection of photographs of Trinity
House and Northern Lighthouse Board subjects,
details of which are available from Mr C Nicholson,
5 Broderip, Cossington, Bridgwater, Somerset TA7 8LB

Publications

Annual Review
Information pack
Flash in house magazine (quarterly)

C33
THE COURTNEY LIBRARY AND CORNISH HISTORY RESEARCH CENTRE

The Royal Institution of Cornwall   Tel: 01872 272205
River Street   Fax: 01872 240514
Truro TR1 2ST
e-mail: ric@royal-cornwall-museum.freeserve.co.uk
Website: www.cornwall-online.co.uk/ric

Learned society and registered charity

Facilities

Enquiries to the Librarian
Information provided by phone, post, fax and e-mail
Members' library but open to the public for research
only (closed access to book stacks): Monday-Saturday
1000-1300 and 1400-1700 (closed Bank Holidays)
Limited photocopying facilities - maximum 10 sheets
per visit and subject to copyright. No photocopies
supplied from rare, fragile or tightly bound volumes
Limited research service available - 1 hour maximum,
£10 donation to Library Book Fund

Subject coverage
All fields, but special emphasis on the history of
Cornwall, including shipbuilding, shipwrecks, lifeboats

Special collections:
Noall Collection: lifeboats/lighthouses
Dunn Collection: lifeboats
Dunn Collection: shipwrecks, 1800-1964
Philorick Collection: Post Office Packet Service, 17th-19th century
The Ernest Hicks Collection, 1927-1958
© Captain George Hogg: shipbuilding database, 1790-1914
'Lloyds' Registers', 1780, 1850, 1880, 1894-2002 (some gaps)
'Lloyds' Register of Yachts', 1889-1980 (some gaps)
'Mariners' Mirror', 1936-1002

Specific databases
'Shipsalvage and Wreck: Plymouth area, 18-19th century' Gary Hicks

Publications
'Sources for Maritime Research (at the RIC)' - 20p plus postage

---

C34
COWES MARITIME MUSEUM
Branch Library and Maritime Museum
Beckford Road   Tel: 01983 293341
Cowes
Isle of Wight PO31 7SG

Local government organisation

Facilities
Enquiries to the Librarian, Cowes Library and Curator of Human History (01983 823433)
Information provided by phone, post and fax
Open to the public: Monday-Friday (closed Thursday) and Saturday 0930-1630
Appointment necessary for the research of specific information
Photocopying facilities

Subject coverage
Maritime history of the Isle of Wight, including ship and boat building; yachting; lifeboats - building and rescue; hovercraft; revenue and customs services; Trinity House, Uffa Fox

Special collections
Photographic collection from John Samuel White & Co. Ltd.
Photographic collection of yachting by Kirk of Cowes
Plans of locally built ships and boats
Approx. 7,000 maritime books and periodicals

Specific companies or groups
John Samuel White & Co. Ltd.

C35
THE CRUISING ASSOCIATION
CA House
1 Northey Street   Tel 020 7537 2828
Limehouse Basin   Fax 020 7537 2266
London
E14 8BT
Email office@cruising.org.uk
Website: www.cruising-association.com/

Amateur sailing association

Facilities
Enquiries to the General Secretary
Information given by phone, post, fax or email to members only
Open to members only
Loans to members only
Fullsize copies can be supplied on request
On-line information service available

Subject coverage
Sailing boats and cruising

Special collections
Some rare books held

C36
CUMBRIA ARCHIVE SERVICE - BARROW-IN-FURNESS
Cumbria Record Office and Local Studies Library
140 Duke Street   Tel: 01229 894363
Barrow-in-Furness   Fax: 01229 894364
Cumbria LA14 1XW
e-mail: barrow.record.office@cumbriacc.gov.uk
Website: www.cumbria.gov.uk/archives

Local government organisation. A joint operation between Cumbria Archive Service and Cumbria Library Service

Facilities
Enquiries to the Area Archivist
Information provided by phone, post, fax and e-mail
Open to the public (CARN network readers' tickets required for Archives sources)
Archives Sources - Monday-Friday 0930-1700,
Wednesday 1700-1900 and Saturday 0930-1600
Local Studies Library - Monday-Wednesday, Friday 0930-1900, Thursday 0930-1700 and Saturday 0930-1600
Photocopying facilities
Research service available - £19 per hour (normally 3 hours maximum for individual enquiry) plus £1 postage

Subject coverage
Archive sources from local authorities, businesses and general community of Southwest Cumbria; books and printed material relating chiefly to Barrow and the Furness area

Special collections

Vickers (Barrow): naval armaments plans (chiefly gun mountings), c.1898-1951; naval architecture records, c.1900-c.1960; apprenticeship records, early 20th century; Port of Barrow records, 19th-20th century, including Registers of Shipping, 1868-1925; some crew lists, 1868-1913

Royal National Lifeboat Institution (Barrow) records, 1895-1973

Diaries of voyages: *Montmorency* (Liverpool-Brisbane, 1863), *Oakhurst* (Liverpool-Australia, 1898)

Microfilm sources: Port of Lancaster shipping registers, 1786-1905, Ulverston Canal Company minutes, 1797-1850

Specific companies and groups

Vickers (Barrow) - as above (other records have been dispersed to other repositories)

Publications

Brief information sheet on sources for ships and shipbuilding

Catalogues on websites currently being developed

C37
CUMBRIA ARCHIVE SERVICE - CARLISLE

Cumbria Record Office   Tel: 01228 607285
The Castle   Fax: 01228 607270
Carlisle CA3 8UR
e-mail: carlisle.record.office@cumbriacc.gov.uk
Website: www.cumbria.gov.uk/archives

Local government organisation

Facilities

Enquiries to the Assistant County Archivist, Carlisle
Information provided by phone, post, e-mail and paid research
Open to the public: Monday-Friday 0900-1700
Official proof of name, current home address and signature required
Photocopying facilities
Research service available - £20 per hour

Subject coverage

Shipping registers, registration records for the ports of Carlisle, Maryport, Silloth, 1786-1974; crew lists and agreements for ships from Allonby, Carlisle and Maryport

Publications

Crew lists available on website

C38
CUMBRIA ARCHIVE SERVICE - KENDAL

Cumbria Record Office   Tel: 01539 773540
County Offices   minicom: 01228 606336
Stricklandgate
Kendal
Cumbria LA9 4RQ
Website: www.cumbria.gov.uk/archives

Record office

Facilities

Enquiries to the County Archivist
Information provided by phone, post, or fax
Open to the public: Mondays-Fridays 0900-1700
Microfilm, microfiche and microprint readers; microcopies and fullsize copies can be provided
Research service provided; £18 per hour, plus postage and handling

Special collections

Orders in Council relating to seamen, 1738-1744
Letters, referring to press gang in Liverpool (1801) and Southwark, London (1790-91)
Shipping registers 1823-1858

C39
CUMBRIA ARCHIVE SERVICE - WHITEHAVEN

Cumbria Record Office and Local Studies Library
Scotch Street   Tel: 01946 852920
Whitehaven   Fax: 01946 852919
Cumbria CA28 7NL
e-mail: whitehaven.record.office@cumbriacc.gov.uk
Website: www.cumbria.gov.uk/archives

Local government organisation

Facilities

Enquiries to the Acting Area Archivist
Information provided by phone, post, fax and e-mail
Open to the public: Monday-Tuesday, Thursday-Friday 0930-1700, Wednesday 0930-1900 and Saturday 0900-1300
No appointment necessary but readers need CARN ticket (proof of ID required)
Readers must request documents in advance on Wednesday evenings and Saturdays
Photocopying facilities
Research service available (can search across other Cumbria Record Offices in Barrow, Carlisle and Kendal) - £20 per hour

Subject coverage

Records relating to West Cumberland, including local government, family estates, businesses, religious organisations, schools, solicitors, census returns for West Cumberland, 1841-1901

IGI; maps; newspapers; GRO index; local studies library

Special collections
Registers of ships and crew lists, etc. Whitehaven and Workington, 1786-20th century
Whitehaven Town and Harbour Trustees records, 1812-1894
Whitehaven Harbour Commissioners, 1924-1956 (registers of cargo vessels)

Specific databases
Card index of vessels, masters, owners, shareholders and shipyards in shipping registers
Card index of vessels, subjects and persons mentioned in 'Cumberland Pacquet', newspaper, 1774-mid 19th century

Publications
'Cumbrian Ancestors' for family historians

Customs and Excise
See HM Customs and Excise

C40
THE CUTTY SARK TRUST
2 Greenwich Church Street   Tel: 020 8858 2698
Greenwich   Fax: 020 8858 6976
London SE10 9BG
e-mail: info@cuttysark.org.uk
Website: www.cuttysark.org.uk

Museum/clipper ship

Facilities
Enquiries to the Research Assistant
Information provided by phone, post, fax and e-mail
Open to the public
Research service available - each request considered on its merits; prices on request

Subject coverage
Archive of documents, photographs, books and artefacts relating to the *Cutty Sark;* the clipper ship genre; the Merchant Navy; international trade; Robert Burns

Special collections
Sydney Cumber's Merchant Navy figurehead collection
Indentures and certificates relating to apprentices, officers and crew of the *Cutty Sark*
Logs of the *Cutty Sark*

D1
DARTMOUTH MUSEUM
The Butterwalk   Tel: 01803 832923
Dartmouth
Devon TQ6 9PZ
e-mail: dartmouth@devonmuseums.net
Website: www.devonmuseums.net/dartmouth

Museum (voluntary organisation)

Facilities
Enquiries to the Honorary Curator
Information provided by phone, post, fax and e-mail
Open to the public
Photocopying facilities
Limited research service available

Subject coverage
Ship models, maps, pictures, photographs and general local artefacts

Publications
Brief catalogues/guides available on entry

D2
DEAL MARITIME AND LOCAL HISTORY MUSEUM
22 St George's Road   Tel: 01304 381344
Deal
Kent CT14 6BA
e-mail: dealmuseum@lineone.net
Website: www.dealmuseum.org.uk

Voluntary organisation and museum with a small library

Facilities
Enquiries to the Secretary
Information provided by phone, post, fax and e-mail
Open to Friends of the Museum only (minimum annual subscription £5 includes free entry and newsletter), 1st April - 30th September 1400-1700
Supervised access, appointment necessary
Limited research service available

Subject coverage
Parish registers (transcripts); cemetery documents: burial register, plots, etc.; directories; photographs

Special collections
MS journal of William Stanton, 19th century Deal pilot
Will Honey collection of photographs (boats and local maritime scenes)

Defence Research Agency
See QINETIQ

D3
DENBIGHSHIRE RECORD OFFICE
46 Clwyd Street   Tel: 01824 708250
Ruthin   Fax: 01824 708258
Denbighshire LL15 1HP
e-mail: dcc-archives@denbighshire.gov.uk
Website: www.denbighshire.gov.uk

Local government organisation and archive

Facilities
Enquiries to the County Archivist
Information provided by phone, post, fax and e-mail
Open to the public: Monday-Thursday 1000-1645 and Friday 1000-1615
Appointment preferred and advisable for use of microfilm/fiche
Photocopying facilities
Research service available

Subject coverage
Denbighshire public records, including quarter sessions; hospital records; parish records

---

D4
DEPARTMENT OF TRANSPORT, LOCAL GOVERNMENT AND THE REGIONS
76 Marsham Street   Tel: 020 7944 2002
London SW1P 4DR   Fax: 020 7944 4716
Website: www.dtlr.gov.uk

Government departmental library

Facilities
Enquiries to the Librarian
Information provided by phone, post, fax and e-mail
Open to departmental employees, other government departments and the public (by appointment for unique collections only)
Photocopying facilities
Research service for departmental staff only

Subject coverage
Transport by rail, air, sea, road; government

Special collections
Departmental publications from DTLR, DETR and DOT
For information relating to First and Second World War shipwrecks covered by the Government War Risks Insurance Scheme, contact DTLR Defence and Civil Contingencies Planning or e-mail john.neary@gsi.gov.uk

Publications
See website

Department of Transport Marine Library
See: Maritime and Coastguard Agency

D5
DERBYSHIRE RECORD OFFICE
County Hall   Tel: 01629 580000
Matlock   Ext. 35202
Derbyshire DE4 3AG   Fax: 01629 57611
e-mail: record.office@derbyshire.gov.uk
Website: www.derbyshire.gov.uk

Local government organisation/county record office

Facilities
Enquiries to the County Archivist
Information provided by e-mail or post (phone enquiries only for opening hours, etc. please) and published guides include annual list of accessions
Open to the public who have registered as readers: Monday-Friday 0930-1645
Appointment advisable: tel.: 01629 585347
Photocopying facilities subject to conservation and copyright requirements (staff use only)
Research service available - searches undertaken in DRO holdings and charged at half-hourly rate (please enquire for details of current charges)

Subject coverage
Official and public records of Derby and Derbyshire; ecclesiastical parish and diocesan records of Derbyshire; family and estate papers; business records; archives of societies and voluntary groups; nonconformist church records; maps and plans

Publications
Derbyshire Record Office Guide
Selected family and estate series and Derbyshire Quarter sessions records on www.a2a.pro.gov.uk

---

D6
DEVON RECORD OFFICE
Castle Street   Tel: 01392 384253
Exeter   Fax: 01392 384256
Devon EX4 3PU
e-mail: devrec@devon.gov.uk
Website: www.devon.gov.uk/dro/homepage.html

Local government organisation

Facilities
Enquiries to the Archivist
Information provided by phone, fax, post and e-mail
Open to the public: Monday-Thursday 1000-1700 and Friday 1000-1630. Proof of identity required and subject to payment of a charge (exemptions for certain categories of use e.g. education)
Photocopying facilities
Research service available - £18 per hour, minimum charge £10 per half hour, 2 hours work maximum at a time, 4-6 weeks response time

Subject coverage

Shipping Registers of Dartmouth, 1824-1900 from which were formed Brixham, 1864-1905 and Salcombe, 1867-1918; Exeter, 1786-1934 from which was formed Teignmouth, 1853-1939

Special collections

Brixham apprentices, 1891-1912
Crew lists and cognate papers, a selection from the Public Record Office, general series, 1863-1914 and fishing vessels, 1884-1914
Exeter City records including customs records of local dues on vessels inwards, 1302-1610, Town Customs books, 1699-1856 and wharfinger records, 1581 to 19th century
Exeter Admiralty Court records, 1623-1719, civil cases
Topsham River Commissioners records, 1840-1976
Teignmouth Harbour Commissioners records, 1836-1924; also Swedish and Norwegian consulate, 1853-1990
Unofficial register of shipping, 1869-1885
Exeter Whale Fishery ledger, 1754-1759
Holman Bequest, log books and ledgers, 1711-1895
Addington Family papers, including letters of Nelson and other figures of Napoleonic wars, documentation of Captain Manby's life-saving apparatus and late 19th century midshipman's log books
Seymour Family papers, letters on maritime affairs c.1590-1610, papers of 12th Duke of Somerset as 1st Lord of the Admiralty, 1859-1866

Publications

'Ports of the Exe Estuary' E A G Clark
Ship's Crew Lists
Guides to sources, leaflets on Family History, Maritime History and Transport History
Sources for 'The New Maritime History of Devon'
'The New Maritime History of Devon', 2 volumes (University of Exeter, 1992 and 1994)

Specific databases

Crew list, etc., catalogues available online (Access2.Archives) at www.a2a.pro.gov.uk

---

Devon Record Office

See also: North Devon Record Office (Barnstaple)
Plymouth and West Devon Record Office
Plymouth Central Library

Discovery (RRS)

See Dundee Heritage Trust - RRS (Royal Research Ship) Discovery

---

D7
THE DOCK MUSEUM - BARROW

North Road   Tel: 01229 894444
Barrow-in-Furness   Fax: 01229 811361
Cumbria LA14 2PW
e-mail: dockmuseum@barrowbc.gov.uk
Website: www.dockmuseum.org.uk

Museum

Facilities

Enquiries to the Collections and Exhibitions Officer
Information provided by phone, post, fax and e-mail
Open to the public and fully accessible to wheelchair-users: Tuesday-Friday 1000-1700 and Saturday-Sunday 1100-1700 (last admissions 16.15 each day)
Photocopying facilities
Research service available - basic enquiries answered free of charge, detailed research enquiries charged at £5 per hour

Special collections

Vickers photographic archive of 10,000 glass plate negatives, cine film, etc
Photographs of Barrow shipyard from 1860-1960s can be viewed on the Museum website (see above); small collection of Barrow-built ships' plans and ship models

Publications

Vickers photographic archive available online - see website

D8
DOLPHIN SAILING BARGE MUSEUM

Crown Quay Lane   Tel: 01795 421549
Sittingbourne
Kent ME10 3SN
Website: www.kentaccess.org.uk.artmuse/dolphin

Museum and charitable trust

Facilities

Enquiries to the Honorary Secretary
Information provided by phone and post
Open to the public
Research service available by arrangement only - free but limited to museum opening hours

Subject coverage

All aspects of the Thames spritsail barges

Special collections

Collection of documents and photographs relating to barges, apprenticeships and bills of lading

---

D9
DONCASTER ARCHIVES

King Edward Road   Tel: 01302 859811
Doncaster DN4 0NA
e-mail: doncasterarchives@doncaster.gov.uk
Website: doncaster.gov.uk/education/

Local government organisation

Facilities
Enquiries to the Principal Archivist
Information provided primarily by personal visit
Limited information provided by phone, post and e-mail
Open to the public: Mondays-Fridays 0900-1245; 1400-1645
Photocopying facilities available
Research service provided. £10.30 charged for half-hour search; more detailed searches are referred to a record agent

Subject coverage
Usual range of local authority records

Special collections
Register of vessels plying waterways in the Doncaster area, 1795-1803 (AB/5)

Records of specific companies
Richard Dunston of Thorne, shipbuilders, 1913-1970

Publications
'A Guide to Doncaster Archives', B J Barber, 2001
See website

D10
DORSET RECORD OFFICE

Bridport Road   Tel: 01305 250550
Dorchester
Dorset DT1 1RP

Local government organisation

Facilities
Enquiries to the County Archivist
Information given by phone and post
Open to the public
Microfilm and microfiche readers
Microcopies and fullsize copies provided
Charges made for research by staff

Special collections
Letterbook of Robert Gregory, Mayor of Weymouth, Vice-Admiral of Dorset and Starcher at Poole, c. 1560-1610 (original at Harvard)
Customs and Excise: Poole accounts, 1559-1560, 1562-1563
List of ships under command of Sir Clowdisley Shovell to go before Dunkirk

Rules of discipline on board HM ships, 1730
Notes of wrecks of ships on Portland, 1795-1840
Memoranda on Portland wrecks, 1815-1876
Papers concerning the naval career of Vice-Admiral Robert Fitzroy, 1818-1863
Papers of Rear-Admiral H W Battiscombe, 1846-1863
Complement of HMS *Victory* before paying off, 1868
Records of Royal National Lifeboat Institution, Swanage, 1876-1975
Three volumes of the diary of Sir George Bingham KCB, Lt Col. 53rd Reg. during the voyage from Plymouth to St Helena on board HMS *Northumberland* which took Napoleon to St Helena
Shipping registers and crew lists:

Poole	Shipping registers, 1855-1893
	Summary of shipping registers, 1855-1913
	Crew lists and agreements, 1863-1913
Weymouth	Summary of shipping registers, 1786-1913
	Crew lists and agreements, 1863-1913
Bridport	Summary of shipping registers, 1832-1880
	Crew lists and agreements, 1863-1880
Lyme Regis	Shipping registers, 1786-1880 and summary
	Transactions book, 1836-1855
	Crew lists and agreements, 1863-1880

Records relating to Bridport harbour

D11
DOVER HARBOUR BOARD (PORT OF DOVER)

Harbour House   Tel: 01304 240400
Dover   Fax: 01304 240465
Kent CT17 9BU
e-mail: pr@doverport.co.uk
Website: www. doverport.co.uk

Statutory board operating cross-channel terminals, cruise terminals, a deep sea cargo berth and a marina

Facilities
Enquiries to the Managing Director

Subject coverage
Port administration, particularly cross-channel passenger trade and roll-on roll-off traffic

Publications
Annual Report
Annual Performance Report
Statistical digests
Service brochures

D12
DOVER MUSEUM AND THE BRONZE AGE BOAT GALLERY

Market Square	Tel: 01304 201066
Dover	Fax: 01304 241186
Kent CT16 1PB	

e-mail: museum@dover.gov.uk
Website: www.dovermuseum.co.uk

Museum

Facilities
Enquiries to the Curator
Information provided by phone, post, fax and e-mail
Open to the public by appointment only: Research
Library open Monday-Friday 1000-1600
Photocopying facilities
Research service available - first half hour free, costs
negotiable thereafter

Subject coverage
Dover Bronze Age Boat - all excavation and research
records; photographic collection of ferries, merchant
ships and other Channel vessels; 'crazy crossings' -
photographs and research on unusual methods of
crossing the English Channel; Channel swimming archive;
Cinque Port Pilots' archive; Channel Passage archive

Specific companies and groups
Cinque Port Pilots' Association

Specific databases
Digital image database comprising all paintings and
photographs in the museum collection, searchable by
subject and keyword (currently 20,000 images)

Publications
Dover Museum Guide
Dover Bronze Age Boat Gallery Guide

D13
DOVER TRANSPORT MUSEUM SOCIETY

Port Zone	Tel: 01304 822409
Unit 26	
White Cliffs Business Park	
Dover CT16 2HJ	

The museum is expected to relocate in 2004

Voluntary association

Facilities
Enquiries to the Secretary
Library open to the public by appointment
Postal queries answered if SAE provided

Subject coverage
Development of the port of Dover; construction of
the Admiralty Harbour; Richborough port; Dover train

ferry dock; cross-channel travel including railway
involvement; charts of the English Channel

Downing College
See: Cambridge University

D14
DUDLEY ARCHIVES AND LOCAL HISTORY SERVICE (DUDLEY MBC)

Mount Pleasant Street	Tel: 01384 812770
Coseley	Fax: 01384 812770
West Midlands WV14 9JR	

e-mail: archives.ed@dudley.gov.uk
Website: www.dudley.gov.uk

Local government organisation

Facilities
Enquiries to the Archivist
Information provided by phone, post, fax, e-mail and
personal visit
Open to the public`; Tuesday, Wednesday, Friday 0900-
1700, Thursday 0930-1900 and 1st and 3rd Saturdays in
the month by appointment only 0930-1230
Material must be ordered in advance for Saturday
appointments (appointments are also advisable for
microform material)
Member of the CARN scheme
Photocopying facilities
Research service available - £15 per hour, £7.50 per
half-hour (minimum charge), payable in advance

Subject coverage
Local authority records (records of our parent
authority and its predecessors); records of local firms,
organisations, individuals and churches; of special note,
the archive of the Earls of Dudley, 12-20th centuries

Special collections
N Hingley and Sons Ltd., chain cable and anchor
manufacturers and associated companies
Jones and Lloyd, chain manufacturers
Walter Somers Ltd., naval forging manufacturers
TW King - collection of canal photographs

D15
DUKE OF NORFOLK'S LIBRARY

Arundel Castle	Tel: 01903 882173
Sussex BN18 9AB	Fax: 01903 885801

e-mail: info@arundelcastle.org

Private library

Facilities
Enquiries to the Librarian
Information provided by phone, post, fax and e-mail
Facilities available to accredited scholars by written

appointment
Opening hours: Tuesdays & Wednesdays 1000-1700, by written appointment
Photocopying facilities
Research service not provided

Subject coverage
Family papers relating to Lord Howard of Effingham and Admiral Lord Lyons

Publications
Four printed catalogues, ed. F W Steer, West Sussex County Council

---

Dumbarton District Libraries
See: West Dunbartonshire Libraries

D16
DUMFRIES AND GALLOWAY COUNCIL LIBRARIES, INFORMATION AND ARCHIVES

Central Support Unit	Tel: 01387 253890
Ewart Library	Fax: 01387 264126
Catherine Street	
Dumfries DG1 1JB	

e-mail: libs&1@dumgal.gov.uk
Website: www.dumgal.gov.uk/lia

Local government organisation

Facilities
Enquiries to the Archivist and Records Management Officer
Information provided by phone (limited enquiries only), post, fax and e-mail
Open to the public: Monday-Wednesday and Friday 0915-1930, Thursday and Saturday 0915-1700. Some material is held in the Archive Centre, which has very limited opening hours. Please see website (or telephone) for further information
Photocopying facilities
Fee-based research service available by post, e-mail or personal consultation - £15 per hour. Please see www.dumgal.gov.uk/lia

Subject coverage
Burgh court, administrative, financial and planning records for Dumfries and Sanquhar; county records re. roads, poor relief, records of families, estates, businesses and societies throughout Dumfries and Galloway; local church records, architectural drawings, maps and motor vehicle licensing records - period covered c1450 to date; diaries of sea voyages. Approximately 250 records relate specifically to shipping

Special collections
Tonnage of ships in port of Dumfries and impost payable 1731-1802
Customs and Excise records of Dumfries, Kirkcudbright, Langholm, Wigtown and Stranraer, 1824-1973 (indexed online)
Research notes on Solway shipping - ships, cargoes and shipwrecks
Records of the Nith Navigation Commissioners (set up by Royal Commission to improve navigation on the River Nith, 1746-1949
Microfilm of customs records for Dumfries, Port Patrick, Kirkcudbright and Alison Bank, 1665-1830

Specific companies and groups
Records of the Nith Navigation Commissioners, 1746-1949
Records of the Innerwell Salmon Fishery, Garlieston, 1961-1992 (including haaf and stake net fishing on the Solway)

Specific databases
Online (internet) database index to shipping registers to Dumfries, Kirkcudbright, Wigtown and Stranraer, 1824 to mid 1850s. Access is via Historical Indexes on our website www.dumgal.gov.uk/lia

Publications
Most of the holdings guide is on website
Information on indexing projects on Friends of the Archives of Dumfries and Galloway site - www.dgarchives.fsnet.co.uk
Pamphlets and source lists also available

Dunbartonshire Libraries
See: East Dunbartonshire Libraries
West Dunbartonshire Libraries

D17
DUNDEE CENTRAL LIBRARY

Central Library	Tel: 01382 434377
The Wellgate	Fax: 01382 434036
Dundee DD1 1DB	

e-mail address: local.studies@dundeecity.gov.uk
Website: www.dundeecity.gov.uk/centlib/

Local studies library

Facilities
Enquiries to the Local Studies Librarian
Library open to the general public: Monday, Tuesday, Friday: 0930-1800; Wednesday: 1000-1800; Thursday: 0930-2000; Saturday: 0930-1700
Information given by phone, post, fax, e-mail,
Photocopying facilities
Limited research by library staff available on specific enquiries about ships or seafarers or incidents with Dundee connection. Minimum charge of £2 to cover costs.

Special collections
Local newspapers

Wilson Collection of glass negatives of ships in Dundee Harbour and the Tay, late 19th century
John Ingram, Shipping Correspondent of the Dundee Evening Telegraph, shipping notebooks (history of Dundee-owned and -built ships, history of shipping in the Tay, North Fife and County Angus, 18th century-c1975)
Books about local shipping companies

D18
DUNDEE CITY ARCHIVES

Support Services' Department Tel: 01382 434494
21 City Square   Fax: 01382 434666
Dundee DD1 3BY
(callers enter by 1 Shore Street)
e-mail: archives@dundeecity.gov.uk
Website: www.dundeecity.gov.uk/archives

Local government organisation

Facilities
Enquiries to the City Archivist
Information provided by phone, post, fax or e-mail
Open to the public by appointment only
Photocopying facilities

Subject coverage
Shipbuilding; Dundee harbour

Special collections
Dundee Port Authority records 1814-1992
Robb Caledon, Dundee, plans and photographs, 1876-1965
Gourlay Brothers, Dundee, plans 1859-1908

Publications
Website: www.dundeecity.gov.uk/archives

D19
DUNDEE INDUSTRIAL HERITAGE TRUST - RRS (ROYAL RESEARCH SHIP) DISCOVERY

Discovery Point   Tel: 01382 201 245
Discovery Quay   Fax: 01382 225 891
Dundee DD1 4XA
e-mail: info@dundeeheritage.sol.co.uk
Website: www.rrsdiscovery.com

Museum

Facilities
Enquiries to the Operations Director
Information provided by phone, post, fax and e-mail
Open to the public all week, all year round except Christmas and New Year
Appointment necessary for Reference Library
Photocopying facilities
Research service available - cost and limitations vary at

discretion of Director (e.g. small searches usually free)

Subject coverage
Archives, photographs, objects and reference material relating to the history of RRS Discovery, the ship built in Dundee for the 1901-04 British National Antarctic Expedition led by Captain Robert Falcon Scott

Special collections
The Colbeck Collection of papers, letters, photographs and objects relating to Captain William Colbeck of the Morning and his son, Captain William R. Colbeck of the Discovery

---

D20
DUNDEE UNIVERSITY ARCHIVES, RECORDS MANAGEMENT AND MUSEUM SERVICES

University of Dundee   Tel: 01382 307095
Tower Building   Fax: 01382 29190
Nethergate
Dundee DD1 4HN
e-mail: archives@dundee.ac.uk
website: www.dundee.ac.uk/armms/

University archives

Facilities
Enquiries to the Archivist
Open to the public
Information given by phone, post or fax
Microfiche reader
Fullsize copies can be provided

Subject coverage
Coastguard service; ferries; fishing (whaling, sealing); harbours; investment; jute processing (use of whale oil in); marine engineering; naval history; pollution; seamanship; shipbuilding/manufacture; shipowning; trade (including disputes over damage to cargoes)

Special collections
Baxter Brothers, linen and jute manufacturers, Dundee (Admiralty contracts)
Dorothy Whale Fishing Co. and Friendship Whale Fishing Co.
Dundee Harbour Commissioners
Dundee, Perth and London Shipping Co., Dundee
Gourlay Bros. (Dundee), engineers and shipbuilders
James Allison and Sons (sailmakers) rope, sail and tent makers, ship chandlers and ship owners, Dundee
James Dalyell (1798-1870), naval officer, HM Coastguard, Buckie and Carnoustie
John Ingram (d.1984), shipping correspondent
Jute Importers Association
Tay Whale Fishing Co., Dundee.

Specific database
Ingram shipping database of information on ships built at Dundee 1767-1980

Publications
Shipping source list available.
On-line library catalogue.

D21
DUNDEE UNIVERSITY LIBRARY

University of Dundee   Tel: 01382 344089
Nethergate   Fax: 01382 229190
Dundee DD1 4HN
e-mail: library@dundee.ac.uk
Website: www.dundee.ac.uk/library

University library

Facilities
Enquiries to the Librarian
Information provided by phone, post, fax and e-mail to all; loans to members only
Library open to the public: Mondays-Fridays 0900-midnight (term time); 0900-1700 (vacation); Saturdays 1200-1700; Sundays 1200-1900 (term time)
Microfilm, microfiche, microcard/microprint readers; Microcopies provided; CD-ROM; on-line information service

Subject coverage
Local history collection (books only) on local shipbuilding, fishing and disasters

---

D22
DUNFERMLINE CARNEGIE LIBRARY

Abbot Street   Tel: 01383 312994
Dunfermline   Fax: 01383 314314
Fife KY12 7NL
e-mail: Lib.Admin@fife.gov.uk

Local government organisation

Facilities
Enquiries to the Librarian
Information provided by phone, post, fax or e-mail; books or other material loaned
Library open to the public
Photocopying facilities: microfilm and microfiche readers; fullsize copies provided

Subject coverage
General local history section covering mainly West Fife including some maritime topics

---

D23
DURHAM COUNTY RECORD OFFICE

County Hall   Tel: 0191 3833253
Durham DH1 5UL   Fax: 0191 3834500
e-mail: record.office@durham.gov.uk

Website: www.durham.gov.uk/recordoffice
Local government organisation

Facilities
Enquiries to the County Archivist
Information provided by phone, post, fax and e-mail
Open to the public: Monday-Tuesday, Thursday 0945-1645, Wednesday 0845-2000 and Friday 0845-1615
Photocopying facilities
Research service available - restricted to 3 hours maximum for any specific search request, subsequent requests allowed - £20 per hour

Special collections
Austin and Pickergsill, shipbuilders, mainly plans of ships, 1870s-1890s
Board of Trade fishing boat records, 1859-1914
Londonderry Papers
Strathmore Papers

Specific databases
Database of complete catalogues of all material held is available in searchroom and on website at www.durham.gov.uk /recordoffice

Publications
Numerous publications, including handlists, subject guides and user guides available from the County Archivist

---

D24
DURHAM UNIVERSITY LIBRARY

Archives and Special Collections
Palace Green   Tel: 0191 334 2972
Durham   Fax: 0191 334 2942
Co. Durham DH1 3RN
e-mail: pg.library@durham.ac.uk
Website: www.dur.ac.uk/library/asc

University department

Facilities
Enquiries to the Head of Heritage Collections
Information provided by phone, post, fax and e-mail link on website
Open to the public at the discretion of the librarian
Search Room (vacation) Monday-Friday 0900-1700; (term time) Monday and Friday 0900-1700, Tuesday 0900-2000, Wednesday 0900-1800 and Saturday 1000-1300
Photocopying facilities
Research service not available, although a list of family record agents is held

Subject coverage
Public records: diocesan records, probate records, Halmote Court records, bishopric estate records; political and family papers; antiquarian collections; scientific mss and papers, including University Observatory records; University records

Special collections
1st Earl Grey papers: including material on joint army and naval expedition to the West Indies, 1793-4
2nd Earl Grey papers: he was the First Head of the Admiralty in 1806
4th Earl Grey papers: some material concerning the North of England Steam Ship Owners' Association

Specific databases
'Pictures in Print' records pre-1850 printed maps and prints of County Durham held in the University Library, Cathedral Library and Durham Public Library (www.dur.ac.uk/library/asc/pip)
See website (see above) for detailed handlists, etc.

Publications
See website for catalogues

Dyfed Archives Service

See Carmarthenshire Archive Service
Ceredigion Archives
Pembrokeshire Record Office

E1
EAST ASIAN HISTORY OF SCIENCE LIBRARY

Needham Research Institute   Tel: 01223 311545
8 Sylvester Road   Fax: 01223 362703
Cambridge CB3 9AF
e-mail: jm10019@cus.cam.ac.uk
Website: www.nri.org.uk

Voluntary organisation

Facilities
Enquiries to the Librarian
Information provided by phone, post, fax and e-mail
Open by appointment only to scholars working on the history of Chinese science, technology and medicine: 0930-1700
Photocopying facilities

Subject coverage
History of Chinese science, technology and medicine

Special collections
Entire collection was formerly the private research collection of Dr Joseph Needham, author of the multi-volume series, 'Science and Civilisation in China'

Publications
See website above

EAST DUNBARTONSHIRE LIBRARIES - INFORMATION AND ARCHIVES

William Patrick Library   Tel: 0141 776 8090
2 West High Street   Fax: 0141 776 0408
Kirkintilloch
Glasgow G66 1AD
e-mail: libraries@eastdunbarton.gov.uk
Website: www.eastdunbarton.gov.uk

Local government organisation

Facilities
Enquiries to the Assistant Manager - Information and Archives
Information provided by phone, post, fax and e-mail
Open to the public: Monday-Thursday 1000-2000, Friday-Saturday 1000-1700
Photocopying facilities
Limited research service available - information provided by staff on specific enquiries that do not involve prolonged searches

Subject coverage
Marine engineering (canal and coastal vessels); general history of canal and canal vessels - especially the Clyde puffers

Special collections
Archives of J & J Hay

Publications
Forth and Clyde canal information on SCRAN database - www.scran.ac.uk

---

E3
EAST KENT ARCHIVES CENTRE

Enterprise Zone   Tel: 01304 829306
Honeywood Road   Fax: 01304 823640
Whitfield
Dover
Kent CT16 3EH
e-mail: eastkentarchives@kent.gov.uk
Website: www.kent.gov.uk/e&l/artslib/archives/archekac.html

Local government organisation

Facilities
Enquiries to the Manager
Information about collections provided by phone, post and e-mail
Research in person or by post (fee payable for postal research)
Open to the public (appointment and readers ticket required): Tuesday-Thursday 0900-1700
Photocopying facilities
Research service - £28 per hour, £52 for 2 hours (maximum 4 hours)

Subject coverage

Cinque Ports; shipping registration; harbour boards

Special collections

Dover Harbour Board, c.1520-1968
Margate Pier and Harbour Board (uncatalogued - notice required)
Registers of shipping: Deal, Dover, Folkestone, Ramsgate and Sandwich, 1786-1970
Crew lists: Deal, Dover, Folkestone and Ramsgate, 1863-1914
Cinque Ports Confederation, 1327-1959

E4
EAST RIDING OF YORKSHIRE ARCHIVES SERVICE

County Hall   Tel: 01482 392790
Beverley   Fax: 01482 392791
East Riding of Yorkshire
HU17 9BA
e-mail: archives.service@eastriding.gov.uk
Website: www.eastriding.gov.uk/archives

Local government organisation

Facilities

Enquiries to the Archivist
Information provided by phone, post, fax and e-mail
Open to the public; seats must be booked in advance:
Mondays: 1400-1645; Tuesdays: 0930-2000; Wednesdays & Thursdays: 0930-1645; Fridays: 0930-1600
Research service. Time restricted to half-an-hour at a cost of £12.00

Subject coverage

Goole shipping registers, 1824-1894, transfer registers 1855-1924
Bridlington shipping registers, 1786-1847,
Boats Licensed register, 1808-1832
Board of Trade plans, 1830-1984
North Eastern Sea Fisheries Committee records, 1889-1993
Humber Conservancy Board Minutes & Reports, 1908-1946
Goole Shipbuilding & Repairing Co. Ltd. records, 1922-1968
Hull and Goole shipping records, including log books, crew lists, agreements for vessels, 1864-1909

Records of specific companies

Goole Shipbuilding & Repairing Co. Ltd. records, 1922-1968

Database

CALM2000 database, covering collections held is available on site

Publications

Various guides and some summary lists available on website
Summary information for many collections also available on A2A website

E5
EAST SUSSEX RECORD OFFICE (ESRO)

The Maltings   Tel: 01273 482349
Castle Precincts   Fax: 01273 482341
Lewes
East Sussex BN17 1YT
e-mail: archives@eastsussexcc.gov.uk
Website: www.eastsussex.govcc.uk/archives

Local government organisation

Facilities

Enquiries to the County Archivist
Information provided by phone, post, fax and e-mail
Open to the public: Monday-Tuesday, Thursday 0845-1645, Wednesday 0930-1645, Friday 0845-1615 and one Saturday per month
Appointment strictly advised as space is limited
Photocopying facilities
Research service - £23 per hour - chiefly for family and house history

Subject coverage

Merchant ships agreements, crew lists and logs, Newhaven and Rye, 1863-1914; crew agreements for fishing boats over 25 tons, Newhaven and Rye, 1883-1914; register of shipping, Newhaven, 1856-1895 and Rye, 1855-1946; appropriation book for official numbers for British registered ships, Newhaven, 1855-1989; registers of deeds and transaction, Newhaven, 1886-1989; returns of changes to the shipping register, Newhaven, 1930-1992; registers of sea fishing boats, Newhaven, 1917-1988; registers of sea fishing boats, Rye, (1902)-1988

E6
EDINBURGH CITY LIBRARIES AND INFORMATION SERVICES - EDINBURGH ROOM

Central Public Library   Tel: 0131 242 8030
George IV Bridge   Fax: 0131 242 8035
Edinburgh EH1 1EG
e-mail: edinburgh.room@edinburgh.gov.uk
Website: www.edinburgh.gov.uk/libraries/

Local government organisation

Facilities

Enquiries to Principal Library Officer
Information provided by phone, post, fax, e-mail and in person
Open to the public: Mondays-Thursdays 1000-2000; Fridays 1000-1700; Saturdays 0900-1300
Photocopying facilities
Research service provided free to identify relevant resources, and answer brief factual questions, but cannot undertake lengthy enquiries

Subject coverage

Books, maps, illustrations, newspapers, manuscripts, ephemera relating to the City of Edinburgh, including the Port of Leith. Microfilms and CDROMs available 'Lloyd's Register', 1947/8 onwards; 'Jane's Fighting Ships'

Special collections

Collection of pamphlets on the development of Leith harbour and docks (18th/19th centuries)
Leith Commercial List 1813-1905
Extensive collection of prints and photographs of Leith harbour
Edinburgh and Leith directories 1773-1974
Collection of Edinburgh newspapers from 1719 to date

Publications

Post-1980 additions to the Edinburgh Room's stock are included in the library's online catalogue: www.edinburgh.gov.uk/www-bin/www_talis32

E7
EDINBURGH UNIVERSITY LIBRARY

Special Collections   Tel: 0131 6508379
University Library   Fax: 0131 6506863
George Square
Edinburgh EH8 9LS
e-mail: special.collections.library@ed.ac.uk
Website:
www.lib.ed.ac.uk/lib/resources/collections/specdivision

University department

Facilities

Enquiries to the Special Collections Librarian
Information given by post to all
Library open to members only - all readers must have a current library ticket/consultation card

Special collections

Archives of Christian Salvesen, Ltd., 1857-1963 (whaling)
Ben Line (Leith), voyage books c.1850-1920 (general cargo)

English Heritage

See National Monuments Record Centre

E8
ESSEX RECORD OFFICE - CHELMSFORD BRANCH

Wharf Road   Tel: 01245 244644
Chelmsford   Fax: 01245 244655
Essex CM2 6YT
e-mail: ero.enquiry@essexcc.gov.uk
Website: www.essexcc.gov.uk/ero

Local government organisation

Facilities

Enquiries to the Archive Services Manager
Information provided by phone, post, personal visit, fax and e-mail
Open to the public: Monday 0900-1630, Tuesday-Thursday 0900-1700, Friday and Saturday 0900-1600
Photocopying facilities

Subject coverage

Essex history, including maritime history

Special collections

Crew lists for ports of Harwich, Colchester and Maldon, 1863-1913
Registers of shipping for the port of Maldon, 1786-1880
Shipbuilding records of J W Cook and Co., Wivenhoe, 1948-86

Publications

Catalogue available on website

E9
ESSEX RECORD OFFICE - COLCHESTER AND NORTH EAST ESSEX BRANCH

Stanwell House   Tel: 01206 572099
Stanwell Street   Fax: 01206 574541
Colchester
Essex CO2 7DL
e-mail: ero.colchester@essexcc.gov.uk
Website: www.essexcc.gov.uk/ero

Local government organisation

Facilities

Enquiries to the Archivist
Information provided by phone, post, fax or e-mail.
Open to the public; a CARN (County Archive Research Network) ticket is necessary to view original documents. Appointment necessary
Opening hours: Monday 1000-1715 (second Monday in every month, 1000-2045), Tuesday-Thursday 0915-1715, Friday 0915-1615
Photocopying facilities (excluding large and fragile items); microfilm and microfiche readers available
Research service not provided

Subject coverage

Harbours (Colchester and Harwich); fisheries (Colne Fishery Company); coastal protection

Special collections

Shipbuilding, records of J W Cook & Co, Wivenhoe, 1948-86 and James & Stone (Brightlingsea) Ltd, 1926-1970
Ship registration (Colchester, 1786-1849 and Harwich, 1824-1884)

Specific databases

SEAX is our searchable database for all records in the Essex Record Office

---

E10
ESSEX RECORD OFFICE – SOUTHEND BRANCH

Central Library   Tel: 01702 464278
Victoria Avenue   Fax: 01702 464253
Southend SS2 6EX
e-mail: ero.southend@essexcc.gov.uk
Website: www.essex.gov.uk/ero

Local government organisation

Facilities
Enquiries to the Branch Archivist
Information provided by phone, post, fax, e-mail and personal visit
Open to the public: Monday 1000-1300 and 1400-1715, Tuesday-Thursday 0915-1300 and 1400-1715, Friday 0915-1300 and 1400-1615
Photocopying facilities
Microfilm and microfiche readers
Research service available at Chelmsford office (£18 per hour); enquirer needs to specify which documents are to be searched; free postal service will advise on sources

Subject coverage
Local authority records and records relating to the Southend and Rochford Hundred area; Essex maritime history

Special collections
Records relating to Southend Pier

Specific databases
SEAX is our searchable database for all records in the Essex Record Office

Publications
'Guide to the Essex Record Office'
Catalogue available on website

E11
ESSO UK LIMITED

Information Centre   Tel 01372 223179
Mailpoint 13   Fax 01372 222276
ExxonMobil House
Leatherhead
Surrey KT22 8UX
Email library@exxonmobil.com

Company, wholly owned subsidiary of ExxonMobil Corporation

Facilities
Enquiries to the Librarian.
Not open to the public but information given by phone, fax and email.

Subject coverage
History of the oil industry; North Sea exploration; oil industry management and economics; history of Esso.

E12
EUROPEAN ASSOCIATION OF SHIPS IN BOTTLES

The Crows Nest
72 Pontac Road
New Marske
Redcar and Cleveland TS11 8AN

Voluntary association

Facilities
Members may access archives and library.

Publications
Members receive an A4, 28-page quarterly magazine 'Bottleship'

E13
EXETER UNIVERSITY, LIBRARY AND INFORMATION SERVICES

Stocker Road   Tel: 01392 263873
Exeter EX4 4PT   Fax: 01392 263871
e-mail: library@ex.ac.uk
Website: www.ex.ac.uk/library/

University library

Facilities
Enquiries to the Subject Librarian for History
Information provided by phone, post, fax and e-mail
Full facilities open to members of the University; reference – only access to printed materials available to the general public
Opening hours variable - see website for details or phone/e-mail
Photocopying facilities

Subject coverage
Collection of several thousand volumes of books from 18th-21st centuries on all aspects of maritime history, with emphasis on UK, including runs of relevant journals and series

Specific companies and groups
Navy Records Society

Specific databases
Restricted to members of the University - they include a number of bibliographical services (e.g. Historical Abstracts, Web of Science) and electronic journals collections

Publications
All books and journal are included in online catalogue on website

---

Exeter

See Devon Record Office

F1
FALKIRK MUSEUMS HISTORY RESEARCH CENTRE

Callendar House   Tel: 01324 503779
Callendar Park   Fax: 01324 503771
Falkirk FK1 1YR
e-mail: callendar.house@falkirk.gov.uk
Website: www.falkirkmuseums.org

Local government organisation and museum

Facilities

Enquiries to the Museums Assistant or the Archivist
Information provided by phone, post, e-mail and in person
Open to the public: Mondays-Fridays 1000-1230; 1330-1700; closed local and public holidays
Photocopying facilities
Research service. Short enquiries free of charge; extensive enquiries charged at £15.00 per hour

Subject coverage

Local authority records, records of local businesses and local organisations, local family and personal papers, including estate plans and maps, photographs

Special collections

Grangemouth Dockyard Company, including ship plans and photographs
Forbes of Callendar papers

Specific databases

Shipping database, containing researched information on locally built ships
Collections' database

Publications

Participating archives in the Scottish Archives Network: www.scan.org.uk

---

F2
FALMOUTH LIBRARY - THE MARITIME COLLECTION

Municipal Buildings   Tel: 01326 314901
The Moor   Fax: 01326 315385
Falmouth
Cornwall TR11 3QA
e-mail: cornishstudies.library@cornwall.gov.uk
Website: www.cornwall.gov.uk/library

Local government organisation

Facilities

Enquiries to Maritime Studies Librarian at Cornish Studies Library, the Cornwall Centre, Alma Place, Redruth, Cornwall TR15 2AT
Tel: 01209 216760 Fax: 01209 210283
Information provided by phone, post, fax and e-mail
Open to the public Monday, Tuesday, Thursday and Friday 0930-1800 and Saturday 0930-1600
Chiefly lending collection
Photocopying facilities

Subject coverage

Naval history; merchant shipping company and vessel history; boatbuilding, marine engineering; seamanship; marine environment; fishing industry; voyages; pilots and charts; Falmouth working boats and packets

Publications

General guide to collection on 'Cornwall Library Service: Special Collections' on website

---

F3
FELIXSTOWE MUSEUM
FELIXSTOWE HISTORY AND MUSEUM SOCIETY

Museum: Postal Address:
Ravelin Block   P.O. Box 50
Viewpoint Road   Hamilton Road
Felixstowe   Felixstowe
Suffolk   Suffolk IP11 7JG

Tel: 01394 285 506
Answerphone: 01394 674 355
e-mail: felixstowemuseum@ravelin.freeserve.co.uk

Museum/voluntary organisation

Facilities

Enquiries to the Librarian (for maritime enquiries)
Information provided by post (usually), phone and e-mail
Open to Museum Society members at any time; to non-members by appointment only
Museum open Easter-October, Wednesday, Sunday and Bank Holidays 1300-1730 (at other times by appointment)
Photocopying facilities
Research service available - donations to cover costs - research carried out in spare time of members

Subject coverage

Local, social and military history for Felixstowe and surrounding areas; models; photographs; publications and printed ephemera; artefacts

Special collections

Paddle steamer room - models, artefacts, photographs (including Paddle Steamer Preservation Society items)
HMS *Beehive* room - history of coastal forces in Second World War
Navy room - Royal and Merchant Navy models, artefacts, photographs

---

F4
PORT OF FELIXSTOWE

Tomline House   Tel: 01394 604500
The Dock   Fax: 01394 604949
Felizstowe
Suffolk IP11 3SY
Website: portoffelixstowe.co.uk

Port operator

F5
THE FLAG INSTITUTE

44 Middleton Road   Tel: 01904 339985
Acomb
York Y024 3AS
e-mail: info@flaginstitute.org
Website: www.flaginstitute.org

Voluntary organisation

Facilities
Enquiries to the Editor of 'Flagmaster'
Information provided by phone, post and e-mail
Open to the public for simple enquiries
Research service available pertaining to flags and items appearing on or related to flags. Commercial bodies charged research fee if necessary (£50 per diem, plus travel costs)

Subject coverage
Archives: documentation, pictures, charts, press items

Special collections
This is the only flag-related archive in Britain

Specific databases
Flags of the World

Publications
'Flagmaster' - quarterly magazine

F6
FLEET AIR ARM MUSEUM

Box D6   Tel: 01935 840565
RNAS Yeovilton   Fax: 01935 842630
Near Ilchester
Somerset BA22 8HT
e-mail: info@fleetairarm.com
website: www.fleetairarm.com

Museum

Facilities
Enquiries to the Records and Research Centre
Open to the public
Research service - fees charged.

Subject coverage
Naval aviation; Fleet Air Arm; Royal Naval Air Service

Special collections
Photographic archive
Technical publications relating to naval aircraft and engines used by Great Britain
Catapults and arrester gear
Personal collections of naval aviators
Log books
First World War personnel records

F7
FLEETWOOD MUSEUM

Queens Terrace   Tel: 01253 876621
Fleetwood   Fax: 01253 878088
Lancashire FY7 6BT
e-mail: fleetwood.museum@mus.lancscc.gov.uk
Website: www.nettingthebay.org.uk

Museum; part of Lancashire County Museum Service

Facilities
Enquiries to the Curator
Information provided by phone, post, fax and e-mail
Museum open to the general public; access to archives by appointment
Photocopying facilities
Research service provided, depending on level of detail required

Subject coverage
Deep-sea fishing, inshore fishing, Fleetwood maritime, marine life and coastal biodiversity

Special collections
Horsley trawler collection
Robertsons' archive (winches, etc.)
Former Harris Museum natural history collection

Records of specific companies
Robertsons

Databases
Fleetwood trawler database
Fleetwood fishing collection

Publications
See website

F8
FLINTSHIRE RECORD OFFICE

The Old Rectory   Tel: 01244 532364
Hawarden   Fax: 01244 538344
Flintshire CH5 3NR
e-mail: archives@flintshire.gov.uk
Website: www.flintshire.gov.uk

Local government organisation

Facilities
Enquiries to the County Archivist
Information provided by phone, post, fax, e-mail and personal visit
Open to the public (on production of identification including address and signature so that a Reader's Ticket may be issued): Monday-Thursday 0900-1645, Friday 0900-1615
Pre-booking necessary to ensure a seat
Photocopying facilities
Limited research service available - up to 30 minutes free - if further research required, private record agents need to be used

Subject coverage
Shipping; shipbuilding; River Dee; fishing; wharves; docks; harbours; ports; lighthouses and piers

Special collections
Dee and Clwyd River Authority MSS
Shipping records (Registrar of Shipping and Seamen)
Shipping registers
Board of Trade marine maps
Photographs

Specific companies and groups:
Dee and Clwyd River Authority
J Crichton and Co. Ltd., shipbuilders, Saltney (mainly photographs)

Specific databases
Indexes by place, subject and personal name to collections held, also separate photographic and map indexes

F9
FOLKESTONE LIBRARY, MUSEUM AND SASSOON GALLERY
Grace Hill Tel: 01303 256710
Folkestone Fax: 01303 256710
Kent CT20 1HD
e-mail: janet.adamson@Kent.gov.uk
Website: www.Kent-museums.org.uk

Museum and local government organisation (run by Kent County Council)

Facilities
Enquiries to the Heritage Officer
Information provided by phone, post, fax and e-mail
Open to the public: Monday-Saturday 0930-1700 (Friday to 1900)
Photocopying facilities
Research service available - first 30 minutes free, thereafter £12 per 30 minutes

Subject coverage
Museum: paintings - topographical of area (mainly); local social/maritime history
Local history collection - census, parish registers, maps; lists of local shipping and cross channel files; 16,000 local photographs for Folkestone, Hythe and Romney Marsh areas

F10
FORTH PORTS PLC
Tower Place Tel 0131 555 8700
Edinburgh EH6 7DB Fax 0131 553 7462
Website: www.forthports.co.uk

Port operator

F11
FREIGHT TRANSPORT ASSOCIATION (FTA)
Hermes House Tel 01892 526171
St John's Road Fax 01892 534989
Tunbridge Wells
Kent TN4 9UZ
Email info@tfa.co.uk
Website: www.fta.co.uk

G1
GATESHEAD LIBRARIES ARTS AND INFORMATION
Central Library Tel: 0191 477 3478
Prince Consort Road Fax: 0191 477 7454
Gateshead
Tyne & Wear NE8 4LN
e-mail: enquiries@gateshead.gov.uk
Website: www.gateshead.gov.uk

Public library

Facilities
Enquiries to Local Studies Librarian
Information provided by phone, post, fax and e-mail
Library open to the public: Mondays, Tuesdays, Thursdays, Fridays 0900-1900; Wednesdays 0900-1700; Saturdays 0900-1300
Photocopying facilities available; CD-ROM available
Research service not provided

Subject coverage
Material relating to the history of Gateshead: 18th century coal and salt trade on the Tyne; 18th and 19th century whaling trade from Tyneside

Special collections
Index to whaling articles and advertisements in 18th and 19th century Newcastle newspapers

General Register and Record Office of Shipping and Seamen

See Registry of Shipping and Seamen and Appendix 1

G2
GENERAL REGISTER OFFICE FOR SCOTLAND (GROS)

New Register House   Tel: 0131 334 0380
Edinburgh EH1 3YT   Fax: 0131 314 4400
e-mail: records@gro-scotland.gov.uk
Website: www.gro-scotland.gov.uk

Central government organisation

Facilities
Enquiries to the Registrar General
Information provided by phone, post, fax and e-mail
Certificate ordering service: 0131 314 4411
Internet search service: see website for details
Open to the public: Monday-Friday 0900-1630 (except public holidays)
Research service available for particular events, but not tracing of family trees or for whereabouts of living persons

Subject coverage
Old parish registers, 1553-1854; open census records, 1841, 1851, 1861, 1871, 1881, 1891, 1901; statutory registers of births, deaths, marriages, 1855 to date; statutory registers of divorces, 1984 to date; adopted children register, 1930 to date; minor records (post 1855) including: marine register of births and deaths from 1855, war registers - South African War, 1899-1902, First World War, 1914-18, Second World War, 1939-45

Specific databases
Computerised indexes of births and marriages from 1553
Computerised indexes of deaths from 1855
Computerised indexes to 1881, 1891 and 1901 census records
1891 and 1901 indexes are linked to digital images of the relevant census records (part of a project to digitise all the Department's records)
Internet searches of historical indexes (linked to digital images of the records) available at www.ScotlandsPeople.gov.uk

Publications
Guides available on website

G3
GLAMORGAN RECORD OFFICE

The Glamorgan Building   Tel: 029 2078 0282
King Edward VII Avenue   Fax: 029 2078 0284
Cathays Park
Cardiff CF10 3NE

e-mail: glamro@cardiff.ac.uk
Website: www.glamro.gov.uk

Local government organisation

Facilities
Enquiries to the Glamorgan Archivist
Information provided by: phone, post, fax and e-mail
Open to the public (all users to register - require identification and are encouraged to book): Tuesday-Thursday 0930-1700, Wednesday also 1700-1900 by appointment and Friday 0930-1630
Photocopying facilities
Research service available - usually limited to specific enquiries for up to 2 hours, £15 per hour, payable in advance

Subject coverage
Merchant shipping in Glamorgan; individual seamen

Special collections
Registers of Cardiff-registered ships, 1824-1906
Crew agreements and other papers for Cardiff-registered ships, 1863-1913
Board of Trade shipping enquiries, 1875-1935
Cardiff Pilotage Authority, 1807-1968
Barry Pilotage Authority, 1889-1974

Specific companies and groups:
Evan Thomas, Radcliffe and Co., 1882-1973
Graig Shipping Co. Ltd. plc, 1919-1989
Reardon Smith Line Ltd., 1902-1985
John Cory and Sons Ltd., 1884-1988
Cory Brothers and Co. Ltd., 1888-1943
Evan and Reid Coal Co. Ltd., c.1890-1960
Cardiff Incorporated Chamber of Commerce, 1866-1965
Cardiff Bay Development Corporation, 1987-2000
Cardiff Society of Sailmakers, 1893-1938
Royal Hamadryad Hospital, 1886-1919

Publications
All above records are listed in searchroom catalogues
General office information available on website

G4
GLASGOW LIBRARIES - ARCHIVES AND SPECIAL COLLECTIONS DEPARTMENT

The Mitchell Library   Tel: 0141 287 2988/2910
North Street   Fax: 0141 226 8452
Glasgow G3 7DN
e-mail: lil@cls.glasgow.gov.uk
Website: www.glasgowlibraries.org

Local government organisation

Facilities
Enquiries to the Senior Archivist, Archives and Special

Collections and Senior Librarian, Archives and Special Collections
Information provided by phone, post, fax and e-mail
Open to the public: Monday 0900-2000 and Friday-Saturday 0900-1700
Photocopying facilities - archival material will be copied by staff only
Enquiries will be answered by staff if they do not require large amounts of time

Subject coverage
Navigation; naval history; seamanship; pollution; marine engineering; shipbuilding; ship technology; shipping concerned with the oil industry; shipping and shipbuilding in the Clyde; sailing ships and all kinds of powered craft; ship models; yachting history including America's Cup; the development of the Clyde as a waterway; the maritime trade of the Clyde ports

Special collections
The Sir Thomas Lipton Collection: over 100 large volumes of press cuttings and approximately 50 albums of photographs, mainly relating to Lipton's yachting activities, in particular his attempts to win the America's Cup
The Wotherspoon Collection, 41 folio albums, the personal work of Sir James Wotherspoon (1858-1936)
A pictorial record of the rise and progress of shipbuilding and shipping from 1812 to the 1930s
Archives: various shipyards including Fairfields, Connells, Barclay Curle
Glasgow register of shipping
Clyde Port Authority
Photographic collections
On-line information databases of all Clyde-built ships and the Clyde-owned sailing fleet, 1860-1914

Publications
Information on shipbuilding records on www.glasgowlibraries.org

---

G5
GLASGOW MUSEUM OF TRANSPORT

Kelvin Hall	Tel: 0141 287 2620
1 Bunhouse Road	Fax: 0141 287 2692
Glasgow G3 8DP	

Museum (Glasgow City Council Cultural and Leisure Department)

Facilities
Enquiries to the Curator Communication and Research, Transport
Information provided by phone and fax
Open to the public: Monday-Thursday and Saturday 1000-1700 and Friday and Sunday 1100-1700
Personal visits to view archives by appointment only
Photocopying facilities

Subject coverage
Clyde shipyard lists

Special collections
Napier papers
Dan MacDonald photographic archive

G6
GLASGOW UNIVERSITY ARCHIVE SERVICES

13 Thurso Street	Tel: 0141 330 5515
Glasgow G11 6PE	Fax: 0141 330 2640

e-mail: dutyarch@archives.gla.ac.uk
Website: www.archives.gla.ac.uk

Archive service

Facilities
Enquiries to the University Archivist
Information provided by phone, post, fax and e-mail
Open to the public by appointment: Monday 1330-1700, Tuesday-Friday 0930-1700 and evening opening until 2000 on Thursday by appointment only
Photocopying facilities
Research service available - £30 per hour, excluding VAT

Subject coverage
Shipbuilding on the Clyde - largest collection of records as part of the Scottish Business Archive; shipping company and some trade union records

Specific companies and groups
See website for details

Publications
General guide on www.archives.gla.ac.uk/collects/summary.html
See also www.archives.gla.ac.uk/collects/lists/business/shipping.html

---

G7
GLOUCESTERSHIRE RECORD OFFICE

Clarence Row	Tel: 01452 425295
Alvin Street	Fax: 01452 426378
Gloucester GL1 3DW	

e-mail: records@gloscc.gov.uk
Website: www.gloucestershire.gov.uk

County record office

Facilities
Enquiries to the County and Diocesan Archivist
Information provided by phone, post, fax and e-mail
Open to the public (advisable to ring in advance of a visit): Monday 1000-1700, Tuesday-Wednesday and Friday 0900-1700 and Thursday 0900-2000
Appointment necessary for library

Photocopying facilities
Research service available - £18 per hour

Subject coverage
Naval ordnance rolls of Admiral William Wynter, 1561-69
Correspondence and papers of Captain H Berkeley, RN, including naval service at Zanzibar, 1843-98
Naval correspondence of Reynolds family, 1704-1804
Naval orders and letters of Admiral Sir George Rooke, 1694-1702
Naval orders and papers of Admiral F Sotherson, 1793-1835 and Captain W G B Estcourt, 1819-45
Letters from Admiral Berkeley, c.1870
Log book of East Indiaman *William Fairlie,* 1829-31
Log of East Indiaman *Hillborough,* 1793
Log of surgeon on South Australian Company's barque *Sarah and Elizabeth,* 1836-37
Usual range of local authority and county archives

Publications
'Handlist of the Contents of the Gloucestershire Records Office' 4th edition, 1998 - essential details also available on website

---

G8
GOOLE LIBRARY MUSEUM AND ART GALLERY
Goole Public Library Reference and Local Studies Department
Carlisle Street   Tel: 01405 762187
Goole   Fax: 01405 768329
East Riding of Yorkshire DN14 5DS
e-mail: gooleref.library@eastriding.gov.uk
Website: www.eastriding.gov.uk/learning

Public library

Facilities
Enquiries to the Reference and Local Studies Librarian
Information provided by post, visit and e-mail
Open to the public: Monday and Wednesday 1000-1900, Tuesday, Thursday-Friday 1000-1700 and Saturday 0900-1300
Photocopying facilities in the Lending Department
Microfilm and microfiche readers
Research service available - first half hour free search (i.e. catalogue search), will look up positive references (£12 per hour) but generally no scans

Subject coverage
Maritime information - photographs; other classes for more general topics; bookable film and fiche readers; local newspaper on film, 1870 onwards

Specific companies and groups:
Some material from the Goole Shipbuilding and Repairing Co. Ltd; and the Goole Shipping Co. Ltd.

Publications
Goole Local Studies Brochure
No website guide (only to East Riding of Yorkshire Council Local Authority as a whole)

G9
GRACE DARLING MUSEUM
Radcliffe Road   Tel: 01668 214465
Bamburgh   Fax: 01668 214465
Northumberland NE69 7AF

Museum/voluntary organisation

Facilities
Enquiries to the Honorary Curator
Information provided by phone, post and fax
Open to the public

Special collections
Grace Darling memorabilia - papers, relics, clothes
The coble in which Grace Darling made the rescue
Family tree

G10
GRAY PAGE LTD
Coopers Marmalade Building   Tel: 01865 202720
27 Park End Street   Fax: 01865 202223
Oxford OX1 1HU
e-mail: enquiries@graypagelimited.com
website: www.graypagelimited.com

Independent investigations and security consultants specialising in the maritime industry.

Subject coverage
Resolving issues arising from contractual default, criminal activity and corporate malpractice. Services include asset tracing, corporate veil investigation and vessel tracking, fraud investigation and asset recovery.

Grampian Regional Archives
See Aberdeen City Archives

G11
ss GREAT BRITAIN TRUST
Great Western Dock   Tel: 0117 926 0680
Gas Ferry Road   Fax: 0117 925 5788
Bristol BS1 6TY
e-mail: admin@ss-great-britain.com
Website: www.ss-great-britain.com

Museum

Facilities
Enquiries to the Curator
Information provided by phone, post and fax

Open to the public - paid entrance to ship; archive access by appointment
Photocopying facilities
Research service available

Subject coverage
Copies of passenger diaries written on board the *Great Britain* between 1852 and 1876; passenger lists (copies only); documents relating to the construction, operation and rescue of *Great Britain*

Publications
Internal guides are available to material in the archive
'The Iron Ship: the story of Brunel's ss Great Britain': £10.50

Greater London History Library
Greater London Record Office
See London Metropolitan Archives

G12
GREATER MANCHESTER COUNTY RECORD OFFICE (GMCRO)

56 Marshall Street   Tel: 0161 832 5284
New Cross   Fax: 0161 839 3808
Manchester M4 5FU
e-mail: archives@gmcro.co.uk
Website: www.gmcro.co.uk

Local government organisation

Facilities
Enquiries to the County Archivist
Information provided by phone, post, fax and e-mail
Open to the public
Photocopying facilities
Research service available - £15 per hour on written request, payable by cheque (preliminary research of up to 15 minutes free of charge)

Subject coverage
Records relating to two or more Greater Manchester districts, including estate papers, business records, public records, trade union records and records of various societies; civil registration index and census information

Special collections
Manchester Ship Canal Company
The Rochdale Canal Company

Publications
'Guide to Collections' (see website) - available for purchase on request

---

G13
GREENWICH LOCAL HISTORY LIBRARY

Greenwich Heritage Centre   Tel: 020 8858 2452
Artillery Square
Royal Arsenal
Woolwich
London SE18 4DX
e-mail: local.history@greenwich.gov.uk
Website:
www.greenwich.gov.uk/council/publicservices/lhistory.htm

Local government organisation/local history library

Facilities
Enquiries to the Senior Library Manager
Information provided by phone, post, fax and e-mail
Open to the public: Monday-Tuesday 0900-1730, Thursday 0900-2000 and Saturday 0900-1700
Photocopying facilities plus colour laser copier
Enquiries are answered as fully as possible within the constraints of the service - copying costs are charged

Subject coverage
All aspects of the Thames at Greenwich: shipbuilding; marine engineering; industries; Royal Hospital for Seamen, Royal Naval College; Royal Hospital School; the *Cutty Sark; Gypsy Moth IV;* Greenwich Palace and Park; Royal Dockyards at Deptford and Woolwich; fishing industry

Special collections
800 watercolours and drawings of the Greenwich area and the Thames from the early 18th century
Administrative records of the riverside parishes from the 17th century
Prints, photographs, postcards, magic lantern slides from the 19th century

Specific companies and groups:
Corporation of the Woolwich Ferry Co., 1811-1828
Siemens Bros. and Co. Ltd. - photo albums
Records of Sykes Pumps, Woolwich Road

Publications
Publications listed on website

G14
GUERNSEY ISLAND ARCHIVES SERVICE

29 Victoria Road   Tel: 01481 724512
St Peter Port   Fax: 01481 715814
Guernsey GY1 1HU

Facilities
Enquiries to the Island Archivist
Open to the public: 0900-1630 weekdays
Limited research service

Subject coverage
Material relating to, or having a close connection with, the Bailiwick of Guernsey

Special collections
Guernsey Chamber of Commerce 1808 on

G15
GUERNSEY MUSEUMS AND GALLERIES

Candie Gardens　　　　Tel: 01481 726518
St Peter Port　　　　　Fax: 01481 715177
Guernsey GY1 1UG
e-mail: p.sarl@museums.gov.gg
Website: www.museum.guernsey.net

Museum

Facilities
Enquiries to the Director
Information provided by phone, fax, e-mail and website
Open to the public
Research service available by arrangement if staff resources available

Subject coverage
Channel Island maritime history, including privateering, shipbuilding, marine art and trade

Special collections
Channel Island privateering - letters of marque
Recovered timbers and objects from 3rd century Gallo-Roman vessel
Ship models

Specific databases
Linked to NAVIS project database of historic ships

Publications
All publications listed on website

Guernsey

See also Priaulx Library

G16
GUILDHALL LIBRARY

Aldermanbury　　　Tel: (printed books) 020 7332
London EC2P 2EJ　　1868/70
　　　　　　　　　Tel: (manuscripts) 020 7332 1863
　　　　　　　　　Fax: 020 7600 3384
e-mail: printedbooks.guildhall@corpoflondon.gov.uk
e-mail: manuscripts.guildhall@corpoflondon.gov.uk
Website: www.cityof london.gov.uk

Local government organisation

Facilities
Enquiries to the Principal Reference Librarian

Information provided by post, e-mail and (limited information only) phone,
Open to the public: Monday-Friday 0930-1700 (Printed Books, Print Room) Monday-Friday 0930-1645 (Manuscripts) and Saturday 0930-1700 (Printed Books and Manuscripts)
Photocopying facilities
Research service available - contact search@guildhalllibrary, utilises Guildhall Library's collections only, £50 plus VAT per hour

Subject coverage
Information on ships (technical details and movements); information on masters and mates holding British Certificates of Competency, 1869-1947

Special collections
Lloyds Marine Collection includes:
'Lloyd's Register' (1764 to date minus one year)
'Lloyd's Register of Yachts', 1889-1939; 1947-80 - gaps
'Lloyd's Register of American Yachts', 1909; 1929-42; 1947-77
'Mercantile Navy List', 1857-1940; 1947-76
'Lloyd's List' (1741 to date)
'Lloyd's List Indexes', 1838-1927
'Lloyd's Shipping Index', 1880-1997
'Lloyd's Voyage Record' (1946 to date minus 5 years)
'Lloyd's Weekly Casualty Reports', 1920-1994
'Lloyd's List Weekly Summary', 1880-1920
'Board of Trade Casualty Returns, 1850-1918
'Registrar General's Monthly Returns', 1890-1946
Bureau Veritas Publications, 1896-1938
'Lloyd's Register Casualty Returns', 1900-1989
'Liverpool Underwriters' Casualty Returns', 1934-1939, 1946-1987
Board of Trade Inquiry Reports, 1908-1965
'Lloyd's War Loss Books', 1914-1918, 1939-1945
'Lloyd's Confidential Index' (1886 to date minus 30 years)
'Lloyd's Calendar', 1892-1894, 1896-1985
Voyage Record Cards, (1927-1975) - 48 hours notice required to view
Lloyd's List Supplementary Mail Advices, 1926-1965
Lloyd's Confidential Sheets, 1939-1945
Yacht and Whaler Movements, 1946-1973
Lloyd's Total Loss Returns, 1945-1969
Lloyd's Missing Vessel Books, 1873-1954
Marine Loss Cards, 1939-1990 - 48 hours notice required to view
War Loss Cards, 1939-1975 - 48 hours notice required to view
The following are held in the Manuscripts Section:
Lloyd's Marine Collection (as above)
Lloyd's Subscription Books, 1774-1849
Lloyd's Loss and Casualty Books, 1837-1998
Lloyd's Captains' Registers, 1869-1948
Archives of Trinity House
Archive of the (Thames) Watermen's and Lightermen's Company
Personal archives of Lord Inchcape
The Manuscript Section also holds smaller collections

of records of individual marine insurance companies and shipping agents

Publications
'Guide to Lloyd's Marine Collection' (1994) (hard copy only)
Leaflets on the Marine Collection, voyage record cards, 'Lloyd's List' indexes, passenger and crew lists available in hard copy and on Corporation Library website

---

G17
GWENT COUNTY RECORD OFFICE

County Hall   Tel: 01633 644886
Cwmbran   Fax: 01633 648382
Gwent NP44 2XH
e-mail: gwentrecords@torfaen.gov.uk
Website: www.llgc.org.uk/cac/

Local government organisation

Facilities
Enquiries to the County Archivist
Information provided by phone, post, fax and e-mail
Open to the public: Tuesday-Thursday 0930-1700 and Friday 0930-1600
Advance bookings for the record office desirable
Photocopying facilities
Research service available - UK and European Union £15 per hour, elsewhere £12.87 (payments in sterling only requested)

Subject coverage
Archives and records of Monmouthshire County Council; Gwent County Council; district councils unitary authorities; local public records; quarter sessions; magistrates courts; coroners courts; hospitals; Diocese of Monmouth parish records, donated and deposited collections of archives of landed estates, businesses, antiquarians, trade unions, ports and maritime concerns; civil parish records; Poor Law records; newspapers; microform collections

Special collections
West Wales Steamship Company records, 1910-1997
Newport Dock Company; deeds, 1829-1851
History of the ports and docks of Newport, Alexandra and Chepstow
Bills of sale of the ships *Unity, Tredegar* and *Nye,* 1807-1829
Share certificates and notices of the AGM of the Great Ship Co. Ltd, 1859
Agreements, crew lists etc. of the ships *Sir George Elliot* and *Lady Tredegar* registered at Newport, 1889-1899
Deed of partnership of Alexandra Docks, Newport, 1910-1981
Notes by TT Birkbeck re HMS *Foudroyant*
Notes by Sir H Nicholas re Lord Nelson, including extracts of his letters

Publications
'Guide to Research No. 5: Harbours, Docks and Shipping'

G18
GWYNEDD ARCHIVES SERVICE - CAERNARFON

County Offices   Tel: 01286 679095
Caernarfon   Fax: 01286 679637
Gwynedd LL55 1SH
e-mail: archives@gwynedd.gov.uk
Website: www.gwynedd.gov.uk/archives

Local government organisation

Facilities
Enquiries to the Principal Archivist and Heritage Officer
Information provided by phone, post, fax and e-mail
Open to the public: Tuesday, Thursday-Friday 0930-1230 and 1330-1700 and Wednesday 0930-1230 and 1330-1900
Photocopying facilities
Paid research service available - first half hour (includes postage, copies etc.) £12, each additional hour (charged to nearest quarter hour) £15

Subject coverage
Quarter Sessions; local authority records; guardians; parish; estate; business; industry; maritime

Special collections
Slate quarrying collections
Maritime holdings

Specific databases
RHAGOROL - online database

Publications
Many publications - books, teaching packs (many of maritime interest)
'Cymru a'r Mor/Maritime Wales' annual journal

G19
GWYNEDD ARCHIVES SERVICE - DOLGELLAU

Archifdy Meirionnydd Archives Tel: 01341 424444
Cae Penarlag   Fax: 01341 424505
Dolgellau
Gwynedd LL40 2YB
e-mail: archives.dolgellau@gwynedd.gov.uk
Website: www.gwynedd.gov.uk/archives

Local government organisation

Facilities
Enquiries to the Area Archivist
Information provided by phone, post, fax or e-mail

Open to the public: Monday, Wednesday-Friday 0900-1300 and 1400-1700
Microfilm and microfiche readers
Photocopying
Research service provided; £12 for first half-hour; each additional hour £15 (charged to nearest quarter hour)

Subject coverage
Ecclesiastical, estate, business, public and official records

Special collections
Crew lists, merchant ships agreements and official log books of Aber Dyfi ships, 1863-1913 Barmouth Harbour Trust papers, 1797-1930
Lister family papers including documents relating to the Lister fleet, 1890-1911 and collection of photographs
Maritime records from the Sailors' Institute, Barmouth including sea charts (19th century)
'Mercantile Navy Lists' and maritime directories, 1896-1917
Lloyd's Registers, 1910-1917
Slate quarrying
Tryweryn Papers

Publications
See website

H1
HAKLUYT SOCIETY

c/o Map Library   Tel: 01428 641850
British Library   Fax: 01428 641933
96 Euston Road,
Great Russell Street
London NW1 2DB
e-mail: office@hakluyt.com
Website: www.hakluyt.com

Learned society and publisher

Facilities
Enquiries to the Administrator
Information provided by phone, post, fax or e-mail
Open to members and to the general public
Research service not provided

Subject coverage
Historical navigation; historical voyages; seamanship in the 16th and 17th centuries

Publications
Two volumes per year of historical travel, not always maritime. Extra series volumes published irregularly e.g. 'The Charts and Views of Captain Cook' volumes 1 and 2.

H2
HAMMERSMITH AND FULHAM ARCHIVES AND LOCAL HISTORY CENTRE

The Lilla Huset   Tel: 020 8741 5159
191 Talgarth Road   Fax: 020 8741 4882
London W6 8BJ
e-mail: archives@lbhf.gov.uk
Website: www.lbhf.gov.uk

Local government organisation

Facilities
Enquiries to the Borough Archivist
Information provided by phone, post, fax and e-mail
Open to the public (appointments preferred): Monday 0930-2000, Tuesday 0930-1300, Thursday 0930-1630 and Saturday (1st in month only) 0930-1300
Photocopying facilities

Special collections:
Fulham II and *Fulham III* - colliers supplying Fulham Power Station: porterage accounts, 1938-40, 1946
HMS *Stork* training ship moored at Hammersmith, 1913-50

Specific companies and groups
London Corinthian Sailing Club minutes, 1848-1940

Publications
Short guide to collections on website

H3
HAMPSHIRE NAVAL COLLECTION HAMPSHIRE COUNTY COUNCIL LIBRARIES & INFORMATION SERVICE

Gosport Library   Tel: 023 9252 3431
High Street   Fax: 023 9250 1911
Hampshire PO12 1BT
e-mail: clsonav@hants.gov.uk
Website: www.hants.gov.uk/library/navalcollection

Local government organisation

Facilities
Enquiries to the Naval Librarian
Information provided by phone, post, fax, e-mail and visit
Open to the public: Monday and Wednesday 0930-1700, Tuesday, Thursday and Friday 0930-1900 and Saturday 0930-1600
Photocopying facilities
Limited research service available at no charge and at the Librarian's discretion

Subject coverage
Predominantly Royal Navy, but includes world navies; collection reflects Gosport's special association with

the development of the submarine, naval aviation, naval ordnance and naval medicine

Special collections
Unique file of Gosport editions of the 'Hampshire Telegraph and Post' and 'Naval Chronicle', 1939-1956

Publications
'The Naval and Maritime Libraries and Archives Group Guide to the Collections', pp10-12

H4
HAMPSHIRE RECORD OFFICE

Sussex Street	Tel: 01962 846154
Winchester	Fax: 01962 878681
Hants SO23 8TH	

e-mail: enquiries.archives@hants.gov.uk
Website: www.hants.gov.uk/record-office

Local government organisation

Facilities
Enquiries to the County Archivist
Information provided by phone, post and e-mail
Open to the public: Mondays-Fridays 0900-1900;
Saturdays 0900-1600
Microfilm and microfiche readers but only wills and inventories are on film/fiche; microcopies and fullsize copies provided

Special collections
Archives of the Naval Ordnance Depot, Priddy's Hard, Gosport, 17th-20th centuries
Admiral Sir Augustus Phillimore of Shedfield House, Hants, family, estate and naval papers, 19th-20th centuries
Photographs of Southampton docks, 1940-1981
Plans of Hampshire harbours, docks and piers, 1834-1951
Wills and inventories of mariners and shipwrights, 1517-1857

Publications
'Hampshire and Australia, 1783-1791: Crime and Transportation' £1.00
Portsmouth Record Series - £15.00 each including:
'Records of the Portsmouth Division of Marines, 1764-1800' JA Lowe
'Portsmouth Dockyard Papers, 1774-1783: The American War' RJB Knight

---

H5
HAMPSHIRE AND WIGHT TRUST FOR MARITIME ARCHAEOLOGY

Room W1/95	Tel: 023 8059 3290
Southampton	Fax: 023 8059 3052
Oceanography Centre	
Empress Dock	
Southampton SO14 3ZH	

e-mail: hwtma@soc.soton.ac.uk
Website: www.soc.soton.ac.uk/hwtma/

Charitable trust

Facilities
Enquiries to Garry Momber
Information provided by phone, e-mail and website
Open to the public

Subject coverage
Maritime archaeology of the Solent; maritime archaeological surveys and excavations; services for marine archaeological aspects of EIAs/AAs; advice on aspects of inter-tidal and underwater archaeology

Special collections
Project archives for maritime archaeological investigations of Solent shipwrecks, submerged landscapes and inter-tidal zones

Specific databases
Historic shipwrecks of the Solent

H6
HARTLAND QUAY MUSEUM

Hartland Quay	Tel: 01288 331352
Hartland	
Near Bideford	
North Devon EX39 6DU	

Private museum.

Facilities
Enquiries to the Administrator, The Old Forge, Woolley, Bude, Cornwall EX23 9PP or
Hartland Quay Hotel, Hartland, Bideford, Devon EX39 6DU; Tel: 01237 441371/218

Subject coverage
Detailed history of the coastal area, north west Devon, e.g., local shipping, coastal trades and industries, and marine casualties, c1600-present day

Publications
'Guide to the coast north of Hartland Quay'
'Guide to the coast south of Hartland Quay'
'Hartland Quay: The Story of a Vanished Port'

H7
HARTLEPOOL ARTS AND MUSEUM SERVICE

Sir William Gray House	Tel: 0142 2665229
Clarence Road	Fax: 01429 523477
Hartlepool TS28 8BT	

e-mail: arts-museums@hartlepool.gov.uk
Website: www.destinationhartlepool.co.uk

Museum

Facilities
Enquiries to the Collections Manager
Information provided by phone, post, fax and e-mail
Open to the public but appointment strictly necessary for library, archives and stores
Photocopying facilities available at cost
Research service available - limited to one hour and only to items in collections

Subject coverage
Local and regional shipbuilding; inshore fishing

Special collections
Ship plans of William Gray and Co., 1945-1962
Photographic archive, including many ship photos
Yard books from the 1860s

Specific companies or groups
William Gray and Central Marine Engine Works
Richardson, Westgarth

H8
HARTLEPOOL CENTRAL LIBRARY
124 York Road   Tel: 01429 263778
Hartlepool TS26 9DE   Fax: 01429 275685
e-mail: mary.hoban@hartlepool.gov.uk
Website: www.portcities.hartlepool.gov.uk

Local government organisation

Facilities
Enquiries to the Librarian
Open to the general public

Special collections
William Gray and Co.: incomplete set of manuscript yard books from c.1878 to c.1941 (records kept in the shipyard as the ship was under construction) for: yard nos. 187 - 288 [c.1878 - 1884]; 352 - 428 [c.1889 - 1891]; 530 - 627 [c.1897 - 1900]; 628 - 728 [c.1901 - 1906]; 729 - 828 [c.1906 - 1913]; 829 - 924 [c.1913 - 1920]; 925 - 1021 [c.1919 - 1929]; 1026 - 1125 [c.1929 - 1941].
Volume of photographs of work in progress for yard nos. 1269-1307 [1955-1960]
L. Blumer & Son four volumes of account books 1853 - 1868

Publications
'Shipbuilders of the Hartlepools', Bert Spaldin, 1985

H9
HASTINGS FISHERMEN'S PROTECTION SOCIETY
Fishmarket   Tel: 01424 722322
Rockanore   Fax: 01424 722322
Hastings
East Sussex TN34 3DW

Organisation representing all Hastings fishermen (formed 1831)

Facilities
Enquiries to the Secretary
Information provided by phone and fax
Open to the public
Research service not provided

Subject coverage
Maritime history of Hastings; local fishing families and the fishing industry from 1832

H10
HASTINGS MUSEUM AND ART GALLERY
John's Place   Tel: 01424 781155
Bohemia Road   Fax: 01424 781165
Hastings
East Sussex TN34 1ET
e-mail: museum@hastings.gov.uk
Website: www.hastings.gov.uk/museum

Museum

Facilities
Enquiries to the Curator
Information provided by phone, post, fax and e-mail
Open to the public
Access to archives - Local Studies Room: Wednesday 1000-1600 and Friday 1000-1300 (other times by appointment)
Photocopying facilities
Research service available - first half hour free, then £19.50 per hour

Subject coverage
Maritime history; fishing industry; smuggling; Cinque Ports; local families; Hastings Corporation records

H11
HEREFORDSHIRE RECORD OFFICE
Harold Street   Tel: 01432 260750
Hereford HR1 2QX   Fax: 01432 260066
e-mail: shubbard@herefordshire.gov.uk
web site: www.herefordshire.gov.uk

Local government organisation

Facilities
Enquiries to the Record Office Manager
Information provided by phone, post and e-mail
Open to the public
Microfilm and microfiche readers
Copies can be provided on request
Research service available: 15 minutes for £3, 30 minutes for £7.50, 1 hour for £15.

Subject coverage
Barges; boats; canals; coracles; naval records; navigation; rivers; training ships

Publications
Many catalogues available on the A2A website: www.pro.a2a.gov.uk

---

H12
HERITAGE, ROYAL MAIL
(formerly Post Office Archives)

Freeling House   Tel: 020 7239 2570
Phoenix Place   Fax: 020 7239 2576
London WC1X 0DL
e-mail: heritage@royalmail.com
Website: www.royalmail.com/heritage

Museum and archive

Facilities
Enquiries to Enquiry Officer
Information provided by phone, post, fax , e-mail and personal visit
Search room open to the public: Monday-Friday 0900-1615
Photocopying facilities (done by staff members only)

Subject coverage
Archives of the Post Office, Royal Mail (including Consignia)
Packet service, mail by ship

Special collections
POST 43:   Packet boats and general post, 1683-1949
POST 41:   Packet service, 1807-1837
POST 51:   Contract sea, 1722-1938
POST 12:   Sea, 1744-1965
POST 4:   Packet stations and agents, 1773-1857

Publications
TPO and Seapost Society: www.royalmail.com/heritage
Most catalogues on PRO website : www.catalogue.pro.gov.uk

H13
HERTFORDSHIRE ARCHIVES AND LOCAL STUDIES

Register Office Block   Tel: 01438 737333
County Hall   Fax: 01992 555113
Hertford
Herts SG13 8EJ
e-mail: hertsdirect@hertscc.gov.uk
Website: www.hertsdirect.org/hals

Local government organisation

Facilities
Enquiries to the County Archivist
Information provided by phone, post, fax, e-mail and website
Open to the public: Monday, Wednesday-Thursday 0930-1730, Tuesday 1000-2000, Friday 0930-1630 and Saturday 0900-1300
Pre-ordering of documents required on Tuesday evenings (1700-2000) and Saturday mornings (0900-1300)
Photocopying facilities
Research service available - £12.50 per half hour/£25 per hour

Subject coverage
Items are held under the following subject headings: Admirals; inland navigation; naval history; naval recruitment; privateers and pirates; ships and shipping

Special collections
Francis, 3rd Duke of Bridgewater (1736-1803) - papers, correspondence and plans of canal-building projects, 1768-1794

H14
HIGHLANDS AND ISLANDS ENTERPRISE

Cowan House
Inverness Retail and Business Park
Inverness   Tel: 01463 234171
IV2 7GF   Fax: 01463 244351
e-mail: sir@hient.co.uk
Website: www.hie.co.uk

Government NDPB

Facilities
Enquiries to the Strategic Information Officer
Information provided by phone, post, fax and e-mail
Open to staff only although access can be granted to resources via local enterprise company offices
Appointment necessary for library

Subject coverage
Highlands and islands of Scotland; economic information for the HIE area; fisheries; geographic information

---

H15
HISTORIC WARSHIPS AT BIRKENHEAD

East Float   Tel: 0151 650 1573
Dock Road   Fax: 0151 650 1473
Birkenhead
Merseyside CH41 1DJ
e-mail: manager@warships.freeserve.co.uk
Website: www.historicwarships.org/

Museum with HM Submarine *Onyx*, HMS *Plymouth*, German submarine *U 534* and lightship *Planet*.

Opening times vary.

Facilities
Tours of warships, visitor centre.

Historical Manuscripts Commission (HMC)
See National Archives

H16
HM CUSTOMS AND EXCISE LIBRARY

New Kings Beam House   Tel: 0207 865 5668/9
22 Upper Ground   Fax: 0207 865 5670
London SE1 9PJ
e-mail: library.enquiries@HMCE.gsi.gov.uk

National government organisation

Facilities
Enquiries to Deputy Librarian
Information provided by phone, post, fax and e-mail
Open to the public by prior appointment
Books loaned through inter-library loan
Microfiche reader
Full size copies can be provided

Subject coverage
Ports; import procedures; trade statistic; customs duties and smuggling

---

HM Customs and Excise
See also Merseyside Maritime Museum

H17
HM NAUTICAL ALMANAC OFFICE

Rutherford Appleton Laboratory   Tel 01235 821900
Chilton   Fax 01235 445068
Didcot
Oxfordshire OX11 0QX
Email nao@rl.ac.uk
Web http://www.nao.rl.ac.uk

Government body (Office of Space, Science and Technology, Department of Rutherford Appleton Laboratory).

Subject coverage
Astronomical ephemeredes for astronomy; navigation and land surveying

Publications
'The UK Air Almanac'
'The Astronomical Almanac'
'Astronomical Phenomena'
'NAVPAC and Compact Data'
'Planetary and Lunar Coordinates'
'Rapid Site Reduction Tables for Navigation'

H18
HOLYHEAD MARITIME MUSEUM

c/o 8 Llainfain Estate   Tel: 01407 769745
Llaingoch   (Hon Sec.) 01407 764374
Holyhead
Anglesey LL65 1NF
e- mail: johncave4@aol.com

Museum

Facilities
Enquiries to the Hon. Secretary
Information provided by phone, post and e-mail
Open to the public
Photocopying facilities
Limited research service available at variable cost

Subject coverage
Books; charts; photographs

Special collections
Artefacts belonging to Captain John MacGregor Skinner, 1760-1832

Specific companies and groups
LNWR, LMS, British Railways
Sealink and Stena Line

Publications
Booklets on special subjects, e.g. Captain Skinner, loss of HMS *Tara,* HMT *Scotia*

H19
THE HONOURABLE COMPANY OF MASTER MARINERS

HMS Wellington   Tel: 020 7836 8179
Temple Stairs   Fax: 020 7240 3082
Victoria Embankment
London WC2R 2PN
e-mail: info@hcmm.org.uk
Website: www.hcmm.org.uk

Livery company

Facilities
Enquiries to the Clerk
Information provided by phone, post, fax and e-mail
Open to the public with maritime interests (students, etc.) otherwise members only
Appointment necessary for library
Photocopying facilities

Subject coverage
Records of membership

Special collections
Nautical memorabilia
Maritime art
Library collection

H20
HOUSE OF LORDS' RECORD OFFICE (THE PARLIAMENTARY ARCHIVES)

London SW1A 0PW   Tel: 020 7219 3074
                         Fax: 020 7219 2570

e-mail: hlro@parliament.uk
Website: www.parliament.uk

National government organisation and archive

Facilities
Enquiries to the Clerk of the Records
Information provided by phone, post, fax and e-mail
Open to the public: Mondays-Fridays 0930-1700;
Appointments preferred
Photocopying facilities
Research service not provided, but information
provided about the existence and scope of records

Subject coverage
Records of both Houses of Parliament from 1497,
including Acts, the journals of both Houses, appeal
cases, private Bill records and papers laid before
Parliament. Few records of the House of Commons
survive prior to 1834

Special collections
Access is also provided to the debates of both Houses
and to printed parliamentary papers (including Bills,
Select Committee reports, commissions of enquiry)

Databases
An automated catalogue is in preparation. Of
particular note is a database of witnesses on private
Bills

Publications
'Guide to the Records of Parliament' M F Bond,
London, 1971

H21
HOVERCRAFT MUSEUM TRUST

HMS Daedalus   Tel: 023 9255 2090
Lee-on-Solent   Fax: 023 9255 2090
Gosport
Hampshire PO13 9NY
e-mail: chris@hovercraft-museum.org
Website: www.hovercraft-museum.org

Museum/voluntary organisation

Facilities
Enquiries to the Trustee and Manager
Information provided by phone, post, fax and e-mail
Open to the public: Monday-Friday 1000-1600 and
Saturday 1000-1200
Photocopying facilities
Research service available - £20 per hour

Subject coverage
Hovercraft - all aspects, plans, manuals, archives, photos
and film

Special collections
Early history - Cockerell's patents
Early photos
Early services
Actual craft - over 50 hovercraft in store

Specific databases
Westlands British Hovercraft Corporation archives

Publications
'The Hovercraft Bulletin', quarterly, £25

H22
HULL CITY ARCHIVES

79 Lowgate   Tel: 01482 615102
Kingston upon Hull HU1 1HN   Fax: 01482 613051
e-mail: City.Archives@hullcc.gov.uk
Website:
www.hullcc.gov.uk/libraries/hull_city_archives/index.ph

Local government organisation

Facilities
Enquiries to the Archivist
Information provided by phone, post, fax and e-mail
Open to the public by appointment only: Tuesday-
Thursday 0900-1215 and 1330-1645
Photocopying facilities

Subject coverage
The port of Hull, including docks, merchant shipping,
deep sea fishing, marine engineering and ship building;
some material relating to Goole

Special collections
Hull registers of shipping, 1804-1902
Running agreements with crews of fishing vessels,
1884-1914
Associated British Ports and its predecessors - Hull,
1788-c.1975 and Goole, 1828-1951
Humber Conservancy, 1852-1946
Hull Fish Merchants Society, 1954-1976
Hull and Goole Port Sanitary Authority, 1873-1974
Water Bailiffs (collecting dues payable to Hull
corporation), 16th-19th centuries

Specific companies and groups
Brigham and Cowan, ship repairers, c.1870-c.1970

Hellyer Bros., trawler owners, and subsidiaries, c.1891-c.1970
Thomas Hamling and Co., trawler owners, and subsidiaries, c.1956-c.1975

Publications
'Transport by Sea, Rail and Inland Navigation, - guide to sources in Hull City Archives' GW Oxley, 1983

H23
HULL CITY LIBRARIES
Business and Technology Library/Local Studies Library/Central Library

Albion Street	Tel: (Bus. & Tech.) 01482 210055
Hull HU1 3TF	Tel: (Local Studies) 01482 210077
	Fax: 01482 616858

e-mail: technical.library@hullcc.gov.uk
Website: www.hullcc.gov.uk

Local government organisation

Facilities
Enquiries to the Librarian
Information provided by phone, post, fax and e-mail
Open to the public: Monday-Thursday 0930-2000, Friday 0930-1730 and Saturday 0900-1630
Photocopying facilities
Research service available for local studies (local and genealogical research) £10 per half hour

Subject coverage
Directories; company histories; monographs - shipping lines, history

Special collections
Whaling log books (local studies)
Local directories (local studies)
Electoral lists (local studies)
'Lloyd's Register of Shipping': Register of Ships, 1764 to date (incomplete)
Fishing industry
Trade and industry of the port of Hull (local studies)
Bills of entry, charts, local newspapers (local studies)

Specific databases
Access to DIALOG, DIALTECH
Company and business databases, e.g. Dun & Bradstreet, KBG 200, Jordans FAME, Kompass Western Europe, Companies House CD ROM, Marquesa Trade Names
Bibliographical databases
Institute of Management IMID
Abstracts in New Technology and Engineering and many more

Publications
Local studies catalogue available via East Yorkshire Bibliography at http://library.hull.ac.uk:81

H24
HULL MARITIME MUSEUM

Queen Victoria Square	Tel: 01482 63902
Hull	Fax: 01482 61370
East Yorkshire HU1 3DX	

e-mail: arthur.credland@hullcc.gov.uk
Website: www.hullcc.gov.uk/museums

Museum

Facilities
Enquiries to the Keeper of Maritime History
Information provided by phone, post, fax and e-mail
Open to the public (displays and exhibitions) - free entry; appointment necessary for reserve collections: Monday-Friday 1000-1700
Limited research service available - no charge but only one member of staff

Subject coverage
Hull whaling (Arctic) in 18th-19th centuries; fishing in the North Sea and North Atlantic in 18th-19th centuries; Hull steamship companies (especially Wilson Line, Bailey and Leetham); Hull marine painting, 18th century to present; decorative arts of the mariner

Special collections
Largest collection of Scrimshaw (decorated whalebone and whales' teeth)
Hull marine painting, 18th century to present
Arctic whaling 18th-19th centuries, journals, logs and artefacts

Specific companies or groups
Wilson Line
Bailey and Leetham
Beverley Shipyard
Selby Shipyard

Publications
'Scrimshaw - The Art of the Whaler' J West and AG Credland
'Marine Painting in Hull through Three Centuries' AG Credland
'Hull Whaling Trade' AG Credland
'The Wilson Line' AG Credland
'Fishing from the Humber' AG Credland

Hull, The University of
See Brynmor Jones Library

H25
HUMBER KEEL AND SLOOP PRESERVATION SOCIETY LIMITED
52 Glenwood Close
Lambwalk Road
Hull HU8 0EP

Voluntary association

Humberside Libraries
See Hull City Libraries

Hydrographic Office
See UK Hydrographic Office

11
ICC INTERNATIONAL MARITIME BUREAU

Maritime House   Tel: 020 8591 3000
1 Linton Road   Fax: 020 8594 2833
Barking
Essex IG11 8HG
e-mail: ccs@icc-ccs.org
Website: www.icc-ccs.org

Membership organisation, a specialist division of the International Chamber of Commerce

Facilities
Information provided to members only by phone, post and e-mail.

12
ICHCA INTERNATIONAL LTD

Suite 2   Tel: 01708 735295
85 Western Road
Romford
Essex RM1 3LS

Trade association

Subject coverage
Cargo handling, ships, equipment, terminals

13
IMMINGHAM MUSEUM

Margaret Street   Tel: 01469 577066
Immingham
North East Lincolnshire DN40 1RB
e-mail: immingham@bmummery.freeserve.co.uk
Website: www.nelincs.gov.uk

Museum

Facilities
Enquiries to the Curator
Information provided by post and e-mail
Open to the public

Subject coverage
Display and records of the history of the town and docks from 1906 to present

Special collections
Photograph collection of Humber Graving Dock

Shipping registers for Immingham, 1912-1965
Specific companies and groups
Sutcliffe (agents)
Humber Graving Dock

Publications
'Immingham and the Great Central Legacy'
'Shipping on the Humber'

14
IMPERIAL WAR MUSEUM - DEPARTMENT OF DOCUMENTS

Lambeth Road   Tel: 020 7416 5222
London SE1 6HZ   Fax: 020 7416 5374
e-mail: docs@iwm.org.uk
Website: www.iwm.org.uk/collections/docs.htm

National museum department

Facilities
Enquiries to the Keeper, Department of Documents
Information provided by phone, post, fax and e-mail
Open to the public by appointment: Monday-Saturday 1000-1700
Photocopying facilities

Subject coverage
20th century naval history

Special collections
Admiral of the Fleet, the 1st Marquess of Milford Haven (Prince Louis of Battenberg), microfilm held by permission of the Broadlands Archive Trust
Papers of over 80 other flag officers, including Admirals Sir Ernest Archer, Sir Francis Bridgeman, Sir John Crace, Sir Dudley de Chair, Sir Vernon Haggard, Sir Cecil Harcourt, Sir Vaughan Morgan, Sir Edward Parry, Sir Richard Phillimore, Sir Ernest Troubridge, Sir Frederic Wake-Walker and Sir William Whitworth, Vice-Admirals Sir Geoffrey Barnard, Sir Alastair Ewing, Sir John Hayes, J Hughes-Hallett, JSC Salter and Sir Cecil Talbot and Rear Admiral H Miller
Unpublished diaries, letters and memoirs of several hundred officers and men who served in the Royal Navy during the 20th century

Specific databases
Many of the collections are included on a departmental database

Publications
Departmental website has details of a selection of our holdings

---

15
IMPERIAL WAR MUSEUM - FILM AND VIDEO ARCHIVE

Lambeth Road	Tel: 020 7416 5291/2/3/4
London SE1 6HZ	Fax: 020 7416 5299

e-mail: film@iwm.org.uk
Website: www.iwm.org.uk

National museum department

Facilities
Commercial enquiries to the Production Office -
020 7416 5291/2
Non-commercial enquiries to Public Services -
020 7416 5291/3/4
Information provided by phone, post, fax, e-mail and by visiting the Archive
Open to all by appointment: Monday-Friday 1000-1700
Photocopying facilities
Research service available (free) and range of charges for film viewing

Subject coverage
Film and video records of naval aspects, including merchant marine, of the Museum's terms of reference ('all aspects of all conflicts involving Britain or the Commonwealth since 1914'); naval operations; training; shipbuilding; convoys

Publications
A working guide to the film archive

16
IMPERIAL WAR MUSEUM - HMS BELFAST

Morgan's Lane	Tel: 020 7940 6300
Tooley Street	Fax: 020 7403 0719
London SE1 2JH	

hmsbelfast@iwm.org.uk
Website: www.iwm.org.uk

Second World War cruiser
National museum department; outstation of the Imperial War Museum

Facilities
Enquiries to the Marketing Officer
Information provided by phone, post, fax and e-mail
Open to the public: seven days, from 1000; admission charged, group discount
Photocopying facilities

Subject coverage
Naval history of Second World War and the development of the British warship

---

17
IMPERIAL WAR MUSEUM - PHOTOGRAPHIC ARCHIVES

Lambeth Road	Tel: 020 7416 5333
London SE1 6HZ	Fax: 020 7416 5355

e-mail: photos@iwm.org.uk
Website: www.iwm.org.uk

National museum department

Facilities
Enquiries to the Keeper, Photographic Archives
Information provided primarily by post
Open to the public by appointment: Monday-Friday 1000-1700. The street address is All Saints Annexe, Austral Street
Photocopying facilities
Limited research service (free) available from curators (e.g. references of pictures for 1 or 2 ships) - personal visit is recommended for intensive research (no charge for personal access to visitors' room)

Subject coverage
Official photographic record of the Royal and Merchant Navies during the First and Second World Wars; material relating to pre-First World War and post-1945 conflicts

Special collections
The Director of Naval Construction's collection forms a comprehensive photographic record of British warships in home waters, principally during the Second World War

Publications
Limited number of images available for viewing online at www.iwm.org.uk/collections/photos/album.htm

---

18
IMPERIAL WAR MUSEUM - DEPARTMENT OF PRINTED BOOKS

Lambeth Road	Tel: 020 7416 5342
London SE1 6HZ	Fax: 020 7416 5246

e-mail: books@iwm.org.uk
Website: www.iwm.org.uk

National museum department

Facilities
Enquiries to 020 7416 5342 (enquiry line roster applies); written enquiries to Keeper, Printed Books
Information provided by phone, post, fax and e-mail
Open to the public (visitors of 14 years and under must be accompanied by an adult when visiting the Reading Room): Monday-Saturday 1000-1700
Appointment necessary for the Reading Room (please call 020 7416 5342)
Photocopying facilities

No research service available but free enquiry service offered by Library staff (limited to 30 minutes per enquiry)

Subject coverage
Naval and maritime history of the 20th century, including operations, records, technical handbooks and personal accounts

Special collections
National Roll of the Great War, 1914-18
Cross of Sacrifice
Seedie's Rolls of Honour and Awards
Admiralty Register of Deaths (Officers and Naval Ratings), 1939-48
Unpublished ships' histories (mainly RN vessels in service, Second World War and after)
Royal Naval Division Rolls of Honour
Lloyds War Losses
Periodicals and newspapers

Specific databases
UK National Inventory of War Memorials

Publications
'Tracing Your Family History' guides, includes RN and Merchant Navy (N.B. post 1914).
See website for catalogue of publications
Library collections catalogue is due to be available on website in 2003

I9
IMPERIAL WAR MUSEUM - SOUND ARCHIVE
Lambeth Road   Tel: 020 7416 5363
London SE1 6HZ   Fax: 020 7416 5378
e-mail: sound@iwm.org.uk
Website: www.iwm.org.uk/collections/sound.htm

National museum department

Facilities
Enquiries to the Office Manager, Sound Archive
Information provided by phone, post, fax , e-mail and website
Open to the public (free of charge): Monday-Friday 1000-1700
Appointment necessary for library of recordings
Analogue or digital copies may be purchased, subject to copyright
Photocopying facilities
Research service not available except for provision of lists of recordings relating to specified subjects - short list provided free (post, email or fax); lengthy list charged at 25p per page, plus postage

Subject coverage
Recorded eye-witness accounts of naval experience, both civilian and services, at sea and on shore, by men and women of all ranks; coverage from 1890s to the

present with greatest emphasis on First and Second World Wars, includes relevant speeches, poetry, sound effects, etc.

Specific databases
Own database lists and summarises the recordings in the collection - fully searchable inhouse and on the IWM website

Publications
Printed catalogues listed on website
Catalogues can be produced to order from the database on any relevant subject (price approx. £10)

110
INFORMA GROUP PLC
Mortimer House   Tel: 020 7553 1000
37-41 Mortimer Street
London W1T 3JH
Website: www.group.informa.com

Business information provider

Publications
'Bunkernews'
'International Freight Weekly'
'Lloyd's Law Reports'
'Lloyd's List'
'Lloyd's Maritime Law Newsletter'
Maritime directories

111
INLAND WATERWAYS ASSOCIATION (IWA)
PO Box 114   Tel: 01923 711114
Rickmansworth WD3 1ZY   Fax: 01923 897000
e-mail: iwa@waterways.org.uk
Website: www.waterways.org.uk

Voluntary association in a specific interest.

Facilities
Enquiries to the Operations Manager
Information provided by phone, post, fax and e-mail
Open to the public
Photocopying facilities available
Research service: IWA archive available at the Boat Museum, Ellesmere Port, Wirral, tel: 0151 355 5017 (q.v.)

Subject coverage
History and restoration of the inland waterways

Special collections
(at Ellesmere Port see Waterways Trust)
Fellows, Morton and Clayton Collection
John Heap Collection

Publications
'Waterways' magazine for members, three times a year
Facts sheets (write for list)
Inland waterways guide.

112
INSTITUTE OF ACTUARIES
LIBRARY

Main library:
Napier House   Tel: 01865 268208
4 Worcester Street   Fax: 01865 268211
Oxford OX1 2AW

Library of pre-1960 historical texts:
Staple Inn Hall   Tel: 020 7632 2100/2114
High Holborn   Fax: 020 7632 2111
London WC1V 7QJ

e-mail: institute@actuaries.org.uk
Website: www.actuaries.org.uk

Professional association

Facilities
Enquiries to the Librarian/Webmaster
Information provided by phone, post, fax, e-mail, and visit.
Open to the public, appointment recommended:
Monday-Friday 0900-1700
Members and registered students may borrow items
Photocopying facilities

Subject coverage
Main coverage is the actuarial basis of life insurance, and includes life assurance in relation to seamen and their dependants. Coverage of the history of marine insurance and reinsurance is more limited.

Special collections
Miscellaneous documents on marine insurance and related matters 17th to 20th centuries, including prospectuses of marine insurance companies
Life assurance available to merchant marine and Royal Navy personnel

Publications
Guide to libraries and publications available on the website.

113
INSTITUTE OF CHARTERED
SHIPBROKERS

3 St Helen's Place   Tel: 020 7628 5559
London EC3A 6EJ   Fax: 020 7628 5445
e-mail: info@ics.org.uk
Website: www.ics.org.uk

Professional association

Facilities
Enquiries to the Director General
Information provided by phone, post, fax and e-mail
Open to members and the public by appointment

Subject coverage
General Maritime Business library

Special collections
Lloyd's Law Reports, 1919 to date

Publications
'The Shipbroker' - quarterly

114
INSTITUTE OF COMMONWEALTH
STUDIES

University of London   Tel: 020 7862 8844
27-28 Russell Square
London WC1B 5DS
Website: www.sds.ac.uk/commonwealthstudies

University research institute

Facilities
Enquiries to the Librarian
Information provided by phone, post and fax
Library open to University of London graduates and those involved in advanced study of the Commonwealth of Nations
Microfiche and microfilm readers

115
INSTITUTE OF EXPORT

Export House   Tel: 01733 404400
Minerva Business Park   Fax: 01733 404444
Lynchwood
Peterborough PE2 6FT
e-mail: institute@export.org.uk
Website: www.export.org.uk

Professional educational and training charity

Facilities
Enquiries to the Administrator
Information provided by phone, fax, e-mail and training/education by examination, home study and via colleges
Open to the public and members

Subject coverage
International trade - export and import

Publications
'International Trade Today' journal

116
INSTITUTE OF HISTORICAL RESEARCH

University of London	Tel: 020 7862 8760
Senate House	Fax: 020 7862 8762
Malet Street	
London WCIE 7HU	
e-mail: ihrlib@sas.ac.uk	
Website: www.ihr.sas.ac.uk	

University department

Facilities
Enquiries to the Librarian
Library open to members (small annual fee but free to teachers or registered postgraduate students at a UK or other EU university), free to anyone for one week during any academic year
Limited information provided by phone, post, e-mail and visit
Microfilm and microfiche readers
Photocopying facilities
CD-ROM available.

Subject coverage
Modern British naval history

___

117
INSTITUTE OF LOGISTICS AND TRANSPORT

Logistics and Transport Centre	Tel: 01536 740100
Earlstree Court	Fax: 01536 740102
Earlstree Road	
Earlstree Industrial Estate	
Corby	
Northants NN17 4AX	
Email enquiries@iolt.org.uk	
Web http://www.iolt.org.uk	

Professional Institute

Facilities
Enquiries to the Librarian
Information given by phone, post, fax and e-mail
Open to the public
Books loaned to members only.

Subject coverage
Business and management aspects of commercial transport, passenger transport and logistics.

Publications
'Logistics and Transport Focus'

___

118
THE INSTITUTE OF MARINE ENGINEERING, SCIENCE AND TECHNOLOGY (IMarEST)

80 Coleman Street	Tel: 020 7382 2648
London EC2R 5BJ	Fax: 020 7382 2670
e-mail: mic@imarest.org	
Website: www.imarest.org	

Professional society

Facilities
Enquiries to the Information Scientist
Information provided by phone, post, fax and e-mail
Open to members and the public: Monday-Friday 0900-1700
Photocopying facilities

Subject coverage
Marine engineering; marine technology, marine science; offshore engineering; navigation; naval history

Specific databases
Marine Technology Abstracts

Publications
See website

___

119
INSTITUTE OF MARITIME LAW

School of Law	Tel: 023 8059 5767
University of Southampton	Fax: 023 8059 3789
Highfield	
Southampton SO17 1BJ	
e-mail: sjlb@soton.ac.uk	
Website: www.iml.soton.ac.uk	

University department

Facilities
Enquiries to the Librarian
Information provided by phone, post, fax and e-mail
Open to the public - prior contact must be made with either Librarian or Director of the Institute
Loans made to Members
Appointment necessary
Photocopying facilities
Research service available - cost varies depending on time and information requested

Subject coverage
Maritime law; marine insurance; marine pollution; international trade law; charter party disputes; cargo claims; carriage of goods and passengers by sea international conventions; salvage law, contract law

Publications
Catalogue accessible through Institute computers

___

120

INSTITUTE OF NAVAL MEDICINE

Alverstoke	Tel: 023 9276 8101/2
Gosport	Fax: 023 9250 4823
Hampshire PO12 2DL	

e-mail: lib@inm.mod.uk

Government organisation (MOD)

Facilities
Enquiries to the Librarian
Information provided by phone, post, fax and e-mail
Open to MOD staff - others by appointment at discretion of the Medical Officer in Charge: Monday-Friday 0900-1700 (visits by appointment only)
Photocopying facilities

Subject coverage
Naval (medical) history; underwater medicine; survival; thermal medicine; physiology

---

121

INSTITUTE OF PETROLEUM (IP)

61 New Cavendish Street	Tel: 020 7467 7100
London W1G 7AR	Fax: 020 7255 1472

e-mail: ip@petroleum.co.uk
Website: www.petroleum.co.uk

Institute

Facilities
Enquiries to the Senior Information Officer
Information provided by phone, post, fax and e-mail
Open to the public (fee charged to non-members):
Monday-Friday 0915-1700
Photocopying facilities
Research service available: non-members - £100 per hour of staff time, plus expenses, IP members - £50 per hour of staff time, plus expenses

Subject coverage
All aspects of petroleum industry - history to modern

Special collections
Complete sets of 'AAPG' (1917-); 'Petroleum Times' (1919-1988); long runs of 'Oil and Gas Journal' (1911-)

Specific databases/publications
Web-based library collection of monographs and periodicals
IP Publications for sale
IP consultants
IP corporate members
IP test methods
International Petroleum Abstracts - bibliographic news in brief
Forthcoming conferences
CD ROM: Petroleum Abstracts

122

INSTITUTE OF TRANSPORT ADMINISTRATION (IOTA)

Mill House	Tel: 01403 242412
11 Nightingale Road	
Horsham	
West Sussex RH12 2NW	

e-mail: director.iota@btclick.com
Website: www.iota.org.uk

Institute

Facilities
Enquiries to the Director
Library open to members only
Information given by phone or post
Books and other materials loaned to members only

Subject coverage
Maritime transport management

123

INSTITUTION OF CIVIL ENGINEERS (ICE)

1-7 Gt George Street	Tel: 020 7222 7722
London SW1P 3AA	Fax: 020 7976 7610

e-mail: library@ice.org.uk
Website: www.ice.org.uk

Professional society

Facilities
Enquiries to the Librarian
Information provided by phone, post, fax or e-mail to non-members with a bona-fide interest in civil engineering, otherwise members only; books and other material loaned to members only
Library open to non-members by appointment, otherwise members only
Opening hours: Mondays-Fridays 0915-1750
Microfilm and microfiche readers; fullsize copies can be provided on request; CD-ROM and on-line information database service offered; charges for all services
Research services provided for members; biographical searches, £10

Subject coverage
Civil engineering including ports; harbours; docks; offshore and marine structures; historical naval architecture; marine pollution and public health engineering

Special collections
Telford and Rennie papers contain material on various harbours and docks on which they were consulted
Coode Collection relates to the work of Coode and Partners

Publications
See website

International Association of Cape Homes
See Shanty Crew

International Cargo Handling Co-ordination Association
See ICHCA International Ltd.

124
INTERNATIONAL CHAMBER OF SHIPPING (ICS)

12 Carthusian Street   Tel: 020 7417 8844
London EC1M 6EZ   Fax: 020 7417 8877
e-mail: ics@marisec.org
Website: www.marisec.org

Trade association with consultative status to IMO

Facilities
Enquiries to the Publications Officer
Information provided by phone, fax and e-mail
Open to the public by appointment only: Monday-Friday 0900-1645

Subject coverage
Industry guidance on technical and operational issues

Publications
See website

125
INTERNATIONAL COUNCIL OF MARINE INDUSTRY ASSOCIATIONS

Marine House   Tel: 01784 223702
Thorpe Lea Road   Fax: 01784 223705
Egham
Surrey TW20 8BF
e-mail: info@icomia.com
Website: www.icomia.com

International trade association

Facilities
Enquiries to the Secretary
Information provided by phone, e-mail and website
Open to the public with members-only section of website
Appointment necessary for library

Special collections
ISO standards and EU standards for recreational marine craft

Publications
Bi-monthly newsletter

126
INTERNATIONAL FEDERATION OF SHIPMASTERS' ASSOCIATIONS (IFSMA)

202 Lambeth Road   Tel: 020 7261 0450
London SE1 7JY   Fax: 020 7928 9030
e-mail: HQ@ifsma.org
Website: www.ifsma.org

Professional body

Facilities
Enquiries to the Secretary General
Information provided by phone, post, fax and e-mail (preferred)
Open to members; others on a case-by-case basis upon request, and by appointment
Photocopying facilities

Subject coverage
IFSMA conference papers, and IMO circulars and reports; IMO committees and sub-committees records are held for 3 years and reports for 10 years

127
INTERNATIONAL MARITIME FEDERATION (IMIF)

The Baltic Exchange   Tel: 0207 493 4559
39 St Mary Axe   Fax: 0207 491 0736
London EC3A 8BH

Voluntary association in a specific interest

Facilities
Enquiries to the Secretary

Subject coverage
Commercial information on maritime industries

Publications
Quarterly newsletter

128
INTERNATIONAL MARITIME ORGANISATION (IMO)

4 Albert Embankment   Tel: 020 7735 7611
London SE1 7ER   Fax: 020 7587 3210
e-mail: info@imo.org
Website: www.imo.org

United Nations specialised agency

Facilities
Information provided by phone, post, fax or e-mail; books and other material loaned to libraries
Library open to the public; access by appointment only
Fullsize copies provided; online information retrieval

using IMOCAB and IMOLIB
Research service provided: simple search of library
catalogue

Subject coverage
Maritime safety; navigation; ship design and equipment;
dangerous goods; bulk chemicals; radiocommunications;
life-saving; search and rescue; training and
watchkeeping; fire protection; containers and cargoes;
environmental protection; pollution; conventions;
technical cooperation; facilitation

Special collections
Complete collection of IMO documents in English,
French and Spanish since 1959
Reports of main committees in Russian, Chinese and
Arabic

Publications
Codes, Conventions, Regulations
IMO Library Current Awareness Bulletin (monthly)
IMO Library Acquisitions List (quarterly)
IMO News (quarterly)

129
INTERNATIONAL OIL POLLUTION COMPENSATION FUNDS

Portland House   Tel: 020 7592 7100
Stag Place   Fax: 020 7592 7111
London SW1E 5PN
e-mail: info@iopcfund.org
Website: www.iopcfund.org

Inter-governmental organisation established under a
convention adopted under the auspices of the IMO

Facilities
Enquiries to External Relations and Conference
Department
Information provided to all by 'phone, post, fax, e-mail
and website
Open to the public
No photocopying facilities

Subject coverage
Liability and compensation for oil pollution damage

Publications
General information on IOPC Fund
Annual report on the IOPC Fund
Statistics
Claims manual

130
INTERNATIONAL SALVAGE UNION

PO Box 32293   Tel: 020 7345 5122
London W5 1WZ   Fax: 020 7345 5722

e-mail: isu@randell.fsnet.co.uk
Website: www.marine-salvage.com

International trade association

Facilities
Enquiries to the Secretary-General
Information provided by phone, post, fax and e-mail
Open to the public
Photocopying facilities

Subject coverage
Private association records

Publications
Annual bulletin

131
INTERNATIONAL SHIP SUPPLIERS ASSOCIATION

The Baltic Exchange   Tel: 020 7626 6236/7
St Mary Axe   Fax: 020 7626 6234
London EC3A 8BH
e-mail: issa@dial.pipex.com
Website: www.shipsupply.org

International trade association

Facilities
Enquiries to the ISSA Secretary
Information provided by phone, post, fax and e-mail
Open to the public

Subject coverage
Information on supply of all stores to ships

Publications
ISSA Ship Stores Catalogue

132
INTERNATIONAL TANKER OWNERS' POLLUTION FEDERATION LTD (ITOPF)

Staple Hall   Tel: 020 7621 1255
Stonehouse Court   Fax: 020 7621 1783
87-90 Houndsditch
London EC3A 7AX

e-mail: central@itopf.com
Website: www.itopf.com

Industry organisation

Facilities
Enquiries to the Information Officer
Information provided by phone, post, fax and e-mail
Open to the public by appointment only
Photocopying facilities

Subject coverage
Oil pollution; clean-up techniques; environmental impact of oil; contingency planning

---

133
INTERNATIONAL TRANSPORT WORKERS FEDERATION (ITF)

49-60 Borough Road   Tel: 020 7403 2733
London SE1 1DR   Fax: 020 7357 7871
e-mail: mail@itf.org.uk
Website: www.itf.org.uk

Trade union

Facilities
Enquiries to the Information Centre Manager
Information provided by phone, fax and e-mail
Certain facilities for members only, some facilities available to students
Appointment necessary for access
Photocopying facilities

Subject coverage
General transport policy; transport sectors - maritime, docks, fishing, railways, roads, inland navigation, urban transport, civil aviation and tourism

Special collections
Archive material - ITF publications

Specific databases
Factiva
Lloyd's List and other maritime publications available online

---

Ipswich
See Associated British Ports - Ipswich

134
ISLE OF MAN SHIP REGISTRY

Marine Administration   Tel: 01624 688500
Peregrine House   Fax: 01624 627238
Peel Road
Douglas
Isle of Man IM1 5EH
Website: www.gov.im/dti/marineadmin/

Government department

135
ISLE OF WIGHT COUNTY RECORD OFFICE

26 Hillside   Tel: 01983 823821/0
Newport   Fax: 01983 823820
Isle of Wight PO30 2EB
e-mail: record.office@iow.gov.uk

Website: www.iwight.com/library/record_office

Local government organisation

Facilities
Enquiries to the County Archivist
Information provided by phone, post, fax and e-mail
Open to the public: Monday 0930-1700, Tuesday - Friday 0900-1700 and Wednesday evening 1700-1930 (1st Wednesday of each month only by prior application)
Appointment only necessary to view microfilm/fiche
Photocopying facilities
Research service available - £15 per hour

Subject coverage
Naval history; ships and shipbuilding

Special collections
Cowes Protest Book 1755-1761
Cowes Registry of Shipping Records - registers of ships 1855-1899, index to ships 1885-1988, appropriation of official numbers 1855-1971, annual returns 1935, fees and deeds 1927-1970, 1983-1989, droit books 1944-1962, transcript of register of ships 1786-1885 and 1923-1930
J. Samuel White of Cowes, shipbuilder: plans of boats, financial records, correspondence and other material c.1860s-1960s (prior notice advised for this collection)

136
ISLES OF SCILLY MUSEUM

Church Street   Tel: 01720 422337
St Mary's
Isles of Scilly TR21 0JT
e-mail: info@iosmuseum.org
Website: www.iosmuseum.org

Museum/voluntary organisation

Facilities
Enquiries to the Curator
Information provided mainly by phone, post and e-mail
Most facilities open to the public, some for members only
Photocopying facilities
Research service available for a small fee

Subject coverage
Logbooks of pilot cutters; records of wrecks (newspaper and oral accounts); family history archives; local history and natural history

J1
JERSEY ARCHIVE

Clarence Road
St.Helier
Jersey JE2 4JY
e-mail: archives@jerseyheritagetrust.org
Website: www.jerseyheritagetrust.org

Tel: 01534 833300
Fax: 01534 833301

Archive

Facilities
Enquiries to the Archivist
Information provided by phone, fax, e-mail and visit
Open to the general public: Tuesdays-Saturdays: 0900-1300, 1400-1700
Photocopying by staff only
Research service available. Initial small enquiries are free; £20.00/hour for more extensive enquiries

Subject coverage
States of Jersey records, church and parish records, business, personal and society records, film archive, sound archive

Special collections
Harbours Department Collection
Customs Department, giving details of shipping, piers' and harbours' correspondence
Harbours' Committee Minutes
Jean Jean shipping research archive

Databases
All Jersey Archive documents are catalogued on an open public access database; see website

---

Jewell And Esk Valley College
No longer have a nautical collection

K1
KENSINGTON AND CHELSEA, ROYAL BOROUGH OF

Chelsea Library
King's Road
Chelsea
London SW3 5EZ

Tel: 0171 352 6056

Public library

Facilities
Enquiries to the Reference Librarian
Library open to the public
Information provided by: phone, post, e-mail and visit
Microfilm and microfiche readers available

Subject coverage
The Thames at Chelsea, especially prints and pictures of Chelsea Creek.

K2
KENTISH STUDIES, CENTRE FOR

Sessions House
County Hall
Maidstone
Kent ME14 1XQ
e-mail: archives@kent.gov.uk
Website: www.kent.gov.uk/e&l/artslib/archives

Tel: 01622 694363
Fax: 01622 694379

Local government organisation

Facilities
Enquiries to the County Archivist
Information provided by phone, post fax and e-mail
Open to the public: Tuesday, Wednesday and Friday 0900-1700, Thursday 1000-1700 and Saturday (2nd and 4th in each month) 0900-1600
Photocopying facilities
Research service available for records at the Centre only - £28 per hour, £7 per 15 minutes (minimum)

Subject coverage
Records relating to the County of Kent

Special collections
Correspondence (18th-20th centuries)
Officers' appointments (17th-19th centuries)
Bills of Sale (15th-19th centuries)
Ships' Logs (17th-19th centuries)
Registers of Shipping - Faversham (19th and 20th centuries)

Publications
Catalogues and guides only at the Centre

K3
KING GEORGE'S FUND FOR SAILORS

8 Hatherley Street
London SW1P 2YY
e-mail: seafarers@kgfs.org.uk
Website: www.kgfs.org.uk

Tel: 020 7932 0000
Fax: 020 7932 0095

Grant making charity

Facilities
Enquiries to the Executive Assistant to the Director General
Information provided by phone, post, fax and e-mail
No records held

K4
KING'S COLLEGE - LIDDELL HART CENTRE FOR MILITARY ARCHIVES

King's College London
Strand
London WC2R 2LS
e-mail: archives.web@kcl.ac.uk

Tel: 020 7848 2015/1867
Fax: 020 7848 2760

Website: www.kcl.ac.uk/lhcma/top.htm

University department and archive

Facilities
Enquiries to the Senior Archive Services Manager
Information provided by phone, post, fax and e-mail
Open to all, providing a letter of introduction is
produced: Monday-Friday 0930-1730, appointment
preferred
Photocopying facilities
No research service is provided, but guidance will be
provided to assist enquirers

Subject coverage
Over 500 collections of senior defence personnel's
private papers since the late 19th century and papers
television documentaries - all relating to modern
conflict, including high level strategy, special forces,
science of war and peace-keeping

Specific databases
Please see website (above) for summary descriptions
of most holdings and detailed catalogues to many sites
Research guide by theme
Location register of senior defence personnel

Publications
Please see research guides on website

Kingston upon Hull

See   Hull City Archives
      Hull City Libraries
      Hull Maritime Museum

K5
KINGSWEAR CASTLE TRUST, PADDLE STEAMER

The Historic Dockyard	Tel: 01634 827648
Chatham	Fax: 01634 827648
ME4 4TQ	

e-mail: kc@pskc.freeserve.co.uk
Website: www.pskc.freeserve.co.uk

Historic ship

Facilities
Enquiries to John Megoran
Information provided by phone, post, fax and e-mail
Open to the general public; archives open by
appointment
No photocopying facilities
Research service available; cost depends on work
involved

Subject coverage
Paddle steamers in the UK and abroad

Special collection
Archive of the River Dart Steamboat Company

Paddle steamer *Kingswear Castle*

Publications
The website: www.pskc.freeserve.co.uk has regular
features on paddle steamer operations and history,
both in the U.K. and overseas

Kirkleatham Museum
See: Redcar and Cleveland

L1
LAMBETH PALACE LIBRARY

London SE1 7JU	Tel: 020 7898 1400
	Fax: 020 7928 7932

Website: www.lambethpalacelibrary.org

Specialist library and record repository (focusing on
history of the Church), historic library of Archbishops
of Canterbury

Facilities
Enquiries to the Librarian
Information provided by phone, post and fax
Open to the public on production of two passport
photographs, identification with address, and a letter of
introduction: Monday-Friday 1000-1700
Photocopying facilities, microfilm, microfiche -
microcopies and other photography can be provided

Subject coverage
Principal library and record office for the Church of
England: mainly ecclesiastical history, includes history of
art and architecture, colonial and Commonwealth
history, English social, political and economic history,
local history and genealogy, maritime history - voyages
and travel

Special collections
Maritime history collections include Elizabethan and
Stuart voyages of discovery
18th century navigation MSS (in Court of Arches
exhibits)
Appointments of notaries public, some involved in
maritime and Admiralty affairs, 17th century onwards

Publications
See website
Handlist of indexes and catalogues available (by post)
for a charge

L2
LANCASHIRE RECORD OFFICE

Bow Lane	Tel: 01772 263039
Preston PR1 2RE	Fax: 01772 263050

e-mail: record.office@ed.lancscc.gov.uk
Website:
www.lancashire.gov.uk/education/lifelong/recordindex.shtm

Local government organisation

Facilities
Enquiries to the County Archivist
Information provided by phone, post, fax and e-mail
Open to the public: please telephone for opening hours
Photocopying facilities; microfilm and microfiche readers
Research services: telephone for details

Special collections
Preston port records, including arrivals and sailings books, plans, financial records and correspondence 19th-20th centuries
Crew lists of ships registered at Fleetwood, Lancaster and Preston
Fishing vessel crew lists 19th-20th centuries
Nautical newspaper cuttings including the ports of Preston, Liverpool, Manchester and North Lancashire, 19th-20th centuries

Publications
'Guide to the Lancashire Record Office' (3rd edition, 1985)
'Supplement to the Guide', 1977-1989 (1st edition, 1992)

L3
LANCASTER MARITIME MUSEUM
Custom House   Tel: 01524 64637
St. George's Quay   Fax: 01524 841692
Lancaster LA1 1RB
e-mail: awhite@lancaster.gov.uk
Website: www.lancaster.gov.uk/council/museums

Museum

Facilities
Enquiries to the Head of Museums
Information provided by phone, post, fax and e-mail; information retrieval on Lancaster Ship Database
Library open to the public by appointment: Easter-October 1100-1700; November-Easter 1400-1700
Photocopying facilities
Research service provided; free for basic information; at cost for detailed research

Subject coverage
Shipping records for port of Lancaster; documents relating to Lancaster canal; maritime history (Lancaster and district); fishing industry (Morecambe Bay); shipbreaking (Morecambe); shipping; shipbuilding; ferry operations; ports of Glasson Dock, Heysham, Morecambe and Lancaster

Special collections
City museum photographic collection - many with local shipping interest
Willmott Collection of material on Heysham Harbour

Database
Lancaster ships' database

Publications
'The Lune Shipbuilding Company' A White
'Shipbuilding in Glasson Dock' N Daiziel
'Lancaster and the African Slave Trade' M Elder

L4
LEEDS LIBRARY AND INFORMATION SERVICES PATENTS INFORMATION UNIT
Library HQ   Tel: 0113 2143347
32 York Road   Fax: 0113 2143349
Leeds LS9 8TD
e-mail: piu@leeds.gov.uk
Website: www.leeds.gov.uk

Local government organisation

Facilities
Enquiries to the Patents Librarian
Information provided by phone, post, fax and e-mail
Open to the public: Monday-Friday 0900-1700 and Saturday 0900-1300
Photocopying facilities at a charge
Commissioned searches available; if subscription databases used, then cost of search and handling fee if passed on, otherwise enquiries and information are free

Subject coverage
All areas of marine engineering; pollution control devices; navigational aids; underwater equipment

Special collections
Includes all early British patents back to 1617
Patents on any aspect of marine engineering

Specific companies or groups
Copies of all British patents and an extensive collection of US, DE, FR, EP, WO, AU, CH patents

Specific databases
Access to Derwest World Patents index
Marquesa UKTM/CTM database
INPADOC database
JAP:o CD ROMS
Globalpat indexes
PRS - family and legal status database
Access to all free internet-based databases

L5
LEEDS UNIVERSITY LIBRARY – THE LIDDLE COLLECTION

Special Collections   Tel: 0113 343 5518
Brotherton Library   Fax: 0113 343 5561
University of Leeds
Leeds LS2 9JT
e-mail: r.d.davies@leeds.ac.uk
Website: www.leeds.ac.uk/library/spcoll/liddle

University department.

Facilities
Enquiries to the Keeper
Information provided by phone, post, fax and e-mail
Library open to the public by appointment: Mondays-Thursdays 0930-1900; Friday 0930-1900; Saturday 1000-1300 (times vary in summer vacation)
Photocopying facilities
Limited research service provided

Special collections
Pre-1914 and 1914-20 Royal and Merchant Navy personal experience documentation; logbooks; letters; diaries; photographs; official papers; artefacts; recollections by manuscript; typescript and tape recording; all 1914-18 battles, engagements and aspects of maritime service covered; papers held of many junior officers who later rose to flag rank
Similar material for Second World War

Publications
Detailed catalogues covering names, ships and aspects of Royal and Merchant Navy service
See website

L6
LEICESTERSHIRE, LEICESTER AND RUTLAND RECORD OFFICE

Long Street   Tel: 0116 257 1080
Wigston Magna   Fax: 0116 257 1120
Leicester LE18 2AH
e-mail: recordoffice@leics.gov.uk

Local government organisation

Facilities
Enquiries to the Chief Archivist
Information provided by phone, post, fax and e-mail
Open to the public (Readers' Ticket system): Monday-Tuesday, Thursday 0915-1700, Wednesday 0915-1930, Friday 0915-1645 and Saturday 0915-1215 (unless before Bank Holiday)
Closed for one week in October
Detailed catalogues covering names, ships and aspects of Royal and Merchant Navy service
Photocopying facilities. Normal microfilm/microfiche copying facilities. Digital copies
Research service available - £22 for first hour, thereafter £18 per hour (plus copying charges, if required)

Subject coverage
Logbooks and diaries relating to travel by sea; papers relating to service in Royal Navy

Special collections
Private journal of Arthur Packe, RN aboard HM surveying vessels *Rattlesnake* and *Bramble* in the Pacific (mainly Australia), 1846-1847 (DE 1672/15)

L7
LEWISHAM LOCAL STUDIES AND ARCHIVES

Lewisham Library   Tel: 020 8297 0682
199-201 Lewisham High Street
London SE13 6LG   Fax: 020 8297 1169
e-mail: local.studies@lewisham.gov.uk
Website: www.lewisham.gov.uk

Local government organisation

Facilities
Enquiries to the Archivist
Information provided by phone, post, fax or e-mail
Library open to the public: Mondays 1000-1700; Tuesdays & Thursdays 0900-2000; Wednesdays closed; Fridays and Saturdays 0900-1700; Sundays 1300-1600
Photocopying facilities
Microfilm and microfiche readers; microcopies and fullsize copies can be provided

Subject coverage
Naval history and specialist information regarding Deptford Dockyard

---

LGSA Marine
See: Liverpool and Glasgow Salvage Association

The Liddle Collection
See Leeds University Library

Liddle Hart Centre for Military Archives
See King's College

L8
LINCOLNSHIRE ARCHIVES

St Rumbold Street   Tel: 01522 526 204
Lincoln LN2 5AB   Fax: 01522 530 047
e-mail: lincolnshire.archive@lincolnshire.gov.uk
Website: www.lincolnshire.gov.uk/archives

County archives

Facilities
Enquiries to the Archivist
Information provided by phone, post, fax and e-mail
Open to the public: Monday (March-October) 1300-1900, (November-February) 1100-1700, Tuesday-Friday 0900-1700 and Saturday 0900-1600
Reprographic service
Research service available - £27 per hour

Subject coverage
Records relating to merchant shipping at the ports of Boston and Gainsborough, including shipping registers, steam boat certificates and crew agreements

Special collections
Records relating to the Grimsby-registered barque *Enchanter,* 1875-1887

Specific companies and groups
Records of the Boston Deep Sea Fishing and Ice Company Ltd., 1885-1967

Lincolnshire
See also North East Lincolnshire

L9
LINEN HALL LIBRARY
17 Donegall Square North   Tel: 028 9032 1707
Belfast BT1 5GB   Fax: 028 9043 8586
e-mail: info@linenhall.com
Website: www.linenhall.com

Subscribing library

Facilities
Open to members: Monday-Friday 0930-1730, Saturday 0930-1600
Books loaned to members only
Microfilm readers
Access to CD-ROM publications and the Internet
Photocopying facilities

Special collections
Irish and local studies collections

Publications
Newsletter
Annual report

L10
LITTLE SHIP CLUB
Bell Wharf Lane   Tel: 020 7236 7729
Upper Thames Street   Fax: 020 7236 9100
London EC4R 3TB
e-mail: cluboffice@little-ship-club.co.uk
Website: www.little-ship-club.co.uk

Private members yacht club

Facilities
Enquiries to the Club Secretary
Information provided by post
Open to members only
Photocopying facilities

Publications
Quarterly magazine and special book commemorating 75 years

L11
LIVERPOOL ATHENAEUM
Church Alley   Tel: 0151 709 7770
Liverpool L1 3DD   Fax: 0151 709 0418
e-mail: library@athena.force9.net
Website: www.athena.force9.co.uk

Private club

Facilities
Enquiries to the Librarian
Information provided by phone, post, fax and e-mail
Open to members and researchers for material otherwise unavailable, on written request - members: Monday-Friday 0900-1600, non-members: Tuesday-Thursday 1300-1600
Photocopying facilities

Subject coverage
Mainly local atlases, maps and charts; printed material on local shipping companies; general collection of voyages, ships and shipping

Special collections
Some manuscript material on voyages
Log of a nautical club, 1776-1781
Holden's Tide Tables
Richard Piper, master of brig *Henricus* - business papers, 1807-10 and 1815-20

Publications
Printed catalogue, 1864 and supplements, 1892 and 1905
'The Athenaeum Liverpool, 1797-1997' N Carrick and EL Ashton

L12
LIVERPOOL AND GLASGOW
SALVAGE ASSOCIATION
(LGSA MARINE)
Mariners House   Tel: 0151 707 2233
Queens Dock   Fax: 0151 707 2170
Commercial Centre
61 Norfolk Street
Liverpool L1 0BG
e-mail: liverpool@lgsamarine.co.uk
Website: www.lgsamarine.co.uk

International marine surveying company

Facilities

Enquiries to the General Manager and Secretary
Open to the public
Photocopying facilities
Research service available

Subject coverage

Minute books for cases involving marine salvage prior to 1968

L13
LIVERPOOL JOHN MOORE'S UNIVERSITY

Avril Robarts Learning Resource Centre
79 Tithebarn Street   Tel: 0151 231 4020
Liverpool L2 2ER   Fax: 0151 231 4479
Website: www.livjm.ac.uk/lea

University department. The University comprises the former Liverpool Polytechnic, the Liverpool Regional College of Technology, the City of Liverpool College of Technology, Central Municipal Technical School and the Liverpool School of Sciences

Facilities

Enquiries to the Learning Resource Manager
Access see webpage: cwis.livjm.ac.uk/lea/rights.htm
Opening hours see webpage:
cwis.livjm.ac.uk/lea/hours.htm
Photocopying facilities
Microfilm and microfiche readers; CD-ROM and on-line information retrieval service; charges for external users
Research service not provided

Subject coverage

Maritime law; transportation; oceanography; meteorology; nautical engineering; naval architecture; marine engineering; seamanship; navigation; pollution/safety

Special collections

Archive material on nautical education, including that from the Liverpool Nautical College from 1895

L14
LIVERPOOL NAUTICAL RESEARCH SOCIETY

c/o Maritime Archives and Library,
Merseyside Maritime Museum,
Albert Dock
Liverpool L3 4AA.

Voluntary organisation of shipping researchers and historians

Facilities

Monthly meetings held in Liverpool
Members also have certain access facilities at the Maritime Archives and Library, Merseyside Maritime Museum

Subject coverage

All aspects of shipping history, with a bias towards Merseyside

Special collections

The Liverpool Nautical Research Society's archives are held at the Merseyside Maritime Museum (q.v.)

Publications

The Bulletin, published four times a year, with material resulting from members' researches

---

L15
LIVERPOOL RECORD OFFICE

Central Library   Tel: 0151 233 5817
William Brown Street   Fax: 0151 233 5886
Liverpool L3 8EW
e-mail: recoffice.central.library@liverpool.gov.uk
Website: www.liverpool.gov.uk

Local government organisation

Facilities

Enquiries to the Archivist
Basic enquiries and bookings by phone, other enquiries by post, fax and e-mail
Open to the public: Monday-Thursday 0900-2000, Friday 0900-1900, Saturday 0900-1700 and Sunday 1200-1600. Annual closure last two weeks of June, restricted hours over Christmas period
Photocopying facilities
Research service available - initial enquiry free if it can be completed in 15 minutes, thereafter charged at £10 for 30 minutes or £16 per hour (business rate £40)

Subject coverage

Records of some shipping companies, business records and family and estate papers, plus records relating to slavery including logbooks of slave ships

Special collections

Records of Booth Steamship Co., 1866-1971
Indefatigable and National Sea Training School for boys, 1860s-1980s
Inman Steamship Company, late 19th century
Papers of Captain George Peacock, (1805-1883), 1798-1958
Crew lists
Accounts of the *Enterprise* (slave ship including crew list)

Specific databases

Crew list indexing project on CD

L16
UNIVERSITY OF LIVERPOOL LIBRARY - SPECIAL COLLECTIONS AND ARCHIVES

Sydney Jones Library   Tel: 0151 794 2696
University of Liverpool   Fax: 0151 794 2681
PO Box 123
Liverpool L69 3DA
Website: www.sca.lib.liv.ac.uk/collections/index.html

University department

Facilities

Enquiries to the Head of Special Collections and Archives
Information provided by phone, post, fax and e-mail
Open to members of the University and (with an appointment) to bona fide researchers: Monday-Friday 0930-1645
Photocopying by staff, subject to condition of material

Subject coverage

University archives: some research papers relating to maritime history; Cunard archives; Cunard-related deposits

Publications

Lists held in the reading room

L17
LLOYD'S OF LONDON

1 Lime Street   Tel: 020 7327 6398
London EC3M 7HA   Fax: 020 7327 6400
e-mail: lloyds-external-enquiries@lloyds.com
Website: www.lloyds.com

Insurance market

Facilities

Enquiries to the Chief Information Officer
Information provided by phone, post, fax or e-mail
Facilities available to market members. Others please apply to the Librarian
Opening hours: Mondays-Fridays 0930-1700
Photocopying facilities available

Subject coverage

General insurance, commercial law, general management

Special collections

Lloyd's history
Nelson Collection
Lloyd's Shipping Archives, Lloyd's Signal Station records and Lloyd's Captains' Registers are now lodged with the Guildhall Library, q.v.

Publications

'The Nelson Collection at Lloyd's' (free)

Information regarding Lloyd's history and the Nelson Collection can be found on the website: www.lloyds.com

L18
LLOYD'S MARINE INTELLIGENCE UNIT

Telephone House   Tel: 020 7553 1683
69-77 Paul Street   Fax: 020 7583 1950
London EC2A 4LQ
e-mail: enquiries@lloydsmiu.com
Website: www.lloydsmiu.com

Data provider

Facilities

Enquiries to the Sales Manager and Marketing Manager
Information supplied to the public subject to charge
Information provided by phone, post, fax, e-mail, CDROM, Intranets etc.
Research service available - charges indicated on request

Subject coverage

The world's merchant fleet over 100gt, including all vessel movements, ownership/name/flag changes and casualty information

Publications

See websites: www.lloydsmiu.com
            www.lloydslist.com

L19
LLOYD'S REGISTER - FAIRPLAY

Lombard House   Tel: 01737 379000
3 Princess Way   Fax: 01737 379001
Redhill
Surrey RH1 1UP
e-mail: info@lrfairplay.com
Website: www.lrfairplay.com

Maritime data provider and publisher

Facilities

Enquiries to Customer Services
Information provided by phone, post, e-mail, or visit by prior arrangement
Research service available subject to fee

Subject coverage

Merchant ships over 100gt, maritime companies (154,000), ports and terminals worldwide, ships on order, casualty data, fixtures, vessel detentions, photographs, electronic news archive from 1996 to date

Publications

'Lloyd's Register of Ships' annually
See website for full list

L20
LLOYD'S REGISTER, INFORMATION SERVICES LIBRARY

71 Fenchurch Street   Tel: 020 7423 2475
London EC3M 4BS   Fax: 020 7423 2039
e-mail: histinfo@lr.org (for historical research)
    ageinfo@lr.org (for commercial research)
    info@lr.org (for Lloyd's Register history and general enquiries)
Website: www.lr.org

Independent safety assurance and risk management organisation

Facilities
Enquiries to the Senior Information Officer and Archivist
Information provided by phone, post, fax and e-mail
The Information Services Library is open to the public: Monday-Friday 0930-1200 and 1300-1630, closed Bank Holidays and between Christmas and New Year
The Archive is a closed collection and applications to view specific items must be made in writing, together with the reason(s) for enquiry
Photocopying facilities available to visiting researchers subject to condition of material and in return for donation to RNLI
Research service available subject to fee, prices on application

Subject coverage
Maritime history; shipping statistics 1878 to date; shipbuilding statistics 1888 to date; shipping casualties 1890 to date; Register of Ships 1764 to date; naval architecture; Lloyd's Register history

Special collections
'Lloyd's Register of Ships' 1764 to date, plus associated volumes ie Appendix
'Lloyd's Register of Yachts', 1878-1980
'Lloyds Register of Classed Yachts', 1981-2002
'Lloyds Register of American Yachts', 1904-1978
'Lloyd's List' 1741-1826 (facsimile)
'Liverpool Underwriter's Register', 1862-1884
'British Corporation Register', 1893-1947 (some gaps)
'Jane's Fighting Ships', 1910 to date (some gaps)
Augustin Francis Bullock Creuze (1800-1852) collection of books on naval architecture
'Mercantile Navy List', 1880-1985 (some gaps)
'Sea Breezes' 1919-date
Good collection of related reference books and periodicals covering shipping industry worldwide, shipping companies and ship types

Specific companies or groups
Lloyd's Register collection, covering 8,000 plus companies

Specific databases
Filemaker Pro databases covering library catalogue and research work done

Publications
44 information sheets, many of which are available on website (see above) including specific ones on the Lloyd's Register collection, how to research a ship and details of where 'Lloyd's Register of Ships' collections are to be found worldwide

---

L21
LONDON CANAL MUSEUM

12-13 New Wharf Road   Tel: 0207 713 0836
London   Fax: 0207 689 6679
N1 9RF
Website: www.canalmuseum.org.uk
Wapsite: www.canalmuseum.org.uk/wap/index.wml

Museum/voluntary organisation

Facilities
Enquiries to the Chairman
Enquiries by phone, post or email but prefer personal visit strictly by appointment with libraries
Opening times: Tuesday-Sunday 1000-1630
Photocopying facilities

Subject coverage
Canals, barges, narrowboats, boatpeople, Regent's Canal

Special collections
Museum is located in a commercial ice house

Publications
Information sheets on ice wells, canal walks, Victorian history, available on request

---

London General Shipowners' Society
See London Shipowners' and River Users' Society

L22
LONDON MARITIME ARBITRATORS ASSOCIATION (LMAA)

Rodwell House   Tel: 020 7377 5055
100 Middlesex Street   Fax: 020 7377 0065
London E1 7HD
e-mail: lmaa@btinternet.com
Website: www.lmaa.org.uk

Professional society

Facilities
Enquiries to the Hon. Secretary by post or fax
Arbitrators appointed at no fee except under small

claims procedure

Publications
Newsletter - 2-3 times a year (free)
Small claims procedure (free)
Conciliation terms (free)
Terms (2002) (free)
FALCA Rules (1996) (free)
Mediation terms (2002) (free)

L23
LONDON METROPOLITAN ARCHIVES
(fomerly Greater London Record Office)

40 Northampton Road	Tel: 020 7332 3820
London EC1R 0HB	Fax: 020 7833 9136

e-mail: ask.lma@corpoflondon.gov.uk
Website: www.cityoflondon.gov.uk/lma

Regional record office and library

Facilities
Enquiries to the Principal Archivist, Enquiries
Information provided by phone, post, fax and e-mail,
and in person
Open to the public: Monday, Wednesday, Friday 0930-
1645, Tuesday, Thursday 0930-1930 and selected
Saturdays (call or see website for details)
Research service available for basic family history
searches only (one hour minimum request at £17.50
per half hour)

Subject coverage
Training ships, e.g. TS *Exmouth* run by Metropolitan
Asylums Board; Coroners' records for *Princess Alice*
disaster; Thames Police Court: riverside incidents;
London County Council/Greater London Council
archives relating to River Thames

Special collections
Photographic collection: includes River Thames, London
Docks, London County Council Steamboat Service;
riverside views of Thames

Specific companies and groups
Thames Iron and Shipbuilding Company

Specific databases
www.eva-eu.org - European Visual Archive has 10,000
images from LMA's photograph collection to browse
online
www.pro.a2a.gov.uk - Access to Archives database
contains information on LCC/GLC records

Publications
Guide to major genealogical sources on website
(please see above)
Certain records covered on Access to Archives
(www.pro.a2a.gov.uk)

L24
LONDON RECORD SOCIETY

c/o Institute of Historical Research

Senate House	Tel: 020 7862 8798
Malet Street	Fax: 020 7862 8793
London WC1E 7HU	

e-mail: heather.creaton@sas.ac.uk
Website: www.history.ac.uk/cmh/lrs

Voluntary association; publishing house

Facilities
Enquiries to Hon. Secretary
Information provided by phone, post, e-mail.

Subject coverage
History of London

Publications
'The Spanish Company, 1604-6'
'Joshua Johnson's Letterbook, 1771-74'
'Trinity House of Deptford transactions, 1609-35'
'The Letters of John Paige, London merchant, 1648-58'
'The Overseas Trade of London: Exchequer Customs
Accounts, 1480-81'

London School of Economics
See: British Library of Political and Economic Science

L25
LONDON SHIPOWNERS' AND RIVER USERS' SOCIETY (incorporating the London General Shipowners' Society)

Carthusian Court	Tel: 020 7417 2830
12 Carthusian Street	Fax: 020 7600 1534
London EC1M 6EZ	

Special collection
Minute books of London General Shipowners' Society
from 1816

L26
LOWESTOFT AND EAST SUFFOLK MARITIME SOCIETY

Sparrows Nest Gardens	Tel: 01502 561963
Whapload Road	
Lowestoft NR32 1XG	

Museum/voluntary organisation (Charity No. 271444
RD 1822)

Facilities
Enquiries to the Curator and Secretary
Information provided by phone and post
Open to the public

Subject coverage
Local fishing, Brooke Marine and Richards Shipyards;

some lifeboat information

Specific companies and groups
Brooke Marine
Richards Shipyards

L27
LYTHAM LIFEBOAT MUSEUM
Central Beach
Lytham St. Annes
Lancashire

Correspondence to
Hon. Curator   Tel: 01253 730155
35 Ripon Road
Ansdell
Lytham St. Annes
Lancashire FY8 4DS
Website: legendol.freeserve.co.uk/

Museum associated with RNLI station/voluntary
organisation

Facilities
Enquiries to the Hon. Curator
Information given by phone and post
Open Tuesday, Thursday, Saturday, Sunday and Bank
Holidays 1030-1630; also 1330-1630 Wednesday in July
and August
Research service; reprints, photocopies at cost plus
donation to RNLI

Subject coverage
Station minute books and returns of service for St.
Annes Lifeboat 1881-1928; station minute book and
returns of service for Lytham lifeboat, 1854-present;
large collection of photographs and drawings of local
lifeboats and some other stations

Special collection
Original letters, reports and books on the wreck of
the *Mexico* of Hamburg, December 1886, the RNLI's
worst disaster

Publications
Local and RNLI brochures

Maitland, Robinson Library
See Cambridge University Downham College

M1
MANCHESTER ARCHIVES AND
LOCAL STUDIES,
MANCHESTER CENTRAL
LIBRARY
St Peter's Square   Tel: 0161 234 1980
Manchester M2 5PD   Fax: 0161 234 1927

e-mail: archives@libraries.manchester.gov.uk
Website: www.manchester.gov.uk/libraries/arls

Local government organisation

Facilities
Enquiries to the Archivist
Information provided by post, fax and e-mail
Archives open to the public (advanced booking
recommended): Monday-Thursday 1000-1630
Photocopying facilities
Paid research service not available but a single specific
source for a specific piece of information may be
researched free of charge

Subject coverage
Records relating to naval history; ships and shipping;
shipbuilding

Special collections
Crew lists and agreements of ships registered at
Manchester, 1894-1913
'The Merchants or Shippers of Goods who shall be
foreigners in the City of Manchester': John Scholes,
1781-1870

Specific companies and groups
Manchester Dry Docks Co. Ltd. records, 1891-1974
United Society of Boilermakers and Iron and Steel
Shipbuilders (Manchester No. 2 Branch), records 1843-
1969
Manchester Steamship Lines Association records, 1894-
1897

Specific databases
Index to crew lists and agreements on disc, part of
crew list index project (CLIP)

Publications
'Guide to Business Collections' available on website

M2
MANX NATIONAL HERITAGE
LIBRARY
Manx National Heritage   Tel: 01624 648000
Douglas   Fax: 01624 648001
Isle of Man IM1 3LY
e-mail: library@mnh.gov.im
Website: www.gov.im/mnh

National organisation

Facilities
Enquiries to the Librarian Archivist
Information provided by phone, post, fax and e-mail
Open to the public: Monday-Saturday 1000-1700
Appointment not necessary for visit, but appreciated
Photocopying, photographic/scanning facilities
Research service not available but a large and

impressive 'national' collection of printed material on general maritime subjects available

Subject coverage
Maritime library of the Isle of Man; ships and shipping; trade; vessel registrations; crews; photographs; private papers; RNLI

Special collections
Records of the RNLI (Isle of Man)
HM Customs and Excise Registers (registrations of vessels for Manx ports)
'Ingates and Outgates' - Manx customs records, 1590s-1765 (after 1765 revenue collection was undertaken by HM Customs and Excise)

Specific companies and groups
Records of the Isle of Man Steam Packet Co. Ltd., 1829-c.1970

Specific databases
Manx crew lists and agreements, 1861-1913 (72,000 names)

Publications
See website

M3
MARINE INFORMATION AND ADVISORY SERVICE (MIAS)

National Oceanographic Library   Tel: 02380 596111
Southampton Oceanography   Fax: 02380 596115
Centre
European Way
Southampton SO14 3ZH
e-mail: mias@soc.soton.ac.uk
Website: www.soc.soton.ac.uk

University department/research

Facilities
Enquiries to the Head of Information Services
Information provided by phone, post, fax and e-mail
Open to the public by appointment
Photocopying facilities
Research service available - please contact MIAS for cost and limitations

Subject coverage
Covers all disciplines in marine sciences, ocean and earth sciences

Special collections
Discovery investigations archive
Expedition reports
Challenger Society for Marine Science Archives

Specific databases
OCEANIS (in-house database)

ASFA
GEOREF
MOFR
Zoological Record
Science Direct

M4
THE MARINE SOCIETY

202 Lambeth Road   Tel: 020 7261 9535
London SE1 7JW   Fax: 020 7401 2537
e-mail: enq@marine-society.org
Website: www.marine-society.org

Charity providing library services to seafarers

Facilities
Enquiries to Head of Library

Subject coverage
Merchant navy and shipping company history

Special collections
Worcester records (contact Head of Training)

M5
MARINE TECHNOLOGY SUPPORT UNIT

AEA Technology plc   Tel: 01235 464335
Abingdon
Oxfordshire

Advisory and executive support unit for Government departments

Facilities
Enquiries to Head of Unit

Subject coverage
Measurement of environmental conditions offshore; offshore and underwater engineering; submersibles; ship operations and propulsion

---

M6
MARINE TRADES ASSOCIATION (MTA)

16 Southview   Tel: 01202 297931
24 St Valerie Road   Fax: 01202 297931
Bournemouth
Dorset BH2 6PJ

Trade association, affiliated to British Marine Federation (BMF)

Facilities
Enquiries to the Secretary
Information given by phone, post or fax

Subject coverage

Manufacturers; wholesalers; retailers of marine supplies and products

---

M7
MARITIME AND COASTGUARD AGENCY

Spring Place   Tel: 023 8032 9297
105 Commercial Road   Fax: 023 8032 9298
Southampton SO15 1EG
e-mail: MCAMIC.gov.uk
Website: www.mcga.gov.uk

Executive agency

Facilities

Enquiries to the Publications Manager
Information provided by phone, post, fax and e-mail
Open to the public by appointment: Monday-Friday
0900-1630 - no loans
Photocopying facilities only for one-off copies

Subject coverage

Research reports; some wreck reports; Acts and regulations relating to maritime issues; accident reports; limited amounts of maritime books; publicity material

Publications

List of publicity material on website

See also **Registry of Shipping and Seamen**

M8
MARITIME HERITAGE EXHIBITION

Fort Victoria   Tel: 02380 593 210
off Westhill Lane   Fax: 02380 593 052
near Yarmouth
Isle of Wight PO41 0RW
e-mail: hwtma@soc.soton.ac.uk
Website: www.soc.soton.ac.uk/HWTMA

Museum

Facilities

Enquiries to the Director
Information provided by phone, e-mail and website
Open to the public
Appointment necessary for library

Subject coverage

Displays of history of the Solent; maritime archaeology; the First Fleet; Fort Victoria; the Hants and Wight Trust for Marine Archaeology; submerged landscapes of the Solent; interactive educational displays

---

M9
MARITIME INFORMATION ASSOCIATION (MIA)

c/o 18 Durrington Avenue
London SW20 8NT
Website: www.maritime-information.org

Professional association of librarians, information officers, archivists, historians, researchers, lecturers and all those having an interest in maritime information and literature.

Facilities

Enquiries to the Honorary Secretary, by post only
Annual conference held in UK or continental Europe
Occasional visits to places of maritime interest and social gatherings.

Subject coverage

Marine science and technology; shipping; shipbuilding; marine engineering and telecommunications; maritime law and economics; maritime history; ports; cargo handling; fisheries; offshore activities (not marine biology or life sciences)

Publications

Newsletter distributed free to members approximately quarterly
'Maritime Information, a Guide to Sources in the United Kingdom', 2004 (4th edition)

The Maritime Trust
See: Cutty Sark Trust

M10
THE MARY ROSE TRUST

HM Naval Base   Tel: 02392 750521
College Road   Fax: 02392 870588
Portsmouth
Hants PO1 3LX
e-mail: maryrose@cix.co.uk
Website: www.maryrose.org

Research organisation and museum with displays in Portsmouth Historic Dockyard

Facilities

Enquiries to Collections Manager
Information provided by post and e-mail

Subject coverage

16th century ships; navigation and ordnance equipment

Publications

List available on request

M11
MARYPORT MARITIME MUSEUM

1 Senhouse Street	Tel: 01900 813738
Maryport	Fax: 01900 819496
Cumbria CA15 6AB	

e-mail: maryport.maritime.museum@allerdale.gov.uk
Website: www.allerdale.gov.uk

Local government organisation

Facilities
Enquiries to the Heritage and Arts Manager
Information provided by phone, post, e-mail and fax

Subject coverage
Local maritime history; collections of photographs and paintings of local ships

Publications
List of publications available

M12
MCLEAN MUSEUM AND ART GALLERY

15 Kelly Street	Tel: 01475 715624
Greenock PA16 8JX	Fax: 01475 715626

e-mail: val.boa@inverclyde.gov.uk
Website: www.inverclyde.gov.uk/museum/index.htm

Local government organisation and museum

Facilities
Enquiries to the Curator
Information provided by phone, post, fax and e-mail
Open to the public

Subject coverage
Maritime history of Inverclyde district (i.e. shipbuilding and shipowning); Greenock and Port Glasgow

Special collections
R B Paterson - collection of steamer photographs, c.1880-1920

Publications
Collections guide available on website for local history material

---

M13
MEDWAY ARCHIVES AND LOCAL STUDIES CENTRE
MEDWAY COUNCIL

Clock Tower Building	Tel: 01634 332714
Civic Centre	Fax: 01634 297060
Strood	
Kent ME2 4AU	

e-mail: local.studies@medway.gov.uk
e-mail: archives@medway.gov.uk

Website: www.medway.gov.uk
Archives database: http://cityark.medway.gov.uk

Local government record office

Facilities
Enquiries to the Local Studies Librarian and/or Archivist
Information provided by phone (basic information only), post, fax, e-mail and visit
Open to the public: Monday, Thursday and Friday 0900-1700, Tuesday 0900-1800, Saturday (1st and 3rd in month) 0900-1300
Photocopying facilities
Research service available - first 20 minutes free, no in-house paid research but clients referred to researchers who may be able to help

Subject coverage
Local studies naval collection - small national collection relating to the history of the Royal Navy (c. 1,500 volumes) comprising mainly printed books, journals/periodicals and Navy List
Archives - shipping records, crew lists, Medway Ports Authority and preceding organisations, 1627-20th century

Special collections
Chatham Dockyard (printed books, plans and newspaper cuttings)
Rochester City Council Oyster and Flat Fishery, 1628-1995
Trinity House Thames Pilots' Association, 1936-1988
Doust and Co. of Rochester, ship repairers, 1902-1950
Port of Rochester shipping records, 1824-1927

Publications
Guides on website

M14
MEDWAY PORTS

Sheerness Docks	Tel: 01795 596596
Sheerness	Fax: 01795 660072
Kent ME12 1RS	

Statutory harbour authority for the River Medway and The Swale operating the commercial docks at Sheerness and Chatham, also the competent harbour authority (responsible for pilotage).
Medway Ports is a wholly-owned subsidiary of Mersey Docks and Harbours Ltd.

M15
MERCHANT NAVY WELFARE BOARD

30 Palmerston Road	Tel: 023 8033 7799
Southampton	Fax: 023 8063 4444
Hampshire SO14 1LL	

e-mail: Enquiries@mnwb.org.uk
Website: www.mnwb.org.uk

Voluntary organisation

Facilities
Enquiries to the General Secretary
Information provided by appointment, phone, post, fax
and e-mail
Research service available - MNWB will research
appropriate organisations to provide financial help to
individuals and to seafarers' welfare organisations (no
charge)

Subject coverage
Information on welfare provision for domiciled and
visiting seafarers within the UK and considerable
information about other national and international
seafarers' welfare agencies

Publications
Advice on making wills and funeral arrangements
Brochure on MNWB services
Database of nautical charities providing assistance to
individuals
Database of seafarers' homes

M16
MERSEYSIDE INDUSTRIAL HERITAGE SOCIETY

c/o Merseyside Maritime Museum Tel: 0151 478 4094
Albert Dock   Fax: 0151 478 4098
Liverpool L3 4AQ
e-mail:adrian.jarvis@nmgmporthist.demon.co.uk

Voluntary organisation

Facilities
Enquiries to the Chairman
Information provided by phone, post, fax and e-mail
Open to members and guests
Appointment necessary for library

Merseyside Maritime Museum
See: National Museums and Galleries on Merseyside

M17
MILLPORT UNIVERSITY MARINE BIOLOGICAL STATION

Millport   Tel: 01475 530581/2
Isle of Cumbrae KA28 0EG

University department, incorporating the Robertson
Museum and Aquarium

Facilities
Enquiries to the Director

Library open to student classes and researchers;
others on written application

Subject coverage
Marine biology; oceanography; pollution

Migration Studies
See Centre for Migration Studies at the Ulster
American Folk Park

M18
MINISTRY OF DEFENCE - ADMIRALTY LIBRARY - NAVAL HISTORICAL BRANCH

Mezzanine 3   Tel: 020 7218 5446
3-5 Great Scotland Yard   Fax: 020 7218 8210
London SW1A 2HW
The Admiralty Library, as part of the Naval Historical
Branch, is due to be relocated to Portsmouth Naval
Base in 2004.

Central government department

Facilities
Enquiries to the Admiralty Librarian
Information provided by phone, post and fax
Open to MOD staff and the public by appointment
Monday-Friday
Photocopying facilities
Limited research service available

Subject coverage
Naval history including administration, policy, doctrine,
operations, strategy, tactics, signal books, naval aviation
and gunnery. After relocation, charts and atlases
c.1600-1900, pilots and sailing directions, voyages,
navigation and seamanship. Other subject areas, and
the manuscripts collection, are currently in the care of
the Royal Naval Museum.

Special collections
Admiralty prints
Sealed patterns for ships' badges

Publications
'Catalogue of the Naval Library, Ministry of Defence':
Boston: GK Hall, 1967 now out of print.
A guide to the manuscripts collection is in preparation
in association with the Royal Naval Museum.

M18A
MINISTRY OF DEFENCE - DEFENCE RECORDS

Records Office   Tel: 020 85733831
Bourne Avenue   Ext. 341/342
Hayes   Fax: 020 8573 9074
Middlesex UB3 1RF
e-mail: navysearch.defencerecords@gtngt.gov.uk

Ministry of Defence establishment

Facilities
Enquiries to Naval Manning Agency Secretariat 3c at the above address
Information provided by post, fax and e-mail
Closed site
Research service available for members of the public to receive details of ancestor's service histories or crew lists between 1939-51 (currently £25 per subject - individual service history or crew list)

Subject coverage
Naval officers of flag rank born between 1890 and 1942; naval ratings who entered for service between 1924 and August 1939; WRNS who entered for service between 1939 and 1955; RNVR ratings mobilised for Second World War

Special collections
Records of service for Royal Naval Division and Royal Naval Reserves passed to Fleet Air Arm Museum at RNAS Yeovilton

---

M19
MINISTRY OF DEFENCE - INFORMATION AND LIBRARY SERVICE
3/5 Great Scotland Yard   Tel: 020 7218 4445
London SW1A 2 HW   Fax: 020 7218 5413
e-mail: info-libsvcsgroupmailbox@defence.mod.uk

Government department library

Facilities
Enquiries to the Chief Librarian
Information provided by post
Admission is usually restricted to MOD and service personnel; however, visitors are admitted by prior arrangement with the condition that the materials to be consulted are unavailable elsewhere
Access is by appointment only (apply in writing) and materials to be consulted must be identified in the letter of application for admission - Monday-Thursday 0900-1700 and Friday 0900-1645
Photocopying facilities

Subject coverage
Defence policy; defence forces world-wide; politics; international affairs; government economic and social issues; management and computers; military technology; electronics and communications; parliamentary information (UK & EC); naval policy; some naval history

---

M20
THE MISSION TO SEAFARERS
St Michael Paternoster Royal   Tel: 020 7248 5202
College Hill   Fax: 020 7248 4761
London EC4R 2RL
e-mail: general@missiontoseafarers.org
Website: www.missiontoseafarers.org

Voluntary organisation

Facilities
Enquiries to the Public Relations Officer
Information provided by post
Open to the public, access by appointment only
Monday-Friday
Photocopying facilities
Limited research service available at no charge
(photocopies of relevant information provided)

Subject coverage
Annual Reports, 1856 to present, Church and Sailor; St Andrew's Waterside Mission Annual Reports

Specific groups
The Mission to Seamen (now Seafarers)
St. Andrew's Waterside Mission

Publications
Please see guide on website
Annual Directory

Mitchell Library
See: Glasgow Libraries

M21
MODEL YACHTING ASSOCIATION
Graham Reeves   Tel: 01789 751800
Information Officer
Arcadia
Pool Close
Welford on Avon CV37 8QB
e-mail: informationofficer@mya-uk.org.uk
Website: www.mya-uk.org.uk

Model yacht racing organisation

Facilities
Enquiries to the Information Officer
Information provided by phone, post and e-mail
Photocopying facilities
Limited research service available

Subject coverage
Model yacht racing

Special collections
Complete collection of books on model yachting published in the UK since 1879

Collection of model yacht plans from 1863
MYA Class Registers 1925 to date

Publications
See website

Modern Records Centre
See University of Warwick

M22
MONTROSE MUSEUM
Panmore Place   Tel: 01674 673232
Montrose DD10 8HE
e-mail: Montrose.museum@angus.gov.uk
Website: www.angus.gov.uk

Museum, part of Angus Council Leisure
Services/Cultural Services' Division

Facilities
Enquiries to the Curator
Information provided by phone, post, fax and e-mail
Open to the public
Photocopying facilities
Research service available - £20 per hour, with VAT @
17.5%, plus administrative charge of £1.50

Subject coverage
Montrose shipping; whaling and fishing from Ferryden

Special collections
Shipping index - Montrose; specific files on the whaler
Eliza Swan and other Montrose vessels; files on other
vessels such as the *Cutty Sark*; general files on
shipbuilding, fishing in Montrose and district, including
salmon fishing; files on whaling; the log of the *Snowdrop*.

M23
THE MORAY COUNCIL - MUSEUMS SERVICE
Falconer Museum   Tel: 01309 673701
Tolbooth Street   Fax: 01309 673701
Forres
Moray N36 1PH
e-mail: museums@moray.gov.uk
Website: www.moray.gov.uk/museums

Museum/local government organisation

Facilities
Enquiries to the Senior Museums Officer
Information provided by phone, post, fax and e-mail
Display areas open to the public, reserve collection to
bona fide researchers only by appointment
Photocopying facilities
Research service available - 20 minutes free, thereafter
£18 per hour

Conditions exist on copyright and access to written
material (details from Falconer Museum)

Subject coverage
Peter Anson Archive:
Pictorial images - watercolours, pen and ink,
photographs
Written material - manuscripts, diaries, books, general
correspondence
Fishing history of the north-east of Scotland

Special collections
As above

Specific databases
List of paintings by accession number
List of slides of above

Publications
Information sheet on Peter Anson
See website for information on Peter Anson
Shipbuilding on the Spey, herring barrel coopering

M24
THE MOTOR BOAT MUSEUM
Wat Tyler Country Park   Tel: 01268 55077
Pitsea Hall Lane   Fax: 01268 584207
Basildon
Essex

Museum

Facilities
Enquiries to the Museum Officer
Information provided by phone, post, fax and e-mail
Open to the public
Appointment necessary for research library
Photocopying facilities
Research service available (written enquiries, please) -
donations and photocopy charges
Refreshments
Gift Shop
Disabled access

Subject coverage
Motorboat archives from 1899 to present; engine and
boat drawings

Special collections
Ailsa Craig archives (engines)
The Carstairs collection (Trophys)
The Bert Savidge Outboard collection

Publications
'Racers and Record Breakers': Museum Guide
'White Lady'
'Skimming the Surface'

M25
MUSEUM OF ARMY TRANSPORT

Flemingate　　　　　　Tel: 01482 860445
Beverley　　　　　　　Fax: 01482 872767
East Yorkshire HU17 0NG
Website: www. museum-of-army-transport.co.uk

Museum

Facilities
Enquiries to the Curator
Information provided by phone, post and fax
Photocopying facilities
Research service available from £12.50

Subject coverage
Photographs; diaries; vessels used by the British Army

M26
MUSEUM IN DOCKLANDS
LIBRARY AND ARCHIVE

No. 1 Warehouse　　　Tel: 020 7001 9825
West India Quay　　　Fax: 020 7001 9801
Hertsmere Road
London E14 4AL
e-mail: bobaspinall@museumindocklands.org.uk
Website: www.museumindocklands.org.uk

Museum

Facilities
Enquiries to the Librarian and Archivist
Information provided by phone, post, fax, e-mail and
research in person
Open to the public, media and commercial
organisations - access strictly by prior appointment
only: Tuesdays and Wednesdays only from 1400-1730
Photocopying facilities
Research service available - subject to the exigencies
of the work - enquiries from general public handled
free of charge, charges for commercial organisations as
follows: first hour free, second and subsequent hours
at £60 per hour, plus VAT

Subject coverage
History and development of the Port of London from
1770 to date; administration of the River Thames from
1770; growth of trade; coming of the enclosed docks;
rise of the Port of London to largest in the world,
followed by decline and closure; regeneration of
former port area into Docklands; ships; cargoes;
statistics; trade; maps of the Port of London and the
docks from 1800 to date

Special collections
30,000 photographs of shipping in the docks and on
the river, 1880s-1970s
Library of books on history and development of the
Port of London, 1770 to date
Minute books of the Corporation of London River

Committee, 1770-1857
Minute books of the Thames Conservancy, 1857-1909
Minute books of the private dock companies, 1799-
1909
Minute books of the Port of London Authority, 1909
to date
Records of the London Wharfingers Association;
British Ports Authority; London Port Employers; strike
records

Specific databases
Database of permanent staff employed by the private
dock companies, (1799-1909) and of the Port of
London Authority (from 1909 onwards)

M27
MUSEUM OF WELSH LIFE

St Fagans　　　　　　Tel: 029 2057 3446
Cardiff CF5 6XB　　　Fax: 029 2057 3490
e-mail: nic.walker@nmgw.ac.uk
Website: www.nmgw.ac.uk/mwl/collections/library/

Museum

Facilities
Enquiries to the Librarian (Library) and Dylan Jones
(for artefacts relating to freshwater and inshore
fishing)
Information provided by phone, post, fax and e-mail
Open to the public - access to reserve collections and
staff by appointment
Photocopying facilities
No research service available but manageable enquiries
are answered free of charge

Subject coverage
Welsh life including freshwater and inshore fishing,
coracles and nets

Publications
Current publications catalogue available from
Publications Officer

N1
NAPIER UNIVERSITY LEARNING
INFORMATION SERVICES (NULIS)

10 Colinton Road　　　Tel: 0131 455 2582
Edinburgh EH10 5DT　　Fax: 0131 455 2377
e-mail: nulis.enquiry@napier.ac.uk
Website: www.nulis.napier.ac.uk

University department

Facilities
Enquiries to Director of Learning Information Services
Information provided by phone, post, fax and e-mail
Library open to the general public; loan and electronic
services available to members only

Opening hours: Mondays-Thursdays: 0845-2100;
Fridays: 0845-1700;
Saturdays & Sundays: 1000-1600
Photocopying facilities available
Research service not provided

Subject coverage
Civil and transportation engineering; water resource management; life science and biological sciences (including pollution and environmental studies; business, health, computing and applied arts)

N2
NATIONAL ARCHIVES
Formerly the Public Record Office

Ruskin Avenue   Tel: 020 8876 3444
Kew   Fax: 020 8878 8905
Richmond
Surrey TW9 4DU
Website: www.national archives.gov.uk

National government organisation

Facilities
Enquiries to the Readers Services Department
Library open to the public
Microfilm and microfiche readers available
Microcopies and fullsize copies can be provided

Subject coverage
Records of the Admiralty; Navy Board; Board of Trade; Registrar General of Shipping and Seamen; Ministry of Transport; Ministry of Shipping; ships wrecked or sunk; *Titanic*

Publications
For sale:
'Battlefront: Sinking of the *Bismarck*'
'*Titanic:* 14th-15th April 1912. The Official Story'
'*Titanic:* the true story'
'Tracing your Naval Ancestors'
'Using Navy Records'
Free leaflets:
Admiralty Charts
Canals: Administrative and Other Records
Coastguard
Merchant Seamen: Abbreviations found in RGSS Registers
Merchant Seamen: Interpreting the Voyages in the Registers of Seamen's Tickets and the Alphabetical Register of Masters
Merchant Seamen: Interpreting Voyage Details in the Registers of Officers' Services;
Merchant Seamen: Interpreting Voyage Details in the Registers of Seamen, Series II
Merchant Seamen: Medals and Honours
Merchant Seamen: Officers' Service Records 1845-1965
Merchant Seamen: Records of the RGSS, A Guide to Leaflets
Merchant Seamen: Registers of Service, 1835-1857

Merchant Seamen: Sea Service Records 1913-1972
Merchant Seamen: Crew Lists and Agreements after 1861
Merchant Seamen: Crew Lists and Agreements, 1747-1860
Merchant Seamen: Registration of Ships, 1786-1994
Passenger Lists
Royal Marines: Further Areas of Research
Royal Marines: Officers' Service Records
Royal Marines: Other Ranks' Service Records
Royal Naval Dockyards
Royal Naval Research and Development
Royal Naval Reserve
Royal Naval Volunteer Reserve
Royal Navy: Logbooks and Reports of Proceedings
Royal Navy: Nurses and Nursing Services
Royal Navy: Officers' Service Records
Royal Navy: Officers' Service Records, First World War, and Confidential Reports, 1893-1912
Royal Navy: Operational Records 1660-1914
Royal Navy: Operational Records, First World War, 1914-1918
Royal Navy: Operational Records, Second World War, 1939-1945
Royal Navy: Pay and Pensions Records: Commissioned Officers
Royal Navy: Pension Records: Ratings
Royal Navy: Pension Records: Warrant Officers
Royal Navy: Ratings Service Records 1667-1923

N3
NATIONAL ARCHIVES:
Formerly the Historical
Manuscripts Commission (HMC)

Ruskin Avenue   Tel: 020 7242 1198
Kew   Fax: 020 7831 3550
Richmond
London TW9 4DU
e-mail: nra@hmc.gov.uk
Website: www.nationalarchives.gov.uk

Facilities
Enquiries to the Secretary
Information provided by post, fax and e-mail
Public searchroom open to the public: Monday-Friday 0930-1700
No appointment necessary
Research service not available, although pleased to answer general enquiries relating to the location of manuscript sources for British history free of charge

Subject coverage
No original documents held
The National Register of Archives (NRA) can be consulted in search room and contains over 43,000 lists of archives held by record offices, libraries, museums, businesses, other public and private institutions and individuals
Indexes to the NRA, which are arranged by the creators of archives - individuals, families, businesses, organisations - are also available on our website

Specific databases
See indexes to the NRA (above)

Publications
NRA indexes and other information about HMC publications and functions on website

---

N4
NATIONAL ARCHIVES OF SCOTLAND
(Formerly Scottish Record Office)

HM General Register House   Tel: 0131 535 1314
2 Princes Street   Fax: 0131 535 1360
Edinburgh EH1 3YY
e-mail: enquiries@nas.gov.uk
Website: www.nas.gov.uk

National government organisation

Facilities
Enquiries to Historical Search Room
Information provided by phone, post, fax and e-mail
Open to the public: Monday-Friday 0900-1645, closed for certain public holidays and part of November for stocktaking
No appointment necessary, but prior contact advised as some material stored off site
Photocopying facilities
Research service available - general advice given; extensive research would require a personal visit or employment of a record agent

Subject coverage
Public records of government and the law; family papers and estate records; church records; maps and plans; Scottish railway archives; records of industrial and commercial firms; charitable institutions and other public bodies

Special collections
(Access via West Register House, Charlotte Square, Edinburgh. Prior contact recommended)
Shipbuilding records from shipyards on the upper and lower Clyde
John Brown and Co. Ltd. - photographic collection
Burntisland Shipbuilding Co. Ltd. - including some records of Hall, Russell & Co., Aberdeen
Robb-Caledon (Leith) Ltd. - including Henry Robb Ltd. and Ramage & Ferguson Ltd.

Publications
Source list of naval, mercantile and shipping records in NAS holdings
General information on website
Fact sheets available on specific topics

N5
NATIONAL ARMY MUSEUM

Royal Hospital Road   Tel: 020 7730 0717
Chelsea   Fax: 020 7823 6573
London SW3 4HT
e-mail: info@national-army-museum.ac.uk
Website: www.national-army-museum.ac.uk

National museum

Facilities
Enquiries to the Head of Department of Archives, Photographs, Film and Sound
Information provided by phone, post, fax, e-mail, but preferably by post
Access to the reading room, where the card index is located, is open to holders of reader's tickets only; requests for reader's ticket application forms should be addressed to Head of Department of Printed Books
Open Tuesdays-Saturdays; closed Bank Holiday weekends and between Christmas and New Year
Photocopying facilities
Research service not provided

Subject coverage
Hodson card index includes biographical and service details of officers of the Indian Navy and ship's officers of the East India Company's fleet up to 1861

N6
NATIONAL FISHING HERITAGE CENTRE

c/o Welholme Galleries   Tel: 01472 323576
Welholme Road   Fax: 01472 323577
Grimsby DN32 9LP
e-mail: Andrew.Tulloch@nelincs.gov.uk

Local government organisation/museum

Facilities
Enquiries to the Documentation Officer
Information provided by phone, post, fax and e-mail
Open to the public
Research service available free but only carried out through existing databases (no original research)

Subject coverage
Photographs of fishing industry and Grimsby and Immingham docks; documentary evidence of fishing industry; marine art; ship model collection

Special collections
Doughty ship model and marine art collection
Hallgarth photograph collection
Pulfrey photograph collection

Publications
'Guide to the Doughty Ship Model Collection'

N7
NATIONAL LIBRARY OF SCOTLAND - MANUSCRIPTS DIVISION

George IV Bridge
Edinburgh EH1 1EW
e-mail: manuscripts@nls.uk
Website: www.nls.uk

Tel: 0131 2264531
Fax: 0131 6224803

National library

Facilities
Enquiries to the Head of Manuscripts Divison
Information provided by phone, post, fax and e-mail
Open to the public: Monday, Tuesday, Thursday and Friday 0900-2030, Wednesday 10.00-2030 and Saturday 09.30-13.00 (excluding Public Holidays)
Please note that archive materials have to be ordered before 1600
Photocopying facilities
Research service not provided

Subject coverage
Naval history includes official naval and Admiralty correspondence; papers relating to overseas maritime trade; personal papers of naval or maritime interest; logs and journals

Special collections
Papers of individuals
John Anderson, pilot of a Dutch fleet to the East Indies, 1640-1643; logbook
Charles Chisholm of Chisholm; business papers and accounts as Master of the East India Company's *Gatton*, 1778-1780
Frederick C Brown, 1914-1918; letters to W K Dickson whilst serving on the east coast of Africa
Lawrence R Burness; naval war correspondence 1940-1947 with his parents and snapshots, 1942, of persons and places mainly in Burma
Cochrane Papers, Admirals Sir Thomas and Sir Alexander Cochrane, 1779-1856
Admiral of the Fleet Viscount Cunningham of Hyndhope; 20 letters, 1941-1958, to the Very Rev. Dr George S Duncan and Professor Douglas Duncan mostly relating to the naval service of the latter 1953-1955
Rear Admiral R K Dickson; letters, diaries and notes
Midshipman A W Dickson RN, killed at Jutland; papers
Captain Colin M Dundas of Ochtertyre, RN; 1833-1877; naval papers including personal logs and journals kept on HMS *Russell, Pearl, Monarch, Orion, Dart, Topaze, Immortalité* and *Eclipse*
Midshipman A W J Findlayson RN; 1904-1906; official naval log book
Admiral Sir Angus Cunningham Graham; notes on life in the Grand Fleet, 1914-1916 and copies of correspondence with Professor A Marder, lecture precis on 'The submarine and anti-submarine war, 1914-18', and accounts of voyage to Murmansk, 1941,

an 'Essay on Signalling at the Battle of Jutland'
JBS Haldane; notes and papers, 1942-1944, concerning experiments on the physiology of diving conducted by the Underwater Physiology Subcommittee
Admiral Sir William H Henderson; correspondence and papers concerning the naval review and the formation of the Naval Society, 1915-1919
Admiral Sir Roger Keyes; letters to Captain (later Rear-Admiral) R K Dickson, 1941
William Leith, Master Mariner, Stromness, Orkney, and his sons; letters and documents relating mostly to their service at sea, 1798-1846
Rear Admiral Frederick L Maitland; papers, 1815-1838
Malcolm of Burnfoot Papers, Admiral Sir Pulteney Malcolm, 1787-1838
Rev. RH Malden, Chaplain on HMS *Valiant*; an account of the Battle of Jutland, 31st May 1916
Melville Papers; (Henry Dundas and Robert Dundas, 1st and 2nd Viscounts Melville); correspondence with various naval commanders and Admiralty business, 1790-1830
Milne Home Papers; Admiral Sir David Milne and Admiral of the Fleet Sir Alexander Milne, 1st Bart, 1817-1900
Minto Papers; papers of Sir Gilbert Elliot, 3rd Bart of Minto as a Lord of the Admiralty and Treasurer of the Navy, 1759-1776
Minto Papers; correspondence of Gilbert Elliot, 1st Earl of Minto, with various naval commanders, c 1794-1813
Minto Papers, correspondence and papers of Admiral John Elliot, 1770-1808
Minto Papers and Elliot Papers; correspondence and papers of Admiral of the Fleet, Hon. Sir Charles GJB Elliot, 1830-1875
Minto Papers, papers of Gilbert Elliot, 2nd Earl of Minto as 1st Lord of the Admiralty, 1835-1841
RC Munday's letters to JBS Haldane, 1916, concerning deaths of personnel saved from ship sunk by mine
Thomas Graham Stirling of Airth; papers as Master of the East India Company's ships, *Busbridge* and *General Goddard*

Papers of organisations
Amalgamated Society of Boilermakers, Shipwrights, Blacksmiths and Structural Workers; records of the Edinburgh Leith branch 1873-1918
The Company of Scotland (the 'Darien Company'); papers including the commissioning, arming and fitting out of ships, wages of crews, and some reports on the voyages to the Isthmus of Darien, 1696-1700
Alexander Houston and Co., Glasgow, merchants, bankers and shipowners, 1729-1798; letter-books
Royal Highland Yacht Club, Oban, 1881-1973; records
National Union of Seamen; minutes of the Greenock Branch, 1918-1953; photocopies of minutes of the Leith Branch, 1918-1967 and of the Ardrossan Branch, 1919-1965
Robert Stevenson and Sons, Civil Engineers, Edinburgh, 19-20th centuries, specialists in lighthouse and harbour building; large archive including extensive harbour and lighthouse plans and works reports

Publications
Published series of 'Catalogue of MSS. Acquired since 1925' (vols. I-viii, 1938-92)
On website: Catalogue of MSS. online; Collections Index

N8
NATIONAL LIBRARY OF WALES

Aberystwyth   Tel: 01970 632800
Ceredigion   Fax: 01970 6323882
Wales SY23 3BU
e-mail: holi@llgc.org.uk
Website: www.llgc.org.uk

Copyright library

Facilities
Enquiries to the Librarian NLW and/or Head of Marketing
Information provided by e-mail
Open to the public: Monday-Friday 0930-1800 and Saturday 0930-1700
Photocopying facilities
Research service

Subject coverage
4.5 million books; over 1 million maps; 700,000 photos; 40,000 works of art; Welsh Political Archive; National Screen and Sound Archive of Wales
By law the NLW has the right to every publication in Wales, the UK and the Republic of Ireland

Special collections
Black Book of Carmarthen (13th century manuscript with earliest Welsh poetry)
Chaucer - Canterbury Tales manuscript written during Chaucer's lifetime

Specific companies and groups
Welsh Political Archive - all Welsh political parties and most pressure groups

Specific databases
Framed works of art - 4,000 digitised paintings on website

Publications
NLW reference books related to the collection: 'Digital Mirror' on website includes many collections

---

N9
NATIONAL MARITIME MUSEUM - CAIRD LIBRARY

Park Row   Tel: 020 8312 6673
Greenwich   Fax: 020 8312 6599
London SE10 9NF
e-mail: library@nmm.ac.uk
            manuscripts@nmm.ac.uk

Website: www.nmm.ac.uk

Museum

Facilities
Enquiries to Head of Library and Manuscripts
            Manuscripts Manager
            Senior Library Assistant
Open to those wishing to undertake maritime research (over 18s only)
Formal ID and completion of an application form on arrival required
Open: Monday-Friday 1000-1645, Saturday by appointment only. Closed during the third week in February
Photocopying facilities, microfilm and microfiche readers
General or genealogical research is not undertaken by staff
Curatorial specific research may be undertaken for a fee
Online research guides are available at www.port.nmm.ac.uk/Research/Research.html

Subject coverage
Astronomy; biography; emigration; exploration; fishing; flags; genealogy; horology, life at sea; marine art; medals; merchant shipping; mercantile history; naval history; navigation; oceanography; piracy; seamanship; ship models; shipbuilding; shipping companies; shipwrecks, uniforms; voyages; warships; World War I; World War II; yachting

Special collections
'Lloyd's Captain's Register' 1851-1947 (microfilm)
'Lloyd's List' - 1741 to date (1933 onwards on microfilm)
'Lloyd's Weekly Shipping Index' 1882 to date
'Index to Lloyd's List' 1838-1927 (microfilm)
'Lloyd's Register' 1764-1785 (incomplete) and 1794 to date
'Lloyd's Register of Yachts' 1879-1980
'Navy List' - 1814 to date
Pilot books
Charts
MacPherson Collection of Atlases
Rare Book Collection 1474-1850

Subject coverage (Manuscript Section)
All aspects of British seafaring history from the fourteenth to twentieth centuries: the administration of the Royal Navy and Merchant Navy, shipping company records and personal papers.

Special collections (Manuscript Section)
SECTION 1. Public Records: Admiralty and Navy Board records, including lieutenants' logbooks 17-19th centuries, Board of Trade records, including masters' and engineers' certificates 1845-1927, crew lists, returns of death 1914-1960 and Lloyd's Register Survey Reports.

SECTION 2. Public Records: Records relating to the Royal Dockyards, Chatham, Deptford, Gibraltar, Halifax, Harwich, Jamaica, Pembroke, Plymouth, Portsmouth, Sheerness and Woolwich, 17-19th centuries.

SECTION 3. Records of business and non-governmental collections, including P&O and amalgamated companies, the Marine Society, Michael Henley & Son and HMS Worcester (Thames Nautical Training College).

SECTION 4. More than 400 collections of papers of individual officers and seamen, including those of Admirals Beatty (1871-1936), Bond (1765-1839), which consists of 40 letters from Admiral William Bligh (1754-1817), Chatfield (1873-1967), Collingwood (1750-1810), Hood (1724-1816), Nelson (1758-1805), Pellew (1757-1833), and of Captain Matthew Flinders (1774-1814), Lady Elspeth Invernairn (fl 1905-1952), which includes material relating to Sir Ernest Shackleton (1874-1922) and John Montagu, Fourth Earl of Sandwich, First Lord of the Admiralty (1718-1792).

SECTION 5. Artificial collections previously assembled, covering a broad range of maritime subjects, including those collections of Roger Charles Anderson (1883-1976) relating to the Royal Navy in the 17-18th centuries and foreign navies, Dr. Philip Gosse (1879-1959), relating to piracy and the Royal United Service Institution.

SECTION 6. Manuscript volumes acquired singly by the Museum, including Royal Navy and merchant logbooks, journals, signal books and letterbooks.

SECTION 7. Manuscript documents acquired singly by the Museum, including autograph letters and papers relating to Royal Navy and merchant administration.

SECTION 8. Copies of manuscripts not held in the Museum's collections.

Specific databases
Library and manuscripts online catalogue (www.nmm.ac.uk)
Port-maritime Information Gateway (www.port.nmm.ac.uk)
Prints and drawings online catalogue (www.nmm.ac.uk)
Historic photographs online catalogue (www.nmm.ac.uk)
Maritime memorials (www.nmm.ac.uk/memorials)
Collections online (www.nmm.ac.uk/collections)

N10
NATIONAL MARITIME MUSEUM - PICTURE LIBRARY

Greenwich   Tel: 020 8312 6600
London SE10 9NF   Fax: 020 8312 6533

e-mail: picturelibrary@nmm.ac.uk
Website: www.nmm.ac.uk/picturelibrary

Museum

Facilities
Enquiries to the Head of Visual Media
Information provided by phone, post, fax and e-mail
Open to the public, commercial researchers, designers, television producers, etc.
Research service available - £20 for first hour, £50 thereafter

Subject coverage
Images from the full range of the Museum's collections, including those of the Royal Observatory, historic photographs from 1840s, 4,000 oil paintings, 63,000 prints, drawings and watercolours, charts, manuscripts, navigational objects and ships' plans

Publication
Guide to Historic Photograph Collection, 1995

N11
NATIONAL MARITIME MUSEUM - SHIP PLANS

National Maritime Museum   Tel: 020 8855 1647
Greenwich   Fax: 020 8317 0263
London SE10 9NF
e-mail: plansandphotos@nmm.ac.uk
Website: www.nmm.ac.uk

Museum

Facilities
Enquiries to the Curators, Ship Plans and Historic Photographs
Information supplied by phone, post, fax and e-mail
However, we prefer enquiries in writing (post, fax or e-mail)
Visits are by appointment only between 10.00-13.00; 14.00-16.30 on weekdays
Photocopying facilities; we can supply full size copies of the plans
Research service. Initial research, based on enquiries, free; further research: current charge is £25.00 per hour (or research can be carried out by recommended researchers)

Subject coverage
Royal Naval vessel plans: c1700-present
Contracts: c1830-1967
Specifications: c1830-c1960
Merchant ship plans: c1850-present
Admiralty Ships' Books: selection to c1975
Admiralty Ships' Covers (ADM.38) (there are gaps)

Records of specific organisations and companies
Admiralty (1680-modern times)

Barclay, Curle & Co
Camper & Nicholson Ltd
William Denny
Richard Dunstan Ltd
Goole Shipbuilding Co.
P.&O. (various vessels)
RNLI
Shell Tankers UK
Smith's Dock Co.
Alexander Stephen & Sons
J I Thornycroft & Co. Ltd.
Vickers
Vosper Ltd

Publications
'The Denny List', D Lyon
'Sailing Navy List', D Lyon

National Maritime Museum Cornwall
See Bartlett Library

N12
NATIONAL METEOROLOGICAL LIBRARY AND ARCHIVE

The Scott Building   Tel: 01344 855960
Sterling Centre   Fax: 01344 855961
Eastern Road
Bracknell
Berkshire RG12 2PW
e-mail: metarc@metoffice.com
Website: www.metoffice.com

National government organisation; part of the
Meteorological Office

Facilities
Enquiries to the Archive Manager
Limited Information provided by phone, post, fax and
e-mail and personal visit (prior notice advisable)
Open to the public: Monday-Thursday 0830-1300 and
1400-1630. Closed on Fridays until further notice
Photocopying facilities
Research service not available but some advice (e.g. on
holdings) will be given

Subject coverage
Meteorological data for surface and upper atmosphere

Special collections
Old data

Publications
General information on website
Partial catalogue on in-house database

N13
NATIONAL MONUMENTS' RECORD CENTRE, ENGLISH HERITAGE

Great Western Village   Tel: 01793 414600
Kemble Drive
Swindon
Wiltshire SN2 2GZ
e-mail: nmrinfo@english-heritage.org.uk
Website: www.english-heritage.org.uk

Local government organisation

Facilities
Enquiries to the Librarian
Information provided by phone, post and e-mail
Open to the general public
Opening hours: Tuesdays-Fridays: 0900-1730 (closed
Mondays); open one Saturday in three; please phone
for details
Photocopying facilities
Research service provided: the library bibliographic
index and the maritime database can be searched.
Cost depends on enquiry type

Subject coverage
The library forms part of the public access collection
of English Heritage, covering the archaeology and
architecture of England. The maritime element of this
collection is primarily reference works on shipwreck
and marine archaeology, including submerged
landscapes

Special collections
'Lloyd's List' 1741-1826 (Facsimile edition)
Some early 'Lloyd's Registers' (Facsimile edition)
'International Journal of Nautical Archaeology'
Nautical Archaeology Society Newsletter
'Diver' magazine, incorporating 'Underwater World',
1978-date
Records and Reports on England's Protected Wreck
Sites

Databases
The National Monuments' Record Centre holds the
National Maritime Record for England. This currently
consists of over 40,000 records, largely comprising
shipwrecks and aircraft lost in England's Territorial Sea
(currently the 12 mile limit) before 31st December
1945. This record complements the National
Archaeological Record also held at the National
Monuments' Record Centre.

N14
NATIONAL MUSEUMS & GALLERIES ON MERSEYSIDE (NMGM) MARITIME ARCHIVES AND LIBRARY

Merseyside Maritime Museum
Albert Dock   Tel: 0151 478 4418/4424
Liverpool L3 4AQ   Fax: 0151 478 4527
e-mail: maritime.archives@nmgm.org.uk
Website: www.nmgm.org.uk

Museum

Facilities
Enquiries to the Curator of Archives
Information provided by phone, post, fax, e-mail and personal visit
Open to the public - Tuesday-Thursday 10.30-16.30; nominal daily charge
Appointment recommended for microfilm readers
Photocopying facilities

Subject coverage
Archives: shipping companies; seafarers; slavery; emigration; Port of Liverpool; maritime charities, missions and educational establishments
Library: maritime history research library of printed books, pamphlets and periodicals and the research collections of Liverpool Nautical Research Society and Docklands History Survey

Special collections
Titanic collection - material relating to the building and sinking of the ship
Lusitania collection - material relating to the building and sinking of the ship
Slavery records - anti-slavery material; papers of slave trade merchants
'Lloyds Register' from 1764
'Lloyd's List' from 1741-1974 (microfilm)
National set of Customs Bills of Entry series for the major ports of Great Britain and Ireland, including complete set for Liverpool, 1820-1939
Liverpool registers of merchant ships
Photographs, map and charts

Specific companies or groups
Thomas and John Brocklebank Ltd. (shipping company)
Ocean Steam Ship Co.
Mersey Docks and Harbour Co.
Alexandra Towing
Bibby Line
Ellerman Line
Hall Line
John Holt
Lamport & Holt
Blue Funnel Line
Elder Dempster
China Mutual SS Co.

Glen Line
Pacific Steam Navigation Co.
Technical records of Cunard Line

Publications
'Guide to the Records of Merseyside Maritime Museum' Vol. 1: comp. Gordon Read and Michael Stammers, 1995
'Guide to the Records of Merseyside Maritime Museum' Vol. 2: Ed. Dawn Littler, 1999

N15
NATIONAL RAILWAY MUSEUM (NRM)

Jack Simmons Library   Tel: 01904 621261; for
Leeman Road   Library bookings, tel:
York YO26 4XJ   01904 686235
                    Fax: 01904 611112
e-mail: nrm.library@nmsi.ac.uk
Website: www.nmsi.ac.uk/nrm

National museum, a department of the Science Museum, London

Facilities
Enquiries to the Librarian and Archivist
Information provided by phone, post, fax and e-mail and personal research by prior appointment is encouraged
Open to the public: Monday-Friday 1000-1700 by prior appointment
Photocopying facilities
Microfilm and microfiche readers
Photographs from archival negative collection
Research service available by prior appointment - no direct charge although charges made for photocopying, supply of photographs and copy drawings

Subject coverage
Monographs; serials; photographs; engineering drawings; archives; railway timetables and posters; maps

Special collections
Photographic archive (1.5 million images), including photographs of railway-owned ships and harbour facilities
Collection of engineering drawings (c.1,000,000 items)

Publications
'A Reader's Guide to Using the Jack Simmons Library Reading Room' (£6.50 including p&p)

National Register Of Archives
See Royal Commission on Historical Manuscripts

N16
NATIONAL SCHOOL SAILING ASSOCIATION

c/o Bellers Bush   Tel: (Home) 01304 613226
Dover Road   Fax: (Work) 01303 226358
Sandwich
Kent CT13 0DG
Website: www.nssa.org.uk

Voluntary organisation open to all organisations working with young people

Facilities
Enquiries to the Secretary
Information provided by phone, post, fax and magazine
Open to the public - especially members or potential members

Subject coverage
Educational activities afloat with young people, especially sailing - recreation and competition
Historical records of all activities since formation in the mid-1950s

Specific databases
Membership only database

Publications
'School Sailing Matters' quarterly magazine

N17
NATIONAL UNION OF MARINE AVIATION & SHIPPING TRANSPORT (NUMAST)

Oceanair House   Tel: 020 8989 6677
750-760 High Road   Fax: 020 8530 1015
Leytonstone
London E11 3B
e-mail: info@numast.org
Website: www.numast.org

Trade union

Facilities
Enquiries to the Communications Department
Information provided by phone, post, fax and e-mail
Books and other material loaned to members only

Subject coverage
Merchant navy history, statistics and law; seafarers' history, statistics, reports on safety; strategic aspects on shipping and seafarers

Special collections
Journals of predecessor unions, including Shipmasters and Radio officers dating back over 100 years

Publications
'The Telegraph': monthly journal, £20 p.a. to non-members

N18
NATIONAL UNION OF RAIL, MARITIME AND TRANSPORT WORKERS (RMT)

Unity House   Tel: 0207 387 4771
39 Chalton Street   Fax: 0207 387 4123
London NW1 1JD
Website: www.rmt.org.uk

Trade union affiliated to the Labour Party and the TUC

Facilities
Enquiries to the National Secretary
Library open to members only

Subject coverage
Industrial relations in the shipping industry

Publications
'RMT News'

N19
NATIONAL WAR MUSEUM OF SCOTLAND

The Castle   Tel: 0131 2257534
Edinburgh EH1 2NG   Fax: 0131 2253848
e-mail: a.carswell@nms.ac.uk

Museum

Facilities
Enquiries to the Secretary
Information provided by phone, post and e-mail
Open to the public - Monday-Friday 0930-1300 and 1400-1700
Appointment necessary for access
Photocopying facilities

Subject coverage
Military history of Scotland and the Scots, including naval history

Special collections
Papers of Admiral Adam Duncan, including private and official correspondence, notebooks, memorandum books, logbooks

---

National Waterfront Museum
New title for Welsh Industrial and Maritime Museum

N20
NATIONAL WATERWAYS MUSEUM

Llanthony Warehouse   Tel: 01452 318200
The Docks   Fax: 01452 318202
Gloucester
Gloucestershire GL1 2EH
e-mail: bookingsnwm@thewaterwaystrust.org
Website: www.nwm.org.uk

Museum/educational charity

Facilities
Enquiries to the Curator
Information provided by phone, post, fax, e-mail and
visit (by prior arrangement)
Open to the public
Photocopying facilities, by staff for a charge
Research service available by appointment only

Subject coverage
Canals and inland waterways: Severn estuary; some
coastal vessels; Gloucester Docks

Publications
Museum Guide
Specialist bookshop
Catalogue on website

N21
NAUTICAL ARCHAEOLOGY SOCIETY

Fort Cumberland   Tel: 023 9281 8419
Fort Cumberland Road   Fax: 023 9281 8419
Eastney
Portsmouth PO4 9LD
e-mail: nas@nasportsmouth.org.uk
Website: www.nasportsmouth.org.uk

Voluntary organisation

Facilities
Enquiries to the Secretary
Information provided by phone, post, fax, e-mail,
website, newsletter and journal
Open to the public and members
Prior appointment necessary for access
Photocopying facilities
Research service available by arrangement, dependent
on individual request

Subject coverage
All aspects of maritime, foreshore (inter-tidal), harbour,
underwater, submerged landscapes, submerged
settlements, lacustrine, estuarine archaeology

Special collections
Archive copies of the 'International Journal of Nautical
Archeology'

Publications
'International Journal of Nautical Archaeology';
Electronic index available for volumes 1-25

Naval Historical Branch
See Ministry of Defence: Admiralty Library

N22
NAVY RECORDS SOCIETY

Department of War Studies
Kings College
London WC2R 2LS
website: www.navyrecordssociety

Voluntary association, publishing house

Facilities
Enquiries to Hon. Secretary
Information provided by post

Subject coverage
Naval history

Publications
List available from Secretary

Needham Research Institute
See East Asian History Of Science Library

N23
THE NELSON MUSEUM, MONMOUTH

Priory Street   Tel: 01600 710630
Monmouth
Gwent NP25 3XA
e-mail: nelsonmuseum@monmouthshire.gov.uk
Website: www.nelsonmuseum.org.uk

Museum

Facilities
Enquiries to the Curator
Information provided by phone, post and e-mail
Open to the public daily throughout the year
Appointment necessary for stored collections
Photocopying facilities
Limited research service

Subject coverage
Personal and commemorative material on Horatio
Nelson

Special collections
Papers from Lady Nelson's collection: Nelson's letters
to his wife, 1785-1802; to his family, 1793-1802;
contemporary pamphlets and documents

Papers from Lady Hamilton's collection: official letter books, 1796, 1799-1800, 1801,1803, 1803-1804; official log books, *Boreas,* 1784-1787, *Vanguard, Foudroyant,* and *Sam and Jane,* 1798-1800, *Victory,* 1803-1805; letters to Lady Hamilton, 1799-1805; collected Nelson MSS, 1782-1813, includes some papers of Sir William Hamilton

Papers from various sources: Nelson holograph correspondence and other papers, 1795-1813; Nelson autograph and signed documents, 1780-1805; Nelson collected documents, 1787-1813; papers of the Hoste family, 1794-1829; papers relative to Lord Nelson's law suit with Lord St Vincent, 1802

N24
THE NELSON SOCIETY

16 Woodside Close   Tel: 01629 812951
Bakewell
Derbyshire DE45 1AY
e-mail: cliffordmansfield@hotmail.com

Voluntary organisation

Facilities
Enquiries to the Archivist/Librarian
Information provided by post (with s.a.e.) and e-mail
Open to members and the public
Photocopying facilities not available except externally, at cost
Research service available at no cost other than direct costs (i.e. postage) when other internal sources consulted

Subject coverage
Naval general service Medal Rolls; accumulation of naval officers' biographical details; small library of 70+ books relating to Nelson and his period

Specific databases
Battle of the Nile musters (incomplete) for all ships

N25
NEWCASTLE-UPON-TYNE LIBRARIES AND INFORMATION SERVICE

City Library   Tel: 0191 277 4100
Princess Square   Fax: 0191 277 4137
Newcastle-upon-Tyne NE99 1DX
e-mail: city.information@newcastle.gov.uk
Website: www.newcastle.gov.uk/libraries

Local government organisation

Facilities
Enquiries to Head of Service, Newcastle Libraries & Information Service
Information provided by phone, post, fax, e-mail, or visit in person

Library open to the general public: Mondays & Thursdays: 0930-2000; Tuesdays, Wednesdays & Fridays: 0930-1700; Saturdays: 0900-1700
Photocopying facilities
Requests for research are assessed on an individual basis. There may be a charge for lengthy searches

Subject coverage
Marine engineering; naval and maritime history; sea disasters; naval war campaigns; 'Lloyd's Registers'; seamanship; yachting

Special collections
Armstrong, Mitchell, Whitworth Ltd. photographic folios, 1880-1914, 1925, 1931
Armstrong, Mitchell, Whitworth launch cards, 1896-1905, 1896-1903
Newcastle upon Tyne Bills of Entry, 1861-1888

Publications
'Black Diamonds by Sea: North East Sailing Colliers, 1780-1880'
'Steamers at the Staiths: North East Steam Collier Ships, 1841-1945'
'Down Elswick Slipways: Armstrong's Ships & People, 1884-1918'
'From Walker to the World: Charles Mitchell's Low Walker Shipyard'
'Looking back at Tyne Liners'
'Ferry Tales: Tyne-Norway Voyages, 1864-2001'
'Mauretania: Pride of the Tyne'
'Turbinia: The Story of Charles Parsons and his Ocean Greyhound'
'Swan Hunter: The Pride and the Tears'
'Palmers Yard'
'Lost Shipyards of the Tyne'

N26
NEWCASTLE-UPON-TYNE – UNIVERSITY SCHOOL OF MARINE SCIENCE AND TECHNOLOGY

Armstrong Building   Tel: 0191 222 6743
Queen Victoria Road   Fax: 0191 222 5491
Newcastle upon Tyne NE1 7RU
e-mail: r.o.carter:@ncl.ac.uk

University Department

Facilities
Enquiries to the Information Officer
Library open to the public
Information given by phone, post and fax
Books and other material loaned to members only
Microfilm, microfiche and microcard/microprint readers available; fullsize copies can be provided, CD-ROM available
On-line information retrieval service offered on marine engineering data bases

Main University Library has complementary stock, including marine technology periodicals, but access is for members only

Subject coverage
Naval architecture; marine technology; shipbuilding; offshore engineering; some marine biology

Special collections
BMT Ltd. library, part of their stock held in the university
Substantial collection of technical material on shipbuilding

Specific databases
British Shipbuilding database of 100,000 entries under development. Enquiries to: Ian.Buxton@ncl.ac.uk

Publications
Subject bibliographies

N27
NEWHAVEN HISTORICAL SOCIETY: LOCAL AND MARITIME MUSEUM

Paradise Park   Tel: 01273 612530
Avis Road
Newhaven, East Sussex BN9 0DH
e-mail: ahelyar@tiscali.co.uk
Website: www.newhavenmuseum.co.uk

Voluntary organisation/museum

Facilities
Enquiries to Hon. Secretary, Mr AG Helyar,
49 Wellington Road, Newhaven, East Sussex BN9 0RD
Information provided by phone, post and e-mail
Museum open to the public: Monday-Friday 1400-1600
Photocopying facilities
Research service may be available by special request

Subject coverage
History of Newhaven-Dieppe ferry service; history of Newhaven port and town; Dieppe raid

Special collections
Photographic archive of Newhaven and its people

Specific database:
Photographic archive

Publications
General information on website

N28
NORFOLK RECORD OFFICE

The Archives Centre   Tel: 01603 222599
Martineau Lane   Fax: 01603 761885
Norwich NR1 2DQ
e-mail: norfrec.nro@norfolk.gov.uk
Website: http://archives.norfolk.gov.uk.

Local government organisation

Facilities
Enquiries to the County Archivist
Open to the public
Information given by phone, post and fax
Microfilm and microfiche readers available
Microcopies and fullsize copies can provided
Charges for searches by staff.

Special collections

General records
Maps of Norfolk and some north east Suffolk coastal parishes, 16th-20th centuries
Parish registers of coastal parishes including occasional references to shipwrecks, 16th-20th centuries
Probate records for mariners, shipwrights, 14th-20th centuries
Rate assessments including ships, 18th-19th centuries
Shipping registers for Cley, 1839-1853 and Wells, 1832-1904
Annual register of vessels registered at Cley, 1867-1901, and at Wells, 1867-1910
Deeds of bills of sale of ships 16th-19th centuries

Great Yarmouth records (documents at Norfolk Record Office)
Borough court rolls including local customs accounts c.1312-1700 and conveyances of ships, early 14th century
Registers of Freemen, 1429-1892 and apprenticeships, 1563-1856
Port and Haven Commissioners' records, 18th-20th centuries
Shipping registers, 1834-1886
Registers of crews engaged, 1881-1913
Appropriation book for official numbers of British registered ships, 1902-1989 (closed to public inspection for 30 years)
Registry reports on registration matters such as the transfer of ownership, including minor accounts of 1899-1957 with lists of yachts of five tons and upwards, tugboats and pleasure boats in passenger service
Register of apprentices, 1884-1907
Register of keels (boats used in internal navigation), 1795-1796
Registers of fishing boats, c.1950-1988 (Accession No. 2002/184, not yet catalogued)

King's Lynn records (documents at Norfolk Record Office)
Register of shipmasters' protests, 1787-1808
Shipping registers, 1836-1922
Register of steam-boat certificates, 1861-1926
Annual register of vessels registered, 1881-1930
Appropriation book for official numbers of British registered ships, 1855-1986 (closed to public inspection for 30 years)
Applications to register ships, 1940-1956
Registers of fishing boats, 1942-1988 (Accession No. 2002/137, not yet catalogued)

King's Lynn (documents at King's Lynn Borough Archives, The Town Hall, Saturday Market Place, King's Lynn PE30 5DQ. To view please make an appointment with the Principal Archivist, Norfolk Record Office)
Registers of Freemen, 1292-1868, and apprentices, 1648-1851 (microfilm copy available in Norfolk Record Office)
Royal writs for supply of ships, 14th-15th centuries
Accounts of building and fitting out of ships in the Chamberlain's accounts, 14th-15th centuries
Admiralty Court books, 1734-1835 and papers, 1604-1830
Register of shipmasters' protests, 1912-1929

N29
NORTHAMPTONSHIRE RECORD OFFICE
Wootton Hall Park   Tel: 01604 762129
Northampton NN4 8BQ   Fax: 01604 767562
e-mail: archivist@nro.northamptonshire.gov.uk
Website: www.nro.northamptonshire.gov.uk

Local government record office

Facilities
Enquiries to the County Archivist
Information provided by phone (please ask for the Enquiries Archivist), personal enquiry during opening hours, post, fax and e-mail
Open to the public: Tuesday-Wednesday 0900-1645, Thursday 0900-1945, Friday 0900-1615 and 1st and 3rd Saturday in month 0900-1215
Photocopying facilities

Subject coverage
Naval affairs - navy, admiralty, ships; harbour; marine; mariner; military; navigation; ship, shipping, shipwreck; seamen; rivers; Nene River; marine engineering

Special collections
Rye of Culworth, including ships' journals, ships' logs, letters, orders, signal books, poems, charts, sketches and watercolours, 1770s-1870s of Rear-Admiral Peter Rye
Logbooks, naval papers, accounts, photograph albums of Admiral Lord Charles Scott of Boughton, 1853-1904 (including photograph album for the *Bacchante* voyage,

1879-1882). Please apply for access in advance for any visit as these papers are currently uncatalogued
Letters of the Rev. Henry Cockayne Cust to Admiral Sir Watkin Owen Pell, as a Captain and Commodore, 1807-1833
Correspondence and papers of Frederick, 4th Earl Spencer, Captain in the Royal Navy, 1817-1830

Publications
'Catalogue of ...Deposited Plans... in Northamptonshire Record Office', Philip Riden, Northampton, 2000

N30
NORTH DEVON MARITIME MUSEUM
Odun House   Tel: 01237 422064
Odun Road
Appledore
North Devon EX39 1PT
e-mail: appledore@devonmuseums.net
Website: www.devonmuseums.net/appledore

Museum

Facilities
Library open to the public
Open: Easter Saturday-31st October 1400-1700;
1st May-30th September Monday-Friday 1100-1300, 1400-1700

Subject coverage
Maritime history of North Devon, including models and photographs of sail and steam vessels, shipbuilding, fishing, wreck and rescue, Second World War experimental beach landings.

N31
NORTH DEVON RECORD OFFICE
Tuly Street   Tel: 01271 388608
Barnstaple EX31 1EL
e-mail: ndevrec@devon.gov.uk
Website: www.devon.gov.uk/dro

Local government organisation

Facilities
Enquiries to the Senior Archivist
Information provided by phone, post and e-mail
Open to the public: Monday, Tuesday, Thursday and Friday 0930-1700, Wednesday 0930-1300 and some Saturdays 0930-1600
Photocopying facilities
Research service - £18 per hour

Subject coverage
Shipping registers of Barnstaple, 1824-1987, merged with Ilfracombe, 1824-1837; Bideford, 1786-1987

Special collections
Port Book, Bideford, 1805-1813
Wreck Books, Appledore, 1919-1982
Shipowners' accounts, 1767-1815

Specific companies and groups
Clarkes, marine engineers of Braunton
PK Harris, shipbuilders of Appledore

Publications
'Guide to Sources for Maritime History' - see website

N32
NORTH EAST LINCOLNSHIRE ARCHIVES

Town Hall	Tel: 01472 323585
Town Hall Square	Fax: 01472 323582
Grimsby	
N.E. Lincolnshire DN31 1HX	

e-mail: john.wilson@nelincs.gov.uk
Website: www.nelincs.gov.uk

Local government organisation

Facilities
Enquiries to the Archivist
Information provided by phone, post (sae required), fax and e-mail
Open to the public - Monday-Friday 1000-1230 and 1330-1600; appointment necessary
Photocopying facilities
Research service available - specific searches on receipt of SAE. First 30 minutes £20 per hour, minimum fee £10

Subject coverage
Local government archives for North Lincolnshire and North East Lincolnshire, 1227-1996; public records for same area (courts, central government departments); gifts, deposits, purchases for same area, 1300-1996

Special collections
HM Customs and Excise, Port of Grimsby registers of British ships, 1824-1918
HM Customs and Excise, Port of Grimsby registers of fishing vessels, 1827-1988
Board of Trade (Grimsby) merchant vessel crew lists, 1863-1913
Board of Trade (Grimsby) fishing vessel crew lists, 1884-1914
Board of Trade (Grimsby) merchant vessel apprentice register, 1879-1919
Board of Trade (Grimsby) fishing apprentice registers, 1880-1937
Grimsby Haven Company, 1747-1847
British Transport Docks Board: records for Grimsby and Immingham Docks, 1848-1960
Immingham Dock: register of sailings and arrivals 1916-27
Papers 1930-65 of Stephen Merceron Burton (1899-1966), author of Burton's Nautical Tables.

Specific companies and groups
Consolidated Fisheries Ltd., 1897-1980, and other trawling companies from 1900.
Humber Graving Dock and Engineering Co. Ltd., Immingham, records, 1909-73
Grimsby: arrival and sailing books (vessels only), 1848-57 and 1918-37

Publications
Guide by John Wilson (1993) ISBN 0-9515240-5-4 out of print
Free information leaflet available on request

N33
NORTH TYNESIDE COUNCIL CULTURAL SERVICES: LEARNING AND LIBRARIES

Central Library	Tel: 0191 200 5424
Northumberland Square	Fax: 0191 200 6118
North Shields	
Tyne and Wear NE30 1QU	

e-mail: local.studies@northtyneside.gov.uk
website: www.northtyneside.gov.uk/libraries/index.htm

Local government organisation

Facilities
Enquiries to Libraries and Information Manager
Information provided by phone, e-mail, post and fax
Open to the public: Monday 0900-1730; Tuesday 0900-1900; Wednesday 0900-1230; Thursday 0900-1900; Friday 0900-1930; Saturday 0900-1700
Photocopying facilities
Research service available, £7.00 per 30 minutes or part thereof plus expenses

Subject coverage
Local newspapers, books

N34
NORTHUMBERLAND RECORD OFFICE

Melton Park	Tel: 0191 236 2680
North Gosforth	Fax: 0191 217 0905
Newcastle upon Tyne NE3 5QX	

Morpeth Records Centre	Tel: 01670 504 084
The Kylins	Fax: 01670 524 815
Morpeth	
NE61 2EQ	

Local government organisation

Facilities
Enquiries to the Senior Archivist
Information provided by phone, post and fax
Open to the public
Melton Park: Wednesday 0930-1300 and 1400-2000,

Thursday-Friday 0930-1300 and 1400-1700
Morpeth: Monday and Wednesday 0930-1300 and
1400-1700, Tuesday 0930-1300 and 1400-2000
Photocopying facilities - charges apply, including those
for postage
Research service available - Archive staff will undertake
a minimum of 1 hour's research with longer periods
available in half hour blocks up to a maximum of 2
hours. Clients should send an initial payment of £16 to
Northumberland County Council (stating maximum
length of search required) - further research will be
charged at £8 per half hour with invoicing for balance
owing submitted with research report

Subject coverage
Public records; records of businesses, commercial
organisations and industrial concerns; local authorities
and other statutory bodies; personal, family and estate
papers; records of charitable and voluntary
organisations; professional associations, employer's
associations, guilds and trades unions; schools, hospitals
and other educational and welfare institutions; clubs
and societies; photographs, maps and plans; audio tapes
and local history publications

Special collections
Crew lists, Blyth, 1863-1913
Shipping registers, Blyth, 1924-66
Blyth, Warkworth, Amble Harbour Commissioners
Royal Northumberland Yacht Club, 1894-1990
Breyen, Richardson & Co., ships' chandlers etc.
Please also see A2A website (www.a2a.pro.gov.uk)

Publications
Please see A2A website (above)

N35
NORTH YORKSHIRE COUNTY
RECORD OFFICE (NYCRO)
Malpas Road	Tel: 01609 777585
Northallerton	Fax: 01609 780447
North Yorkshire	

e-mail: archives@northyorks.gov.uk
Website: www.northyorks.gov.uk/archives

Postal address:
County Hall
Northallerton
North Yorkshire DL7 8AF

Local government organisation

Facilities
Enquiries to the Archivist.
Information provided by phone, post, e-mail and visit.
Appointment necessary, please explain nature of
subject to be studied.
Open to the public: Monday, Tuesday and Thursday 0900-
1645, Wednesday 0900-2045 and Friday 0900-1615

Photocopying facilities

Subject coverage
History of merchant and naval shipping relating to
North Yorkshire

N36
NOTTAGE MARITIME INSTITUTE
The Quay	Tel: 01206 824142
Wivenhoe CO7 9BX	Tel: 01206 824142

e-mail: nottage@rya-online.net

Private library and museum

Facilities
Enquiries to the Institute
Open to the public by appointment
Information given by telephone, post and e-mail.

Subject coverage
Maritime history (River Colne and its estuary);
shipbuilding, especially Wivenhoe; yachting.

N37
NOTTINGHAMSHIRE ARCHIVES
County House	Tel: 0115 958 1634
Castle Meadow Road	Fax: 0115 941 3997
Nottingham NG2 1AG	

e-mail: archives@nottscc.gov.uk
Website:
www.nottscc.gov.uk/libraries/archives/index.htm

Local government organisation

Facilities
Enquiries to the Principal Archivist
Information provided by phone, post, fax and e-mail
(post preferred)
Open to the public - Monday, Wednesday-Friday 0900-
1645, Tuesday 0900-1915 and Saturday 0900-1245
Photocopying facilities
Limited and specific research service available free of
charge, all others referred to private record agents

Subject coverage
Nottinghamshire official and deposited family and
estate records

Special collections
Letter re. trial of Admiral Byng, 1757
Preservation of Sherwood timber for naval affairs,
1630-31
Letters re. impressing Nottinghamshire men for navy,
1700-01
Grant by Lord High Admiral of ship called the
Westgate, 1660
Lord Lumley's evidence at court martial of Admiral
Keppel, 1779

See also references in catalogues of the Portland, Foljame and Savile family and estate collections listed on the A2A website (www.a2a.pro.gov.uk)

Publications
Nottinghamshire Archives website (please see above)
National Register of Archives (ARCHON)
Public Record Office (Access to Archives - www.a2a.pro.gov.uk)

O1
OCEAN LINER SOCIETY

27 Old Gloucester Street
London WC1N 3XX
Website: www.ocean-liner-society.com

Voluntary society

Facilities
Regular meetings held in London
No research facilities.

Subject coverage
Ocean liners of the past and cruise ships

Publications
'Sea Lines', distributed quarterly to members

O2
OCEAN YOUTH TRUST

The Ocean Youth Trust is a co-operative activity between six registered charities, each providing sail training and personal development for people between the age of 12 and 25. Each organisation sails in a different, but overlapping, area and shares the same objectives.

Ocean Youth Trust South
Spur House   Tel: 0870 241 2252
1 The Spur   Fax: 0870 909 0230
Alverstoke
Gosport
Hampshire PO12 2NA
e-mail: oytsouth@aol.com
Website: www.oyt.org.uk

Ocean Youth Trust East
102 Ewe Lamb Lane   Tel: 0115 939 9825
Bramcote
Nottingham NG9 3JW
e-mail: manager@oyteast.org.uk
Website: www.oyteast.org.uk

Ocean Youth Trust North West
Unit 4   Tel: 0151 666 1664
Brandon Street   Fax: 0151 666 1664
Birkenhead
Wirral
Cheshire CH41 5HN

e-mail: info@oytnw.org.uk
Website: www.oytnw.org.uk

Ocean Youth Trust North East
PO Box 91   Tel: 0870 241 6789
Robin Hood's Bay
Whitby
Yorkshire YO22 4WB
e-mail: info@oyt-ne.org.uk
Website: www.oyt.org.uk

Ocean Youth Trust Northern Ireland
Unit 18   Tel: 02893 366776
217 Kilroot Business Centre   Fax: 02893 367670
Larne Road
Carrickfergus
Northern Ireland BT38 7PR

Ocean Youth Trust Scotland
24 Blythswood Square   Tel: 0141 300 5511
Glasgow G2 4QS   Fax: 0141 300 5701
e-mail: office@oytscotland.org.uk
Website: www.oytscotland.org.uk

O3
OFFSHORE ENGINEERING INFORMATION SERVICE

University Library   Tel: +44 (0)131 451 3579
Heriot-Watt University   Fax: +44 (0)131 451 3164
Edinburgh EH14 4AS
e-mail: oeis@hw.ac.uk
Website: www.eevl.ac.uk/offshore/

University department

Facilities
Enquiries to the Senior Information Scientist
Information provided by: phone, post fax and e-mail
Books and other material loaned;
Library open to subscribers
Opening hours: see website
Microfilm and microfiche readers available; CD-ROM available; on-line information retrieval
Photocopying facilities available

Subject coverage
Offshore engineering (oil industry); marine technology (non-oil marine resources); marine environmental protection

Databases
Offshore database, via website

Publications
'Offshore Engineering'
Bulletin (monthly)

04
OLD GAFFERS ASSOCIATION
(OGA)

7 Rathmore Close   Tel: 01242 603375
Winchcombe
Cheltenham
Gloucester GL54 5YX
Website: www.oldgaffersassociation.org/

Voluntary organisation

Facilities
Enquiries to the Membership Secretary

Subject coverage
Coastal sailing craft, including smacks, bawleys,
prawners, pilot cutters and classic yachts

Publications
'Gaffers Log' journal

Oriental and India Office
Collection
See British Library

05
THE ORKNEY LIBRARY AND
ARCHIVE

Junction Road   Tel: 01856 873166
Kirkwall   Fax: 01856 875260
Orkney KW15 1AG
e-mail: archives@orkneylibrary.org.uk
Website: www.orkneylibrary.org.uk

Local government organisation

Facilities
Enquiries to the Principal Archivist
Information provided by phone, post, fax and e-mail
Library services open to the public - Monday,
Wednesday-Thursday 0900-1900, Tuesday, Friday-
Saturday 0900-1700
Archives open Tuesday-Friday 0900-1300 and 1400-1645
Photocopying facilities
Limited research service available - no research fee and
list of reproduction charges available on request

Subject coverage
Shipwrecks; whaling; smuggling; trade, especially with
Europe, North America; harbours; activities of the
'merchant lairds'; shipbuilding; shipping companies;
shipping registers; fishing; Admiralty surveys plus large
photographic and sound/video archive and local
newspapers

Special collections
Balfour of Balfour and Trenabie (merchant laird)
Watt of Breckness and Starll (merchant laird)

Admiralty Court processes
Shipping registers
Specific companies and groups
Bremner and Co. Shipowners, Stromness
Orkney Steam Navigation Co.

Publications
Top level finding aids available on www.scan.org.uk
(Scottish Archive Network)

06
ORKNEY NATURAL HISTORY
SOCIETY MUSEUM TRUST

52 Alfred Street
Stromness
Orkney

Charitable trust

Facilities
Enquiries to the Curator
Information provided by phone and post
Library open to the public

Subject coverage
Fishing; whaling; shipping; shipwrecks; lifeboats and
lighthouses; naval history (Scapa Flow); Hudson Bay Co.

Special collections
Archives of the First World War German fleet scuttling
and salvage

Publications
'The salving of the German Fleet', J Pottinger

P1
PADDLE STEAMER PRESERVATION
SOCIETY (PSPS)

PO Box 356
Worcester WR3 7WH

Voluntary association

Facilities
Enquiries to the National Secretary

Subject coverage
Paddle steamers

Publications
'Paddle Wheels' quarterly

P2
PADDLE STEAMER KINGSWEAR CASTLE TRUST

The Historic Dockyard	01634 827648
Chatham	01634 827648
Kent ME4 4TQ	

e-mail: kc@pskc.freeserve.co.uk
website: www.pskc.freeserve.co.uk

Historic ship and archive

Facilities
Enquiries to John Megoran
Information provided by phone, post, fax and e-mail
Open to the public by appointment
Research by arrangement, cost depending on work involved

Subject coverage
Paddle steamers

Special collections
River Dart Steamboat Company
PS *Kingswear Castle*

Publications
Website has regular features on paddle steamer history and operations

---

Parliamentary Archives
See House of Lords' Record Office

P3
PASSENGER SHIPPING ASSOCIATION

Walmar House	Tel: 0207 436 2449
4th Floor	Fax: 0207 636 9206
288-292 Regent Street	
London W1R 5HE	

Website: www.discover-cruises.co.uk

UK trade association for cruise and ferry operators

Patents Information Unit
See Leeds Library And Information Services

P4
PEMBROKESHIRE RECORD OFFICE

The Castle	Tel: 01437 763707
Haverfordwest	Fax: 01437 768539
Pembrokeshire SA61 2EF	

e-mail: record.office@pembrokeshire.gov.uk
Website: www.pembrokeshire.gov.uk

Local government organisation

Facilities
Enquiries to the County Archivist
Information provided by phone, post, fax and e-mail
Open to the public
Photocopying facilities
Research service available - £15 per hour

Subject coverage
Registers of ships, Cardigan, 1824-1855; registers of ships, Milford Haven, 1827-1906; registers of transactions, Milford Haven, 1855-1934; registers of fishing boats, Milford Haven, 1869-1926 and 1945-1988; registers of transactions, Cardigan, 1855-1856; crew agreements and some log books of Cardigan and Milford Haven registered ships, 1863-1913; Customs and Excise - wrecks, 1920-1986; seamen, crew and ships arriving 1903-1958

Specific companies and groups
Milford Docks Company collection, 1874 on

Specific databases
CLIP (Crew List Indexing Project) 1863,1880 and 1881

P5
PERMANENT INTERNATIONAL ASSOCIATION OF NAVIGATION CONGRESSES (PIANC)

The Institution of Civil Engineers	
Great George Street	Tel: 0207 222 7727
London SW1P 3AA	Fax: 0207 222 7500

Learned society

Facilities
Enquiries to the Librarian of ICE
Information provided by phone, post and fax to all; loans to members only
Library open to members only; on-line information retrieval service offered

Subject coverage
Engineering; financial matters relating to marine engineering

---

P6
PERTH MUSEUM AND ART GALLERY

George Street	Tel: 01738 632488
Perth	Fax: 01738 443505
Tayside PH1 5LB	

e-mail: museum@pkc.gov.uk
Website: www.pkc.gov.uk\ah

Local government organisation

Facilities
Enquiries to the Principal Officer

Information provided by phone, post and fax
Open to the public: Monday-Saturday 1000-1700
Appointment necessary to view material which is not on exhibition
Photocopying at 20p per A4 sheet

Subject coverage

All branches of fine and applied art, human history and natural science with special emphasis on Perth and Kinross District, Scotland. Includes photographs of river and sea-going vessels; Perth harbour and local ferries; ships models and maritime material in medieval archaeology collection associated.

P7
PLYMOUTH CENTRAL LIBRARY - DEVON LIBRARY SERVICES LOCAL AND NAVAL STUDIES DEPARTMENT

Central Library   Tel: 01752 305909
Drake Circus   Fax: 01752 305905
Plymouth
Devon PL4 8AL
e-mail: localstudies@plymouth.gov.uk
Website: www.plymouth.gov.uk/star/library.html
www.plymouth.libraries.info

Local government organisation

Facilities

Enquiries to the Local and Naval Studies Librarian
Information provided by phone, post, fax, e-mail and visit
Open to the public: Monday to Friday 0900-1900 and Saturday 0900-1600
Photocopying facilities - minimum charge £2.40 plus p&p
Research service available - no more than 30 minutes and only specific questions answered (no detailed research); further details on request

Subject coverage

Naval history and current naval studies; Royal Navy; NATO; less detailed coverage of European, Commonwealth and world navies; navigation; voyages; warship construction; warships index; local naval areas of interest (Devonport dockyard and conflicts involving local ships)

Special collections

Wide range of historical and current periodicals
'Navy List' from 1783
'Jane's Fighting Ships' from 1898
Navy Records Society publications
Hakluyt Society publications

Specific databases

Plymouth Library Service's on-line catalogue can be viewed at www.webopac.plymouth.gov.uk

Publications

See 'Naval and Maritime Libraries and Archives Group Guide to Collections' published by Hampshire Libraries and Information
'A Naval Tradition' (4 titles)
'No Place Field' (Royal Naval Memorial Garden, Plymouth)
'Jobs for the Boys' (stories of local men and work)
'Jobs for the Girls' (stories of local women and work)
'Resource Directory" (a guide to the collections)

P8
PLYMOUTH AND WEST DEVON RECORD OFFICE

Unit 3   Tel: 01752 305940
Clare Place
Coxside
Plymouth PL4 0JW
e-mail: pwdro@plymouth.gov.uk
Website: www.plymouth.gov.uk/star/archives.htm

Local government organisation

Facilities

Enquiries to the City Archivist
Information provided by phone, post and e-mail
Open to general public; appointments necessary
Opening hours: Tuesdays-Thursdays 0930-1700;
Fridays: 0930-1600
Proof of identity required for all searchers using the search rooms
Photocopying facilities
Research facilities not provided; list of private researchers supplied

Subject coverage

Maritime history of Plymouth, 1824-c.1920

Special collections

Shipping registers, Plymouth 1824-1920
Plymouth City records, register of arrivals and sailings, 1782-1815
Harbour Master's records for Sutton Pool, 1838-1900
Hawkins, Edward, 1765-1839, papers of the Officer commanding prison hulks, early 19th century
Devonport Dockyard deeds, 1719-1911 and plans, 1763-1917
Plymouth breakwater, superintendent engineer, papers of William Stuart, 1818-1845
Naval officer's log book, 1908-1918

Publications

See website

P9
P&O HISTORY AND ARCHIVES

National Maritime Museum   Tel: 020 8312 6616
London SW1Y 5EJ   Fax: 020 8312 6680
e-mail: stephen.rabson@pogroup.com
Website: www.pogroup.com
Catalogue on www.nmm.ac.uk

P&O employee seconded to the National Maritime
Museum

Facilities
Enquiries to the P&O Historian and Archivist
Information provided by phone, post, fax and e-mail
Brief enquiries can be answered and guidance to
specific sources can be supplied but detailed in-depth
research will have to be done by the enquirer

Subject coverage
Documents, photographs and film and video relating to
the history of P&O since the 1830s, and its major
subsidiary companies including:
Asiatic Steam Navigation Co.
British India Steam Navigation Co.
Coast Lines
Eastern and Australian Steamship Co.
Federal Steam Navigation Co.
General Steam Navigation Co.
Moss Hutchison Line
New Zealand Shipping Co.
James Nourse Ltd.
Orient Steam Navigation Co.
Strick Line and
Trident Tankers

———————————

P10
POLISH INSTITUTE AND SIKORSKI MUSEUM (PISM)

20 Princes Gate   Tel: 020 7589 9249
London SW7 1PT

Museum and archive

Facilities
Enquiries to the Keeper of Archives (for documents)
and the Keeper of Photographic Library (for
photographs)
Information provided by phone (simple queries) or
post
Archives open to the public: Tuesdays-Fridays 0930-
1600
Museum open Mondays-Fridays 1400-1600 and 1st
Saturday of month 1000-1600
Microfilm reader; fullsize copies provided

Subject coverage
Polish naval and maritime history; Polish navy, 1939-
1946 and Polish merchant marine, 1939-1946

Special collections
Documents of Polish Naval GHQ
Documents concerning specific vessels of the Polish
navy and Polish merchant marine
Documents of the Polish Ministry of Trade, Industry
and Marine; Jerzy Bohusz-Syszko papers (civil servant
in Marine Ministry)
Lt-Cdr Julian Ginsbert papers, 1939-41
Captain DN Brunon Jabtonski papers, 1941-1963
Jozef Limbach papers, 1935-1969
Rear-Admiral Tadensz Podjazd-Morgenstern papers,
1937-1973
Captain PN Czestaw Petelenz papers, 1879-1947
Captain PN Eugeniusz Ptauski papers, 1939-1972
Commander Artur Reyman papers, 1903-1964

Publications
Guide to the Archives of the Polish Institute and
Sikorski Museum

———————————

P11
POOLE LOCAL HISTORY CENTRE

4 High Street   Tel: 01202 262613
Poole   Fax: 01202 262622
Dorset BH15 1BW
e-mail: localhistory@poole.gov.uk

Local government organisation

Facilities
Enquiries to the Local History Manager
Information provided by phone, post and e-mail
Open to the public: Tuesdays-Saturdays 1000-1500
Photocopying facilities

Special collections
Maritime book collection
Card index of Poole ship names
Shipping index from 18th/19th century newspapers (in
progress)
Large photographic collection of vessels in port
Historic charts of Poole Bay and Poole Harbour

———————————

P12
PORT OF LONDON AUTHORITY

Bakers Hall   Tel: 0207 743 7900
7 Harp Lane
London EC3R 6LB
Website: portoflondon.co.uk

Port operator

———————————

P13
PORT OF LOWESTOFT RESEARCH SOCIETY

52 Salisbury Road
Lowestoft
Suffolk NR33 0NE

Voluntary association, membership by invitation

Facilities
Enquiries to the Chairman.

Subject coverage
Lowestoft shipping: registered, owned or built
Some coverage of vessels visiting Lowestoft
Lowestoft lifeboats

Special collections
LW Moore collection of photographs of Admiralty motor fishing vessels.
The Society's main photographic and shipping information collections are deposited with Suffolk Record Office (Lowestoft Branch) where they are available to the public.

Publications
Newsletter to members, 10 issues per year

P14
PORTSMOUTH CENTRAL LIBRARY

Guildhall Square   Tel: 023 9268 8046
Portsmouth   Fax: 023 9283 9855
Hants PO1 2DX
e-mail: reference.library@portsmouthcc.gov.uk
Website: www.portsmouth.gov.uk

Local government organisation

Facilities
Enquiries to the Historical Collections Librarian
Information provided by phone, post, fax and e-mail
Open to the public: Monday-Friday 0930-1900, Saturday 0930-1600 and Sunday 1230-1600 (no specialist staff on duty on Sundays)
Photocopying facilities
Research service available - specific enquiries answered free of charge, no open-ended research, small charge for photocopies

Subject coverage
Mainly printed books (no archives); some pamphlets, photographs, cuttings, ship photographs covering: any warship and navy (in theory) at any time, anywhere, strong in biography, R.N. history, ship construction and history, voyages and exploration, First and Second World Wars, 'Navy Lists' 1778 to date, Navy Records Society and other naval periodicals

Special collections
Lily Lambert McCarthy collection (early and rare items on Nelson and his period)

Publications
Entry in NMLAG Guide (2000)

P15
PORTSMOUTH MUSEUMS AND RECORDS SERVICE
CITY MUSEUM AND RECORDS OFFICE

Museum Road   Tel: 023 9282 7261
Portsmouth   Fax: 023 9287 5276
Hants PO1 2LJ
e-mail: kball@portsmouthcc.gov.uk
e-mail: adrew@portsmouthcc.gov.uk
Website: www.portsmouthmuseums.co.uk

Local government organisation - combined museum and records service

Facilities
Enquiries to the Archivists (records) and Local History Officer (museum)
Information provided by phone, post, fax and e-mail
Open to the public
Photocopying facilities
Research service available in both Records Service and Museum
Records charge £8 per half hour, up to 3 hours work
Museums charge £8 per half hour, up to 3 hours work for enquiries, where these could be undertaken by the enquirer using finding aids available in the City Museum and Records Office
Charges are made for general research, not drawing on the collections and for those making commercial use of information provided. Where finding aids are not available and for general access to the collections, there is no fee

Subject coverage
Holdings reflect the impact of the navy, army and Dockyard on the people and local economy of Portsmouth
Service certificates, souvenir programmes and personal letters of naval personnel
Late 18th, 19th and 20th century paintings, prints and drawings of naval and merchant vessels
Photographic and postcards of naval and other vessels in and around Portsmouth harbour and general maritime images
Mementoes of famous ships and wrecks, relics relating to Jack the Painter, naval medals and cannons
D-Day Museum Archive Collection holds books, documents, maps, photographs and oral history recordings on naval aspects of Operation Overlord. A strength of the collection is the role of landing craft in Operation Neptune and most notable are the papers

of Commander Rupert Curtis, DSC RNVR
Development of Mulberry Harbours and the parts
played by McAlpine and Sons Ltd. and the Directorate
of Transportation at the War Office

Special collections
Portsmouth shipping registers, 1820-1870
Fishing registers, Port of Portsmouth, c.1930-1970
Crew lists for ships registered in Portsmouth and
Cowes, 1863-1913
Customs and Excise Registers
Letters relating to the Board of Ordnance, early to
mid 18th century
Records of the Royal Sailors Rest and the Royal
Marine and Naval Orphanage, along with plans,
photographs and postcards of barrack and naval or
military groups and events
Letters regarding Spithead Mutiny, 1797, from Lord
Howe and other miscellaneous papers
Letters, logbooks and family papers belonging to
Hulbert-Jackson, prize agent
Large collection of work by marine artist WL Wyllie,
particularly from the years he lived in Portsmouth.
Watercolours and lithographs by the Deane brothers,
featuring material recovered from wrecks including
Mary Rose, Royal Oak and the East Indiaman *Earl of
Abergavenny.*
Large numbers of works on a maritime theme by
lesser-known and local artists.
Items from HMS *Bounty*
Items relating to 1875-1876 voyage of HMS *Alert* and
HMS *Discovery* and Captain Giffard

P16
PORTSMOUTH UNIVERSITY - THE CENTRE FOR MARINE RESOURCE ECONOMICS (CEMARE)

Milton Site	Tel: 023 9284 4082
Locksway Road	Fax: 023 9284 4614
Southsea	
Hants PO4 8JF	

e-mail: christopher.martin@port.ac.uk
Website: www.port.ac.uk/cemare

University department

Facilities
Enquiries to the Librarian
Open to the public: Monday-Friday 0900-1700
Advisable to phone prior to visit
Photocopying facilities
Research service available

Subject coverage
Multi-disciplinary research into marine resources,
especially fish

Special collections
Large FAO collection

Post Office Archives
See Heritage Royal Mail

P17
PRESS ASSOCIATION

Central Park	Tel: 020 7963 7000
New Lane	Fax:07808 306801
Leeds LS11 5DZ	

e-mail: palibrary@pa.press.net
Website: www.pa.press.net

Media

Facilities
Enquiries to Chief News Librarian
Library open to the public
Information provided by phone, post, fax, e-mail and
visit
Microfiche and microcard/microprint readers
Photocopying facilities
Charges for research: £30 per hour for visitors, £45
per hour for commissioned research, £15 per hour for
students
On-line search facilities for Press Association copy

Subject coverage
14 million press cuttings in total, amongst which are
many dealing with all aspects of shipping and maritime
affairs including shipbuilding, shipping accidents, shipping
lines, fishing industry, the Royal Navy, shipping frauds,
files on personalities

P18
PRIAULX LIBRARY

Candie Road	Tel: 01481 721998
St. Peter Port	
Guernsey	

e-mail: priaulx.library@gov.gg
Website: www.gov.gg/priaulx/

Library

Facilities
Enquiries to the Chief Librarian
Information provided by phone, fax, post, e-mail and
visit
Open to the public: Monday-Saturday 0930-1700,
occasionally by appointment at other times
Loans to members only
Microfilm and microfiche readers
Microcopies can be provided
Photocopying facilities
Research service available at £10 per hour plus cost of
copies

Subject coverage
Channel Island trade, privateering

Special collections
Carteret Priaulx papers, correspondence of Guernsey shipowners

---

Public Record Office
See National Archives

P19
PUBLIC RECORD OFFICE OF NORTHERN IRELAND (PRONI)

66 Balmoral Avenue	Tel: 02890 255900
Belfast BT9 6NY	Fax: 02890 255999

e-mail: proni@dcalni.gov.uk
website: www.proni.nics.gov.uk

Government agency

Facilities
Enquiries to Head of Reader Services
Open to the public: Monday, Tuesday, Wednesday and Friday 0900-1645; Thursday 1000-2045
Limited photocopying facilities

Subject coverage
Governmental, departmental, local authority and court records
Large collection of privately deposited records

Special collections
Board of Guardians
1901 Census
Landed estates
Emigrant letters
Church records (most denominations)
Belfast Harbour Authority

Specific companies
Ulster Transport Authority
Various liner companies

Publications
'Tracing your ancestors in Northern Ireland'
'Local history sources in PRONI'
Deputy Keeper's Report/Annual Report and Accounts

Q1
QINETIQ - (FORMERLY DRA, DERA)

QinetiQ Winfrith Libraries	Tel: 01305 212447

Winfrith Technology Centre
Building A22, Room 046
Dorchester
Dorset DT2 8XJ
e-mail: askalibrarian@qinetiq.com

QinetiQ Library	Tel: 02392 336935

Dstl Portsdown West

Portsdown Hill Road
Fareham
Hants PO17 6AD
e-mail: askalibrarian@qinetiq.com

Research and development company - addresses above for two main sites with marine interests

Facilities
Enquiries to e-mail address above
Information normally available to government departments only, other users by prior arrangement with site services and Information Specialists at individual sites

Subject coverage
Hydrodynamics and hydroacoustics applied to ships and their propulsors: ship model research; ship and submarine structural research; underwater acoustics; propagation of sound in the sea; mines and countermeasures; underwater weapons systems; underwater vehicles; trials

---

Queen Mother Library
See Aberdeen University Library

R1
RAILWAY AND CANAL HISTORICAL SOCIETY (RCHS)

3 West Court	Tel: 01865 240514

West Street
Oxford OX2 0NP
Website: www.bodley.ox.ac.uk/external/rchs

Voluntary organisation

Facilities
Enquiries to the Hon. Secretary
Information provided by phone, post, fax and e-mail
Open to the public

Subject coverage
Information on sources for the history of British waterways and docks

---

R2
RAMSGATE MARITIME MUSEUM

The Clock House	Tel: 01843 587765
Royal Harbour	Fax: 01843 582359

Ramsgate
Kent CT11 8LS
e-mail: museum@ekmt.fsnet.co.uk
e-mail: curator@greatstorm.fsnet.co.uk
Website: www.ekmt.fsnet.co.uk

Museum and charitable trust

Facilities
Enquiries to the Director, EKMT Museums and
Curator
Information provided by phone, post, fax and e-mail
Library and archives open to the public by
appointment only
Museum open: Tuesday-Sunday 1000-1700 (April-
September) and Thursday-Sunday 1100-1630 (October-
March)
Photocopying facilities
Research service available - information retrieval only
from Museum's own internal sources. Advice and
suggestions given for sourcing material from
elsewhere. Copying and postage only charged

Subject coverage
Ramsgate fishing industry; history of Ramsgate
Harbour; geology of the East Kent coast; East Kent
ferry and pleasure steamer operations; marine
archaeology; navigation; shipbuilding; East Kent's naval
role in two world wars; books; artefacts and
interpretive displays

Special collections
Artefacts raised from late Stuart warships wrecked on
the Goodwin Sands in 1703
Board of Trade Ramsgate Harbour Letter Books, 1862-
1918
Board of Trade/Ministry of Transport Ramsgate
Harbour Minute Books, 1918-1921
Register of Ramsgate boatmen's licences, 1948-1975
Register of Margate boatmen's licences, 1898-1975
Ramsgate slipway registers and reports, 1937-1941 and
1946-69
Ramsgate harbour cargo books, 1939, 1947-1967

Specific companies and groups
Public relations and marketing archive of defunct cross-
channel ferry operation Sally Line (Ramsgate-Dunkirk)

Specific databases
Ramsgate fishing smack information, 1880s-1920s

Publications
Introductory website at www.ekmt.fsnet.co.uk
Free leaflet available from reception and tourist centres

R3
REDCAR AND CLEVELAND
MUSEUMS SERVICE

Kirkleatham Museum   Tel: 01642 479500
Kirkleatham   Fax: 01642 474199
Redcar, TS10 5NW
e-mail: museum_services@redcar-cleveland.gov.uk

Museum; local government organisation

Facilities
Enquiries to the Curator

Information provided by phone, post, fax and e-mail
Open to the public: Tuesday-Sunday (not Mondays
except bank holidays), April to September 1000-1700,
October-March 1000-1600. Reserve collections by
appointment.
Photocopying facilities.
Research service available.

Subject coverage
Objects, photographs, paintings, publications

Special collections
Sir James Knott, 1963 Oakley-class lifeboat.
Seamew sailing coble c. 1900.
Volente and *Redcar Lass* double-ended fishing boats.
Zetland lifeboat (on loan to RNLI Zetland Museum,
Redcar).
Inshore fishing and sea rescue collections.
Shipbuilding collections, including c. 4,000 photos of
Smith's Dock, South Bank, Middlesbrough.
Paintings by Staithes Group of artists

R4
REGISTRY OF SHIPPING AND
SEAMEN

MCA Cardiff   Tel: 029 2044 8800
Anchor Court   Fax: 029 2044 8820
Ocean Way
Cardiff CF24 5JW
e-mail: rss@mcga.gov.uk
Website: www.mcga.gov.uk

Postal applications and correspondence can also be
sent to:
Registry of Shipping and Seamen
PO Box 420
Cardiff CF24 5XR

Part of the Maritime and Coastguard Agency

Facilities
Enquiries to the Records Officer
Information provided by phone, post, fax and e-mail -
please write with any historical enquiries
Open to the public: Monday-Thursday 0900-1630 and
Friday 0930-1630
Photocopying facilities
Research service available for merchant seamen's
records which are held in manual record format.
Cost of research will be advised if required

Subject coverage
UK Register of ships, c.1910 to present; merchant
seaman's records, 1973 to present

Specific companies and groups
Merchant seamen's records and data for all UK
registered ships

Specific databases
The office responsible for the registration of all UK
ships - information is maintained on a live database
holding registration details of UK merchant, fishing and
small ships
See also Appendix 1

R5
RENFREW DISTRICT COUNCIL - DEPARTMENT OF LEISURE SERVICES

Local Studies Library   Tel: 0141 887 3672
Central Library   Fax: 0141 887 6468
High Street
Paisley PA1 2BB
e-mail: locstuds.els@renfrewshire.gov.uk
Website: www.renfrewshire.gov.uk

Public library

Facilities
Enquiries to the Local Studies Librarian
Library open to the public
Information provided by phone, post, fax and e-mail
Microfilm and microfiche readers
Photocopying facilities

Subject coverage
Local history, e.g. launches from local shipyards from
newspapers dating from 1824.

R6
RIVER AND ROWING MUSEUM

Mill Meadows   Tel: 01491 415600
Henley-on-Thames
Oxfordshire RG9 1BF
e-mail: michael.rowe@rrm.co.uk
Website: www.rrm.co.uk

Museum

Facilities
Enquiries to the Collections Manager
Open to the public: 1st May - 31st August 1000-1730
and 1st September - 30th April 1000-1700 (closed
Christmas Day, Christmas Eve, New Year's Eve and
New Year's Day)

Subject coverage
General history of the River Thames and the sport of
rowing

R7
THE ROBERT GORDON UNIVERSITY LIBRARY

St. Andrew Street Library   Tel: 01224 262888
Robert Gordon University   Fax: 01224 262889
St. Andrew Street
Aberdeen AB25 1HG
e-mail: saslibrary@rgu.ac.uk
website: www.rgu.ac.uk/library/index.htm

University library

Facilities
Enquiries to the Site Librarian, St. Andrew Street
Library
Limited information provided by phone or e-mail
Library open to the public
Loans to staff, students and members only
Microfilm and microfiche readers
Photocopying facilities

Subject coverage
Offshore engineering

R8
THE ROYAL ALFRED SEAFARER'S SOCIETY

SBC House   Tel: 020 8401 2889
Restmor Way   Fax: 020 8401 2592
Wallington
Surrey SM6 7AH
e-mail: royalalfred@btopenworld.com

Voluntary organisation

Facilities
Enquiries to the General Secretary
Information provided by phone, post, fax and e-mail
Open to the public: Monday-Friday (office hours)
Photocopying facilities
Research service available - space very limited but
access never denied to bona fide students of marine
charity history

Subject coverage
Fairly comprehensive collection of the Society's annual
reports since its foundation in 1867, together with some
committee minutes from that date; record (incomplete)
of the Society's beneficiaries through the years

R9
ROYAL ASTRONOMICAL SOCIETY

Burlington House   Tel: 020 7734 3307
Piccadilly   Fax: 020 7494 0166
London W1J 0BQ
e-mail: info@ras.org.uk
Website: www. ras.org.uk

Learned society

Facilities
Enquiries to the Librarian.

Subject coverage
Astronomy, geophysics and their histories.

___

Royal Commission on Historical Manuscripts
See National Archives

___

R10
ROYAL COMMONWEALTH SOCIETY LIBRARY

Cambridge University Library	Tel: 01223 333146
West Road	Fax: 01223 333160
Cambridge CB3 9DR	
e-mail: rcs@lib.cam.ac.uk	
Website: www.lib.cam.ac.uk	

University department

Facilities
Enquiries to the Smuts Librarian (part-time)
Information provided by post and e-mail
Open to holders of Cambridge University Library
reader tickets and the public by appointment only - the
public should apply in writing to the Smuts Librarian
Details of opening hours available on website
Photocopying facilities - copying is at the discretion of
the Librarian

Subject coverage
Voyages and travel; discovery and exploration; naval
history and mercantile marine aspects of the British
Empire and Commonwealth and their member
countries

Publications
Only a small proportion of the collection has been
retrospectively catalogued, namely periodicals,
monographs on Canada and Africa, poetry and
literature, bibliographies, and the Cobham Collection
on Cyprus. The remainder of printed material in the
Library is accessible via a traditional subject card
catalogue, arranged geographically

___

R11
ROYAL GEOGRAPHICAL SOCIETY

1 Kensington Gore	Tel 020 7591 3000
London SW7 2AR	Fax: 071584 4447
e-mail: rgs@uk.ac.bbk	

Learned society

Facilities
Enquiries to the Librarian for books, to the Map
Curator for maps and to the Archivist for archives and
manuscripts
Information provided by phone, post and fax
Library and archives open to members only
Map room open to the public where photocopying is
available
Loans to members only
Microfilm and microfiche readers
On-line information retrieval for library and archives
only using BLAISE, GEOBASE, JANET

Subject coverage
History of exploration and travel including voyages

Publications
'The Geographical Journal'
'Geographical Magazine'

___

R12
ROYAL INSTITUTE OF NAVIGATION CUNDALL LIBRARY

1 Kensington Gore	Tel: 020 7591 3130
London SW7 2AT	Fax: 020 7591 3131
e-mail: info@rin.org.uk	
Website: www.rin.org.uk	

Charity aiming to further and promote the science of
navigation

Facilities
Enquiries to the Librarian
Information provided by phone, post, fax and e-mail
Library open to the public by appointment: 0930-1630
Photocopying facilities
Research service not provided

Subject coverage
Navigation, sea and maritime, air, land, space;
seamanship; naval history

Publications
'Journal of Navigation' - 3 times a year
'Navigation News' - bi-monthly
Website

___

Royal Institution of Cornwall
See Courtney Library

___

R13
ROYAL INSTITUTION OF GREAT BRITAIN

21 Albemarle Street	Tel: 0207 409 2992
London W1X 4BS	Fax: 0207 629 3569
e-mail: ri@ri.ac.uk	
Website: www.rigb.org.uk	

Learned society

Facilities
Enquiries to the Librarian
Library open to non-members by appointment only
Information provided by phone, post, e-mail and visit
Loans to members only
Microfilm and microfiche readers
Photocopying facilities

Special collections
Lord Stanhope's papers
H. Davey's papers
J Tyndall's papers
WH and WL Braggs' papers

R14
ROYAL INSTITUTION OF NAVAL ARCHITECTS

10 Upper Belgrave Street   Tel: 0207 235 4622
London SWIX 8BQ   Fax: 0207 259 5912
Website: www.rina.org.uk

Professional society

Facilities
Enquiries to the Secretary
Library open to members only
Information given by phone, post and fax to members only
Fullsize copies can be provided

Subject coverage
All fields of maritime technology

R15
ROYAL MARINES MUSEUM

Southsea   Tel: 023 9281 9385
Portsmouth   Fax: 023 9283 8420
Hampshire PO4 9PX
e-mail: info@royalmarinesmuseum.co.uk
       archives@royalmarinesmuseum.co.uk:
       pictures@royalmarinesmuseum.co.uk
Website: www. royalmarinesmuseum.co.uk

Museum

Facilities
Enquiries to the Librarian or the Photographic Librarian
Information provided by phone, post, fax, e-mail and visit
Library open to the public
Microfilm and microfiche readers
Photocopying facilities

Subject coverage
Naval history; Royal Marines history 1664-date; military history, naval/military social history; barracks/buildings; weapons/small arms; medals; biographies

Special collections
George Aston papers
380 personal diaries of Royal Marines
Lewis Rotely letters of Trafalgar

Publications
'The Royal Marines Museum - the story of Britain's sea soldiers'
'Royal Marines and the Victoria Cross'
'The Royal Marine Band Service'

R16
ROYAL NATIONAL LIFEBOAT INSTITUTION (RNLI)

West Quay Road   Tel: 01202 663000
Poole   Fax: 01202 663167
Dorset BH15 1HZ
e-mail: canard@rnli.org.uk
Website: www.rnli.org.uk

Voluntary organisation

Facilities
Enquiries to the RNLI Heritage Trust Collections Administrator
Information provided by phone, post, fax and e-mail
Open to the public by appointment: Monday-Friday 0930-1630
Photocopying facilities

Special collections
Minute books and records since founding in 1824
Lifeboat Journals since 1852

R17
ROYAL NATIONAL LIFEBOAT INSTITUTION, EASTBOURNE

RNLI Museum   Tel: 01323 730717
Royal Parade   Fax:01323 730717
Eastbourne
Sussex BN21 4BY

Museum

Facilities
Enquiries to the Curator
Information provided by post
Open to the public
Appointment necessary for library

Subject coverage
Brief history of Eastbourne lifeboats

Special collections
Historical models, pictures and artefacts

Publications
'The History of Eastbourne Lifeboats' (normally

updated every 10 years)

R18
ROYAL NATIONAL MISSION TO DEEP SEA FISHERMEN (RNMDSF)

43 Nottingham Place   Tel: 020 7487 5101
London W1U 5BX   Fax: 020 7224 5240
e-mail: RNMDSF@charity.vfree.com

National charity

Facilities

Enquiries to the Mission Secretary
Information provided by post and e-mail
Open to the general public
Photocopying facilities
Research service not provided

Subject coverage

History of UK deep sea fishing

Publications

'Toilers of the Deep' (half yearly)

Royal Naval Hospital Haslar

Records transferred to Institute of Naval Medicine

R19
ROYAL NAVAL MUSEUM

HM Naval Base (PP66)   Tel: (Museum) 023 9272 7562
Portsmouth PO1 3NH   Tel: (Library) 023 9272 3795
   Fax: (Museum) 023 9272 7575
   Fax: (Library) 023 9272 3942
e-mail: library@royalnavalmuseum.org
Website: www.royalnavalmuseum.org

Museum

Facilities

Enquiries to the Librarian and Head of Information Services
Information provided by phone, post, fax and e-mail
Open to the public. Collections research by prior appointment with the relevant curator. General public must make a prior appointment for the Library Reading Room but it may be made on the same day as visit: Monday-Friday 1000-1600
Photocopying facilities
Research service available - £10 plus VAT for research over 30 minutes - (Navy List search/over six ship/shore establishments) - commercial organisations £45+VAT

Subject coverage

Naval biographies; naval social history; naval operational history; navigation; ship information; naval architecture; museology

Special collections

Library:
part of the Admiralty Library, including Admiralty Library manuscript collection (leaflet available)
Museum:
WRNS Historic Collection
20th Century oral history
Wright & Logan Photographic Collection

Specific databases

Ship information database (in house)

Publications

'Naval and Maritime Libraries and Archives Group - Guide to Collections'
'Guide to RNM Manuscript Collection', Matthew Sheldon (1997)
'Guide to the Oral History Collection', Val Billing (1998)

R20
ROYAL NAVY SUBMARINE MUSEUM

Haslar Jetty Road   Tel: 02392 510354 ext.
Gosport   226 or ext. 239 for
Hampshire PO12 2AS   Research Asst.
   Fax: 02392 589985
e-mail: archives@rnsubmus.co.uk
or research@rnsubmus.co.uk
Website: www.rnsubmus.co.uk

Museum

Facilities

Enquiries to the Archivist
Information provided by post, fax and e-mail
Open to the public - strictly by appointment
Photocopying facilities
Research service available - commercial charges arranged via Archivist. Family/private research carried out by Research Assistant - donations requested rather than formal charge

Subject coverage

RN submarines from 1900 to present (books in library) including nuclear; underwater weapon technology and tactics; submarine communications and tactics; underwater warfare; marine mechanical and electrical engineering; general naval history; Navy Lists; pink lists; naval staff monographs; information on other navies; complete set of 'Jane's Fighting Ships'

Special collections

All RN submarines service and technical details on database
Submarine patrol reports

Publications

RN Submarine Museum website (see above) Archive page

R21
ROYAL OCEAN RACING CLUB (RORC)

20 St. James's Place　　　Tel: 0207 493 2248
London SW1A 1NN　　　Fax: 0207 493 5252
e-mail: info@rorc.org
Website: www.rorc.org

Yacht club

Facilities
Enquiries to the General Manager
Library open to members only

Subject coverage
Offshore yacht racing

Publications
RORC Annual Race Programmes, published each
January
'Seahorse', monthly magazine

R22
THE ROYAL SOCIETY

6-9 Carlton House Terrace　　Tel: 020 7451 2606
London SW1Y 5AG　　　Fax: 020 7930 2170
e-mail: library@royalsoc.ac.uk
Website: www.royalsoc.ac.uk

Learned society

Facilities
Enquiries to the Library Manager
Information provided by phone, post, fax and e-mail
Open to the public, Fellows and staff of the Society
New readers are encouraged to discuss their area of
research with library staff prior to their first visit:
Monday-Friday 1000-1700
Photocopying facilities
Short enquires can be answered but readers are
encouraged to do their own research

Subject coverage
Archives of the Society from 1660; book collection:
primary scientific works relating to the Fellowship of
the Society (particularly strong in 17th and 18th
century material); history of science collection;
biographies of Fellows; journals from worldwide
scientific academies; modern science policy collection

Publications
Library catalogue, archive catalogue and Sackler
Database of Fellows of the Society are available on
website

R23
ROYAL SOCIETY OF MARINE ARTISTS (RSMA)

17 Carlton House Terrace　　Tel: 020 7930 6844
London SW1Y 5BD　　　Fax: 020 7839 7830
e-mail: info@mallgalleries.com
Website: www.mallgalleries.org.uk

Arts charity. Affiliated with the Federation of British
Artists, who administer eight other national art
societies

Facilities
Enquiries to the Gallery and Events Manager
Information provided by phone, post, fax and e-mail
Open to the public: 0930-1730
Photocopying facilities
Research service available (free) upon request to the
Archivist

Subject coverage
Archive information on past RSMA members;
information on current artist members; details of
RSMA membership, lay membership and exhibitions;
information/submission forms for exhibiting in Society
annual exhibitions (held every October at the Mall
Galleries, London SW1)

Special collections
Past RSMA exhibition catalogues and some past RSMA
publications (some for sale)

Specific databases
Current members
Past exhibitors

R24
ROYAL THAMES YACHT CLUB (RTYC)

60 Knightsbridge　　　Tel: 020 7235 2121
London SW1X 7LF　　　Fax: 020 7245 9470
e-mail: secretary@royalthames.com
Website: www.royalthames.com

Yacht club

Facilities
Enquiries to the Secretary
Information provided by phone, post, fax and e-mail
Library open to members only

Subject coverage
Yachting history and yacht ownership over 150 years

Special collections
'Hunt's Yacht Register'
'Lloyd's Yacht Register'
Yachting magazines and individual rare books

R25
ROYAL YACHTING ASSOCIATION (RYA)

RYA House　　　　　　Tel: 023 8060 4100
Ensign Way　　　　　　Fax: 023 8060 4299
Hamble
Southampton SO31 4YA
e-mail: admin@rya.org.uk
Website: www.rya.org.uk

Voluntary national sport governing body

Facilities
Enquiries to the Administration Manager
Information provided by phone, post, fax, e-mail and website
No library facility but open to anyone interested in boating (by prior appointment)

Subject coverage
Minutes of YRA/RYA Council meetings since foundation in 1875; yachting; motor cruising; powerboat racing; windsurfing

---

S1
SAILORS' FAMILIES' SOCIETY

Newland　　　　　　Tel: 01482 342331
Cottingham Road　　Fax: 01482 447868
Hull
East Yorkshire HU6 7RJ
e-mail: info@sailors-families.org.uk
Website: www.sailors-families.org.uk

Voluntary organisation

Facilities
Enquiries to the Chief Executive
Information provided by phone, post, fax and e-mail
Open to the public (some records restricted)
Access by appointment only
Photocopying facilities

Subject coverage
Records of seafarers' orphans who have been cared for at Newland and a complete history of the Society since 1821

Special collections
Historic memorabilia

S2
ST ANDREWS' UNIVERSITY LIBRARY

North Street　　　　　Tel: 01334 462281
St. Andrews　　　　　Fax: 01334 462282
Fife KY16 9TR
e-mail: lis.library@uk.ac.st-and.ac.uk
Website: www.library.st-and.ac.uk

University department

Facilities
Enquiries to the Librarian
Information provided by phone, post, fax and e-mail
Library open to the public
Opening hours: term: Mondays-Thursdays 0845-2200; Fridays: 0845-1800; Saturdays: 0900-1700; Sundays: 1300-1900; vacation: Mondays-Fridays 0900-1700
Microfilm, microfiche and microcard/microprint readers, fullsize copies provided; CD-ROM and on-line information retrieval service
Research service not provided

Subject coverage
Naval history; history of exploration; maritime archaeology; navigation; shipbuilding and shipping services especially Scottish

Special collections
Manuscript records of several East Fife Burghs, including records of St. Andrews harbour from the 18th century onwards
Early works on seamanship and navigation in the period 1600-1850

S3
SALFORD UNIVERSITY – INFORMATION SERVICES

Adelphi Campus　　　Tel: 0161 295 2444
Peru Street　　　　　Fax: 0161 295 5888
Salford M3 6EQ
e-mail: advisor@salford.ac.uk
Website: www.uis.salford.ac.uk

University library

Facilities
Enquiries to the Research Coordinator (Tel. 0161 295 3188; e-mail m.p.carrier@salford.ac.uk)
Information provided by: phone, post and e-mail
Open to the public: term time 0855-2100, vacation 0900-1700 (details on web pages)
Appointment necessary for non-members
Photocopying facilities

Special collections
Archives of Francis Egerton, 3rd Duke of Bridgewater, the 'Canal Duke'

Publications
See website:
www.uis.Salford.ac.uk/publica/speccoll/bwa.htm

S4
SALT MUSEUM

162 London Road   Tel: 01606 41331
Northwich
Cheshire CW9 8AB
e-mail: cheshiremuseums@cheshire.gov.uk
Website: www.saltmuseum.org.uk

Museum, local government organisation

Facilities
Enquiries to the Curator
Information provided by phone, post, e-mail and visit
Open to the public: Tuesday-Friday 1000-1700, Saturday
and Sunday 1400-1700
Appointment necessary for library
Photocopying facilities (10p/copy)
Research service

Subject coverage
Story of salt industry and local history
Boat building on the River Weaver.

Special collections
Artefacts, books, documents, oral history.

S5
THE SALVAGE ASSOCIATION

5th Floor   Tel: 020 7648 9653
37-39 Lime Street   Fax: 020 7623 0439
London EC3M 7AY
e-mail: salvage@wreckage.org
Website: www.wreckage.org

Marine surveyors

Facilities
Enquiries to the Deputy Chairman or GSS Assistant
Manager

Specific databases
Casualty database

S6
SCIENCE MUSEUM LIBRARY

Imperial College Road   Tel: 020 7942 4242
South Kensington   Fax: 020 7942 4243
London SW7 5NH
e-mail: smlinfo@nmsi.ac.uk
Website: www.sciencemuseum.org.uk/library/

Museum

Facilities
Enquiries to the Readers' Services' Librarian
Information provided by phone, post, fax and e-mail
Library open to the public: full service Mondays-
Saturdays 0930-1700. Extended opening hours in
Imperial College terms and Easter vacation to 2200
Microfilm, microfiche and microcard/microprint
readers; CD-ROM and on-line information retrieval
services
Research service provided, no charge

Subject coverage
Marine engines; water transport; warships; docks/diving;
Froude; navigation

Special collections
Original ships' plans second half of 19th century
MS collections from Maudslay, Sons & Field
Notebooks of Charles Sells (1842-1883)
Notebooks of John Scott Russell
Papers of Simon Goodrich, engineer to the Navy
Board, 1796-1831
Collections of hovercraft drawings
Records of submarine cable-laying projects of Clark,
Forde and Taylor, 1869-1929
Papers of Sir Charles Algernon Parsons, c1896-1915
Bentall yacht design drawings

S7
SCHOOL OF ORIENTAL & AFRICAN STUDIES, UNIVERSITY OF LONDON

Thornhaugh Street   Tel: 020 7637 2388
Russell Square   Fax: 020 7436 3844
London WC1H 0XG
e-mail: docenquiry@soas.ac.uk
Website: www.soas.ac.uk/index.cfm

University library and archives

Facilities
Enquiries to the Archivist
Open to members of the University; access to non-
members by prior application to the Archivist

Special collections
Letters of John Inglis of A & J Inglis, Glasgow
shipbuilder, to Sir William Mackinnon, Chairman of the
British India Steam Navigation Company, 1870-1893;
these letters relate to shipbuilding contracts

S8
SCOTTISH CANOE ASSOCIATION

Caledonia House   Tel: 0131 3177314
South Gyle   Fax: 0131 3177319
Edinburgh EH12 9DQ
e-mail: enquiry@scot-canoe.org
Website: www.scot-canoe.org

Voluntary organisation

Facilities
Enquiries to the Access Officer
Information provided by phone, post and e-mail

S9
SCOTTISH FISHERIES MUSEUM TRUST LTD

Harbourhead   Tel: 01333 310628
Anstruther   Fax: 01333 310628
Fife KY10 3AB
e-mail: info@scottish-fisheries-museum.org
Website: www.scottish-fisheries-museum.org

Museum

Facilities
Enquiries to the Curator
Information provided by phone, post, fax and e-mail
Museum open to the public: Monday-Saturday 1000-1730 (April-September) and 1000-1630 (October-March)
Library and archive open by appointment: Monday-Friday 1000-1600
Photocopying facilities
Research service available - undertaken by volunteers, generally free of charge unless copying required

Subject coverage
Scottish fishing - history, methods, boats, equipment and industries associated with fishing - coopering, fish processing, boat building and marine engineering

Specific companies or groups
Miller Archive - business and technical records of JN Miller & Sons, boatbuilder, St Monans, Fife
Photographic and slide collections

Publications
'Scotland's Sailing Fishermen' R Halliwell, 1991
'The Fleet - a guide to the historic vessels at the Scottish Fisheries Museum' A Walker, 2002
See website

S10
SCOTTISH HISTORY SOCIETY (SHS)

Department of Scottish History
University of Edinburgh
17 Buccleuch Place
Edinburgh
EH8 9LN   Tel: 0131 650 4030

Email: steve.boardman@ed.ac.uk
Web: http://www.gla.ac.uk/centres/hca/shs

Learned Society

Facilities
Enquiries to the Honorary Secretary

Subject coverage
Scottish history

S11
SCOTTISH INLAND WATERWAYS ASSOCIATION (SIWA)

Clifton Staithe   Tel: 0131 333 1231
Newbridge
Edinburgh EH28 8LQ

Voluntary association

Facilities
Enquiries to the Secretary

Subject coverage
Scottish canals

S12
SCOTTISH MARINE INDUSTRIES ASSOCIATION

36 Renfield Street   Tel: 0141 248 6161
Glasgow G2 1BD

S13
SCOTTISH MARITIME MUSEUM

Laird Forge   Tel: 01294 278283
Gottries Road   Fax: 01294 313211
Irvine
Ayrshire KA12 8QE
Website: www.scottishmaritimemuseum.org

Museum

Facilities
Enquiries to the Curator
Information provided by phone, post or fax to all
Open to the public
Opening hours: summer, daily 1000-1700; winter, daily 1000-1600; closed Christmas and New Year
Photocopying facilities, black + white and 4-colour laser
Research service provided at £12 per hour + VAT

Subject coverage
All aspects of Scottish maritime history; tank testing

Special collections
Plan collection of yachts built by William Fife & Sons of Fairlie

Scottish Maritime Museum, other sites
Clydebuilt, Braehead Shopping Centre, King's Inch Road, Glasgow G51 4BN; Tel: 0141 886 1013
Denny Ship Model Experiment Tank, Castle Street, Dumbarton G82 1QS; Tel: 01389 763444

Scottish Record Office
See National Archives of Scotland

S14
SCOTTISH RECORD SOCIETY

Department of Scottish History   Tel: 0141 330 4576
University of Glasgow
Glasgow G12 8QH
e-mail: j.kirk@history.arts.gla.ac.uk

Facilities
Enquiries to the Secretary
No research service

Subject coverage
Historical records relating to Scotland

Publications
List available on request

S15
SCOTTISH SCREEN ARCHIVE

1 Bowmont Gardens   Tel: 0141 337 7400
Glasgow G12 9LR   Fax: 0141 337 7413
e-mail: archive@scottishscreen.com
Website: www.scottishscreen.com

Non-departmental public body

Facilities
Enquiries to the Production Library Administrator
Information provided by phone, post, fax and e-mail
Open to the public, educational bodies, film and media
organisations and the museum and heritage sector
Appointment necessary for viewings and research
Photocopying facilities
Research service available - free of charge for holdings;
a charge may be levied for extensive research enquiries

Subject coverage
Moving image material on Scottish shipbuilding
industry, principally Clydeside; fishing (deep sea, inshore
and rural crofting methods) and industries associated
with fishing; marine engineering; coastal steamer
transport and inter-island ferries

Special collections
'Seawards the Great Ships', 1960; Oscar-winning
documentary on Clyde shipbuilding (35mm colour)
'The Bowler and the Bunnet', 1967; Sean Connery
presents account of industrial relations in Clyde yards
(16mm B&W)

Specific companies or groups
Constituent members of Upper Clyde Shipbuilders
(UCS); films produced 1927-1971
Scott-Lithgow film of construction/launches 1955-1977
MacBraynes, later Caledonian MacBrayne

Publications
'Guide to Scottish Screen Archive Collection'
Catalogue published online in 2003

S16
SCOTTISH SHIP CHANDLERS ASSOCIATION

11 Burns Road   Tel: 01224 313473
Aberdeen   Fax: 01224 310385
AB15 4NT
e-mail: roddy@mccoll/associates.com

Voluntary organisation

Facilities
Enquiries to Roddy McColl
Information provided by phone, post, fax and e-mail
Open to members only
Photocopying facilities
Research service not provided

Special collections
Minute books from inception in 1955

S17
SCOTT POLAR RESEARCH INSTITUTE

University of Cambridge   Tel: 01223 336540
Lensfield Road   Fax: 01223 336549
Cambridge CB2 1ER   Telex: 81240 CAMSPL G
e-mail: wjm13@cam.ac.uk
Website: www.spri.cam.ac.uk

University department, research organisation and
museum

Facilities
Enquiries to the Librarian and Keeper or Archivist and
Curator, depending on nature of inquiries
Information provided by phone, post, fax and e-mail
Library open to the public: Mondays-Fridays 0900-1300
and 1400-1730; Access to Archives by appointment
only
Microfilm and microfiche readers; fullsize copies can be
provided; CD-ROM and on-line information retrieval
service
Research service not provided

Subject coverage
Arctic, southern oceans and adjacent waters; sea ice;
naval history in relation to exploration, particularly the
Northwest and Northeast Passages and the southern
ocean

Special collections
Collection of manuscripts relating to polar exploration,
for comprehensive list - 'Manuscripts in the Scott Polar
Research Institute, Cambridge', C Holland (ed).
published by Garland 1982

S18
SEA FISH INDUSTRY AUTHORITY

18 Logie Mill   Tel: 0131 558 3331
Logie Green Road   Fax: 0131 558 1442
Edinburgh EH7 4HG
e-mail: seafish@seafish.co.uk
Website: www.seafish.co.uk

UK non-departmental public body

Facilities
Enquiries to the Librarian
Information provided by phone, post, fax and e-mail
Library open to the public, by appointment; books and
other material loaned
Photocopying facilities: fullsize copies can be provided

Subject coverage
Marine engineering, fishing boats; fishing gear and net
technology; seabed hazards

S19
SEAFACS INFORMATION AND RESEARCH

PO Box 317   Tel: 01707 334192
Welwyn Garden City   Fax: 01707 324615
Hertfordshire AL8 6DP
e-mail: seafacs@sir.co.uk
Website: www.sir.co.uk

Consultancy

Subject coverage
A marine information broker: locating expertise,
commodity and other commercial information

S20
SEAMEN'S HOSPITAL SOCIETY

29 King William Walk   Tel: 020 8858 3696
Greenwich   Fax: 020 8293 9630
London SE10 9HX
e-mail: shs@btconnect.co

Facilities
Enquiries to the General Secretary
Open to merchant navy seafarers
Photocopying facilities available

Publications
'Welcome Aboard' - history of the Seamen's Hospital
Society and the Dreadnought

S21
THE SHANTY CREW

6 Brafferton Road   Tel: 020 8688 3580
Croydon
Surrey CR0 1AD
e-mail: chrisroche@onet.co.uk
Website: www.shantycrew.co.uk

Performance group

Facilities
Enquiries to Group Leader (Chris Roche)
Information provided by phone, post and e-mail
Limited research services available

Subject coverage
Shanties - the work songs of the sailing ship sailor -
and other sailors' songs
Chris Roche is associated with International
Association of Cape Horners (IACH), membership
open to all those who have voyaged to Cape Horn in
sailing ships

Special collections
Slides of shipwrecks and sailing ships

Publications
Books, manuscripts, LPs, tapes and CDs
'The Cape Horner' journal of the International
Association of Cape Horners

S22
SHETLAND LIBRARY

Lower Hillhead   Tel: 01595 693868
Lerwick   Fax: 01595 694430
Shetland ZE1 0EL
e-mail: info@shetland-library.gov.uk
Website: www.

Library

Facilities
Enquiries to the Assistant Chief Librarian
Information provided by phone, post, fax and e-mail
Open to the public: Monday, Wednesday-Thursday
1000-1900, Tuesday, Friday and Saturday 1000-1700 but
closed temporarily between 1200 and 1300 on Tuesday
and Saturday
Photocopying facilities
Extensive public internet/e-mail access available
(currently free of charge)

Subject coverage
Shetland maritime information

S23
SHETLAND MUSEUM

| Lower Hillhead | Tel: 01595 695057 |
| Lerwick | Fax: 01595 696729 |

Shetland ZE1 0EL
e-mail: museum@sic.shetland.gov.uk
Website: www.shetland-museum.org.uk

Museum

Facilities
Enquiries to the Curator
Information provided by phone, post, fax, e-mail, displays and interpretive leaflets
Open to the public - free admission

Subject coverage
All aspects of Shetland's maritime history

Special collections
Collection of 60,000 photographs

Ships in Focus
See Clarkson

S24
SHIPWRECK AND MARINE LTD

| 'Tamale' | Tel: 01720 423679 |
| Buzza Hill Road | Fax: 01720 423679 |

St. Mary's
Isles of Scilly
Cornwall TR21 0NQ
e-mail: larn@shipwreck-marine.demon.co.uk

Private shipwreck research company; consultancy; publisher

Facilities
Enquiries to the Director
Information provided by phone, post, fax and e-mail
Open to the public
Research service available - SAE requested with initial enquiry, currently £15 per hour, photocopies, photographs, documents extra

Subject coverage
UK, Republic of Ireland, Channel and Channel Isles coast and offshore shipping losses; shipwreck research; shipwreck exploration/survey/recovery; ownership of wreck and seabed recoveries; shipwreck publications; shipwreck artefacts (display, conservation, valuation and disposal)

Special collections
Comprehensive collections of all UK shipwreck standard reference books, plus extensive archive of documents relating to shipwrecks around UK and Ireland
Extensive archive of documents relating to wrecked ships around UK and Ireland
'Lloyd's Lists' 1741 - 1826
'Admiralty Wreck Returns' 1816 - 1854
'Board of Trade Wreck Returns' 1855 - 1919
'Lloyd's Casualty Returns' 1894 - date
Complete set of Admiralty charts for UK and Ireland.
The late Bill Butland's shipwreck card index, research collection, correspondence and library of shipping companies' histories.

Specific databases
UK Shipwreck Computer Index holding details of 90,000 ships wrecked around Great Britain and Ireland by county

Publications
'United Kingdom Shipwreck Index', Volumes 1-6
'The Wreck of the *Cita*' (1997)
'Shipwrecks of the Isles of Scilly'
'Admiral Shovell's Treasure and Shipwreck, on the Isles of Scilly'

S25
SIR MAX AITKEN MUSEUM TRUST

| 83 High Street | Tel: 01983 292191 |
| Cowes | Fax: 01983 200253 |

Isle of Wight PO31 7AJ

Museum

Facilities
Enquiries to the Secretary
Information provided by post
Open to the public
Photocopying facilities
Research service not provided

Subject coverage
Marine paintings; nautical instruments; yachting memorabilia

S26
SOCIETY FOR NAUTICAL RESEARCH

National Maritime Museum   Tel: 020 8312 6712
Greenwich
London SE10 9NF
e-mail: lxveri@nmm.ac.uk
Website: www.snr.org

Voluntary association providing support and encouragement for research into maritime history and nautical archaeology
Research service not provided

Publications
'The Mariner's Mirror' quarterly journal
Quarterly newsletter

S27
SOCIETY FOR SAILING BARGE RESEARCH (SSBR)

5 Cox Road   Tel: 01206 825317
Alresford
Colchester
Essex CO7 8EJ
e-mail: john.white6@talk21.com
Website: www.sailingbargeresearch.org.uk

Voluntary organisation

Facilities
Enquiries to the Hon. Secretary
Information provided by phone, post and e-mail
Research service available: contact the Hon. Secretary
for queries regarding Thames Barges (no charge, but
SAE please for postal enquiries)

Subject coverage
History of the Thames spritsail sailing barge, including
information on individual barges, owners, builders,
ports, wharves and quays

Specific databases
Records of approximately 4,000 vessels dating back to
1751

Publications
'Topsail' annual journal

S28
SOCIETY FOR UNDERWATER TECHNOLOGY

80 Coleman Street   Tel: 020 7382 2601
London EC2R 5BJ   Fax: 020 7382 2684
e-mail: admin@sut.org
Website: www.sut.org

Society

Facilities
Enquiries to the Executive Secretary
Information provided by phone, post, fax and e-mail
Facilities open to members only

Subject coverage
Oceanology; geology; geophysics; geotechnics; subsea
engineering; underwater acoustics; marine technology;
pollution; fisheries; marine environment technology

Publications
'Underwater Technology' (quarterly journal)
Conference proceedings and collected papers

S29
SOCIETY OF GENEALOGISTS

14 Charterhouse Buildings   Tel: 020 7251 8799
Goswell Road   Fax: 020 7250 1800
London EC1M 7BA
e-mail: library@sog.org.uk
Website: www.sog.org.uk

Learned society/educational charity/publisher

Facilities
Enquiries to the Librarian
Information provided by phone, post, fax and e-mail
Open to non-members on payment of fees (1 hour, 4
hours or day): Tuesday-Wednesday, Friday-Saturday
1000-1800 and Thursday 1000-2000
Photocopying facilities
Research service available - half hour maximum,
searches in indexed sources in own library only (£8.80
for members and £11 for non-members)

Subject coverage
Records of births, marriages and deaths; tombstone
inscriptions; census copies and indexes; directories; poll
books; wills; family histories; local, national and social
history; topography (British and overseas); heraldry,
peerages, etc.; professions, occupations, apprenticeships
(including naval/maritime); biography; education (school
and university registers)

Special collections
GRO indexes to marine births and deaths, 1837-1965,
etc.
Navy List, 1756-1990s and East India Company naval
personnel, c.1760-1833
Trinity House Petitions, 1750-1890
Apprentices of Great Britain, 1710-1774
PCC will indexes to 1800 (containing wills of those
dying at sea)

Specific databases
Larger indexes are gradually being digitised on to the
English Origins website (pay per view service) at
www.englishorigins.com

Publications
Bookshop online at www.sog.org.uk
'Maritime sources in the library of the Society of
Genealogists'
'My ancestor was a Merchant Seaman: how can I find
out more about him'
'Trinity House Petitions: a calendar'
'Lloyd's Captains' Register', 1869

S30
SOCIETY OF INTERNATIONAL GAS TANKER AND TERMINAL OPERATORS

17 St. Helens Place　　　Tel: 0207 628 1124
London EC3A 6DG　　　Fax: 0207 628 3163
e-mail: secretariat@sigtto.org
website: www.sigtto.org

Trade association

Facilities
Enquiries to James MacHardy
Information provided by phone, post, fax and e-mail
Facilities available mainly to members
No research service

Subject coverage
LNG and LPG carriers and terminals

Publications
See website

S31
SOCIETY OF MARITIME INDUSTRIES

(Formerly British Marine Equipment Council)
4th Floor　　　　　　Tel: 0207 928 9199
Great Guildford House　Fax: 0207 928 6599
30 Great Guildford Street
London SE1 0HS
e-mail: ce@bmec.org.uk
website: www.maritimeindustries.org

Trade association

Facilities
Enquiries to Office Manager
Information given by e-mail, fax, post and phone (preferred order)
Facilities available to members and potential member companies
Photocopying facilities

S32
SOMERSET ARCHIVE AND RECORD SERVICE

Obridge Road　　　　Tel: 01823 278805
Taunton　　　　　　Fax: 01823 325402
Somerset TA2 7PU
e-mail: archives@somerset.gov.uk
Website: www.somerset.gov.uk/archives

Local government organisation

Facilities
Enquiries to the County Archivist

Information provided by phone, post, fax and e-mail
Open to the public - for opening hours, see website
Photocopying facilities
Research service available - £22 per hour, maximum between 1 and 2 hours

Subject coverage
Naval history; seaborne trade; Navy Office ledger 1631; autobiography of Phineas Pett, master builder of the Navy and naval commissioner 1670-1746; naval charts, ships' plans and sketches of Captain George Wyndham c.1777-c.1833

Special collections
Merchant shipping crew lists for vessels registered at Bridgwater, 1863-1913
Bridgwater shipping registers, 1786-1906
Bridgwater Water Bailiffs' accounts, 1495-1652; 1716-1720
Accounts returned to quarter sessions relating to Bridgwater Quay, 1697-1712, Minehead Harbour, 1823-1903 and Watchet Harbour, 1858-1904
Minehead Harbour accounts, 1753-1865
Minutes of Watchet Harbour Commissioners and successors, 1857-1970
Journals, ships' logs, correspondence of the following: Capt. J G C Everard, 1846-1856; Capt. Alexander Hood, 1775-1798; Rear Admiral Sir Samuel Hood, 1791-1812; Admiral Sir Richard Keats, 1789-1838; Commander George Kenyon, 1837-1849; Rear Admiral Sir Mervyn Medlycott, 1852-1881
Correspondence and accounts of the Dickinson, Alloway and Prankard families, relating to trade from Minehead, Bridgwater and Bristol, 1683-1746

Publications
All catalogues searchable on A2A and available on website

S33
SOUTH WEST MARITIME HISTORY SOCIETY

The Secretary　　　　Tel; 01752 550768
Ground Floor Flat
124 Molesworth Road
Stoke
Plymouth
Devon PL3 4AH
Website: www.swmaritime.org.uk

Voluntary organisation

Enquiries to the Secretary

Publications
'Maritime South West' journal
'South West Soundings' newsletter with details of Society activities
Maritime Monographs: occasional publications

S34
SOUTHAMPTON CENTRAL LIBRARY

Special Collections' Library
Civic Centre
Southampton SO14 7LW
Tel: 023 80 832205
Fax: 023 80 336305
e-mail: local.studies@southampton.gov.uk
Website:
www.southampton.gov.uk/education/libraries/specialc.htm

Public library

Facilities

Enquiries to the Special Collections' Librarian
Information provided by phone, post, fax and e-mail
Library open to the public
Microfilm and microfiche readers; microcopies and fullsize copies provided
Research service not provided

Subject coverage

Mercantile shipping; containerisation; some naval material

Special collections

Titanic Collection
'Lloyd's Registers of Ships', 1764 to date, incomplete

Publications

Catalogue of Maritime Collection, 1981
Southampton's Ships; an index to periodical references, 1978

S35
SOUTHAMPTON CITY ARCHIVES

Civic Centre
Southampton SO14 7LY
Tel: 023 8083 2251
Fax: 023 8083 2156
e-mail: city.archives@southampton.gov.uk
Website:
www.southampton.gov.uk/education/libraries/arch.htm

Local government organisation

Facilities

Enquiries to the Archives and Records Manager
Information provided by phone, post, fax and e-mail - a fee may be payable for other than short queries
Open to the public: Tuesday-Friday 0930-1630 (late evening to 2100 each month by appointment only)
Photocopying facilities
Research service available - maximum 2 hours, £20 per hour

Subject coverage

Merchant navy; seamanship; ship design; trade; port administration; ship movements; ship personnel; legal records; cargoes

Special collections

Southampton crew lists, 1863-1913
Isherwood Collection, 6,500 drawings of elevations of ships by Captain Isherwood
Photographs of ships indexed by ship name
Southampton Harbour Board Records including minutes, 1803-1968, port and harbour ledger, 1868-1896, wharfingers day books, 1881-1968
Thornycroft Shipbuilders Records, c.1850-1968
Central Index register of Merchant Seamen, 1918-41 for personnel serving on British registered ships (arranged alphabetically and by seamen discharge number)
Harrison Collection, papers of a ship's chef, c.1914-1956
Court of Admiralty Records, 1488-1756
Itchen Floating Bridge Co., 1833-1933
Port and petty customs books, 1426-1803
South East Engineering and Shipbuilding Employers Association, 1902-78

Specific companies and groups

John H. Thornycroft

Publications

See website

S36
SOUTHAMPTON CITY COUNCIL - ARTS AND HERITAGE SOUTHAMPTON CITY ART GALLERY

Civic Centre
Southampton SO14 7LP
Tel: 023 8083 2277
Fax: 023 8083 2153
e-mail: art.gallery@southampton.gov.uk
Website: www.southampton.gov.uk/leisure/arts

Local government organisation

Facilities

Enquiries to the Collections Manager
Information provided by phone, post, fax and e-mail
Gallery open to the public
No photocopying facilities

Subject coverage

Seascapes and maritime themes by various artists

Publications

General catalogue of the collection

S37
SOUTHAMPTON HERITAGE SERVICES

Collections Management Centre   Tel: 023 8023 7584
Unit 31
City Industrial Park
Southern Road
Southampton SO15 1HG
website: www.southampton.gov.uk

Local government organisation

Facilities
Enquiries to the Curator of Collections
Open to the public by appointment only
Information given by phone, post and fax, charges on request

Subject coverage
Merchant shipping and the Port of Southampton, with particular reference to passenger ships and cargo handling; local shipbuilding

Special collections
Archival material on Furness Withy; Vosper Thornycroft; British Power Boat Co.; Day, Summers
Photographic archives of British Ports Collection, Mitchell, Kennaway and Philips Collections
Liner ephemera, furnishings and fittings

S38
SOUTHAMPTON INSTITUTE

Mountbatten Library   Tel: 023 8031 9684
East Park Terrace   Fax: 023 8031 9697
Southampton
SO14 0RJ
Email: library.enquiries@solent.ac.uk
Website: www.solent.ac.uk/library

Institute of Higher Education

Facilities
Enquiries to Maritime Information Librarian
Information given by post, phone, fax and e-mail
Open to the public for reference but material loaned only to members or subscribers who have paid an annual fee.

Subject coverage
Shipping, maritime economics, safety at sea, seamanship, cargo handling, navigation, marine engineering, yacht and boat design, oceanography, marine environmental science and management, maritime law, ship history, maritime leisure management

Special collections
A branch library at Warsash Maritime Centre (Newtown Road, Warsash, Southampton, SO31 9ZL,

Tel: 01489 576817) specialises in the education and training of merchant seamen and houses an historical collection of maritime journals and 'Lloyd's Registers' and a current collection of 'Merchant Shipping Notices' and 'Merchant Shipping Statutory Instruments'.

Publications
Library catalogue on website

South Humberside Area Archive Office
See North East Lincolnshire Archives

S39
SOUTH TYNESIDE CENTRAL LIBRARY - LOCAL HISTORY DEPARTMENT

Prince Georg Square   Tel: 0191 4271717
South Shields   Ext. 7860
Tyne and Wear NE22 2PE   Fax: 0191 4558085
e-mail: localstudies.library@s-tyneside-mbc.gov.uk

Local government organisation

Facilities
Enquiries to the Local History Librarian
Information provided by phone, post, fax and e-mail (post or e-mail preferred for detailed enquiries)
Open to the public: Monday-Thursday 0930-1900, Friday 0930-1700 and Saturday 0930-1300
Photocopying facilities in main foyer of building (no copier in department)
Research service available - free limited research but photocopies charged at 30p per A4 copy

Subject coverage
History of South Tyneside shipbuilding/ship repair yards; South Tyneside Merchant Seamen and shipping; limited coverage of the above for Northumberland and Durham

Special collections
All archival material is now held by Tyne and Wear Archives

S40
SOUTHWARK LOCAL STUDIES' LIBRARY

211 Borough High Street   Tel: 020 7403 3507
London SE1 1JA   Fax: 020 7403 8633
e-mail: local.studies.library@southwark.gov.uk
Website: www.southwark.gov.uk

Local government organisation

Facilities
Enquiries to the Librarian

Information provided by phone, post, fax, e-mail and personal visits
Library open to the public: Mondays & Thursdays 0930-2000; Tuesdays & Fridays 0930-1700; Wednesdays closed; Saturdays 0930-1300
Photocopying facilities; microfilm and microfiche readers

Special collections
Beatson Shipbreakers, Rotherhithe, ledger 1831-1856, journal 1835-1858 (includes the 'Fighting Temeraire'); census returns, trade directories, electoral registers, parish registers

---

S41
STAFFORDSHIRE RECORD OFFICE
Eastgate Street　　　　Tel: 01785 278379
Stafford ST16 2LZ　　　Fax: 01785 278384
e-mail: staffordshire.record.office@staffordshire.gov.uk
Website: www.staffordshire.gov.uk/archives/

Local government organisation

Facilities
Enquiries to the County Archivist
Information provided by phone, post, fax and e-mail
Open to the public by appointment: Monday-Tuesday, Thursday 0900-1700, Wednesday 0900-2000, Friday 0930-1630 and Saturday 0900-1230
Photocopying facilities
Research service available - £18 per hour

Subject coverage
Maritime history through family papers, e.g. Anson, Dartmouth, Leveson-Gower

Specific databases
Gateway to the POST database of our holdings on website above

Publications
'Guide to Family Collections' £2.50

States of Guernsey Island Archive Service
See Guernsey

S42
THE STEAM BOAT ASSOCIATION OF GREAT BRITAIN (SBA)
The Hon. Secretary (SBA)　　Tel: 01983 730664
Avoca Cottage
School Lane
Niton
Isle of Wight PO38 2BP
Website: www.steamboat.org.uk

Voluntary society

Facilities
Enquiries to the Honorary Secretary
Information provided by phone, post and website
Open mainly to members; publications are available to non-members
Photocopying facilities
Limited research service provided (volunteer operation) with preference given to members, although non-members' requests for information will be answered within reason. No charge other than for published material

Subject coverage
Details of extant (and some past) steam boats of Great Britain (and to a limited extent, overseas); some historic archives, mainly of steam boat and boat plant builders

Specific companies or groups
Designers
LIFU
Simpson Strickland
Vosper-Thornycroft
Edwin Clarke

Publications
'The Steam Boat Register'
'The Funnel' - quarterly journal
Archive material on CDROMs

S43
STIRLING COUNCIL ARCHIVES
Unit 6　　　　　　　　　　Tel: 01786 450745
Burghmuir Industrial Estate　Fax: 01786 433005
Stirling FK7 7PY
e-mail: archive@stirling.gov.uk

Local government organisation

Facilities
Enquiries to the Council Archivist
Information provided by phone, post, fax and e-mail
Open to the public: Wednesday-Friday 1000-1230 and 1330-1630
Photocopying facilities
Research service available by agreement - £17 per hour

Subject coverage
Shipbuilding; customs and excise records

Special collections
Records of the Board of Customs and Excise, Alloa N.B. The records of the Board of Customs and Excise for Bo'ness and Grangemouth have been transferred to the History Research Centre, Callendar House, Callendar Park, Falkirk FK1 1YR

Strathclyde Regional Archives

See Glasgow City Archives

S44
STRATHCLYDE UNIVERSITY ARCHIVES

University of Strathclyde	Tel: 0141 552 4400
Glasgow G1 1XQ	Ext. 2318

University

Facilities

Enquiries to the Archivist
Information provided by phone, post and fax
Open to the public by appointment
Microcopies and fullsize copies on request;
photographic and microfilm by arrangement

Special collections

University Departments of - Shipbuilding and Naval
Architecture c1880 to present day
School of Navigation c1900-1965 (general department
and university records)
Gem Line (steamship company), c1945-1960

Strathkelvin District Libraries

See East Dunbartonshire Libraries

S45
SUFFOLK COUNTY COUNCIL LIBRARIES AND HERITAGE

Libraries and Heritage	Tel: 01473 584564
St Andrews House	Fax: 01473 584549
County Hall	
Ipswich IP4 1LJ	

Local government organisation

Facilities

Enquiries to the Head of Information and Learning
Information provided by phone, post and fax
Books and other material loaned to members only
CD-ROM and free Internet available in all Suffolk's 42
libraries
Research service available

S46
SUFFOLK RECORD OFFICE - IPSWICH BRANCH

Gatacre Road	Tel: 01473 584541
Ipswich	Fax: 01473 584533
Suffolk IP1 2LQ	

e-mail: ipswich.ro@libher.suffolkcc.gov.uk
Website: www.suffolkcc.gov.uk

Local government organisation

Facilities

Enquiries to the Public Services Manager
Information provided by phone, post, fax and e-mail
Open to the public: Monday-Saturday 0900-1700
Appointment necessary for microform readers
Photocopying facilities
Research service available - charges £20 per hour
(minimum 30 minutes)

Subject coverage

Ships registered at Suffolk ports; seamen registered at
Suffolk ports; port administration

Special collections

Ship registers for Ipswich and Woodbridge
Crew lists for Ipswich and Woodbridge

Specific companies and groups

Ipswich Port Authority Archives
Felixstowe Dock and Railway Co. archive

S47
SUFFOLK RECORD OFFICE - LOWESTOFT BRANCH

Central Library	Tel: 01502 405 357
Clapham Road	Fax: 01502 405 350
Lowestoft	
Suffolk NR32 1DR	

e-mail: Lowestoft.ro@libher.suffolkcc.gov.uk
Website: www.suffolkcc.gov.uk/sro/

Local government organisation

Facilities

Enquiries to the Public Services Manager
Information provided by phone, post, fax and e-mail
Open to the public: Monday, Wednesday-Thursday and
Friday 0900-1730, Tuesday 0900-2000 and Saturday
0900-1700
Appointment necessary for microform readers
Photocopying facilities
Research service available - £20 per hour (minimum 30
minutes)

Subject coverage

Ships; shipbuilding; fishing industry; lighthouses

Special collections

Lowestoft Shipping Registers, 1852-1946
History of the Port of Lowestoft
Port of Lowestoft Research Society Collection
Ships logs and crew lists for Lowestoft, 1863-1914
Fishing boat agreements for Lowestoft, 1880-1914

S48
SULLOM VOE HARBOUR AUTHORITY

Shetland Island Council,
Marine Operations Department.
Port Admin. Building   Tel: 01806 242551
Sella Ness   Fax: 01806 242237
Graven
Shetland ZE2 9QR
e-mail: marine.reception@sic.shetland.gov.uk

Local government organisation

Facilities
Enquiries to the Managing Director
Information provided by phone, post, fax and e-mail
Open to the public for any reasonable request within our area of knowledge
Photocopying facilities
Research service not provided

Subject coverage
Shipping movements; export/import of gas and crude oil

Specific databases
Ships
Ship movements
Pollution/safety incidents

Publications
Port Information Book

S49
HMS SULTAN LIBRARY

Military Road   Tel: 023 9254 2678
Gosport   Fax: 023 9254 2555
Hampshire PO12 3BY
e-mail: sultanlibrary@gtnet.gov.uk

Central government (MOD) establishment

Facilities
Enquiries to the Librarian
Information provided by phone, post, fax and e-mail
Open to members of staff and trainees of HMS *Sultan* (the Royal Naval School of Marine and Air Engineering)
Limited facilities available to the public: Monday-Thursday 0815-1645 and Friday 0815-1615
Public access by appointment only (apply to librarian)
Photocopying facilities not available to personal visitors
Research service available

Subject coverage
Aeronautical, marine, mechanical, electrical and electronic engineering; physical sciences, mathematics, computing, management and defence studies - principally in print format

Special collections
Small collection of general naval history
Collection of works on the history of naval engineering
Archival material relating to the former Royal Naval Engineering College, Plymouth

---

S50
SUPREME COURT LIBRARY

The Court Service   Tel: 020 7947 6587
Royal Courts of Justice   Fax: 020 7947 6661
Strand
London WC2A 2LL
Website: www.courtservice.gov.uk
          www.lcd.gov.uk

National government organisation

Facilities
Enquiries to the Supreme Court Librarian
Open to the public at the discretion of the librarian
Photocopying facilities

Subject coverage
Maritime and international law

Special collections
A large collection of material from the old Admiralty Court, unsorted and uncatalogued

---

S51
SURREY HISTORY CENTRE

130 Goldsworth Road   Tel: 01483 594 594
Woking   Fax: 01483 594 595
Surrey GU21 6ND
e-mail: shs@surreycc.gov.uk
Website: www.shs.surreycc.gov.uk

Local government organisation (absorbed the Guildford Muniment Room in 1998)

Facilities
Enquiries to the County Archivist
Information provided by phone, post, fax and e-mail
Open to the public (CARN or Surrey Library ticket required): Tuesday-Wednesday, Friday 0930-1700, Thursday 0930-1930 and Saturday 0930-1600
Photocopying facilities
Research service not provided

Subject coverage
Personal papers of naval officers and others connected with maritime affairs (very small quantity)

Special collections
Logbook and journal of Commander E C Tufnell, 1904-1907
Two letters of Admiral Sir John Balchin (1670-1744),

1739 and 1742
Papers of Sir William More, Vice-Admiral of Sussex,
c.1559-1591
Papers of Admiral Sir Robert Henry More-Molyneux
(1838-1904), c.1876-1903
Logbooks of Henry More-Molyneux, 1904-1907

Publications
Summary electronic index on website; some catalogues
currently available, very soon to be greatly expanded
electronically

S52
SWANSEA MUSEUM

Victoria Road   Tel: 01792 653763
Maritime Quarter   Fax: 01792 652585
Swansea SA1 1SN
e-mail: swansea.museum@swansea.gov.uk

Museum

Facilities
Enquiries to the Collections Access Officer
Information provided by post and e-mail
Open to the public: Tuesday-Friday 1000-1700
Research tables by appointment only
Photocopying facilities
Basic research service available - up to 1 hour by staff
free of charge, otherwise by researcher in person (by
appointment only)

Subject coverage
History of the Port of Swansea; development of local
shipping; Swansea's trade links with the rest of the
world

Special collections
William Gammon lifeboat
Olga Bristol channel pilot cutter
Helwick light ship

T1
TEESSIDE ARCHIVES

Exchange House   Tel: 01642 248321
6 Marton Road   Fax: 01642 248391
Middlesbrough TS1 1DB
e-mail: teesside_archives@middlesbrough.gov.uk

Archives

Facilities
Enquiries to the Archivist
Information provided by phone, post, fax and e-mail
Open to the public: Monday, Wednesday-Thursday
0900-1700, Tuesday 0900-2100 and Friday 0900-1630
Photocopying facilities
Research service available - searches in archives held
by the service cost £8.50 per half hour

Subject coverage
Archives for the boroughs of Hartlepool,
Middlesbrough, Redcar and Cleveland, and Stockton-
on-Tees

Specific companies or groups
Shipping registers for Hartlepool, Middlesbrough and
Stockton
Archives of Smith's Dock Co. Ltd., shipbuilders
Archives of Furness Shipbuilding Co., Ltd., Haverton
Hill

T2
THAMES POLICE MUSEUM

Wapping Police Station   Tel: 020 7275 4421
98 Wapping High Street   Fax: 020 7275 4490
London E1 9NE
e-mail: bob.jeffries@met.police.uk

Voluntary association and museum

Facilities
Enquiries to the Hon. Curator
Information provided by phone, post and e-mail
Library open to public: access to museum considered
to organisations or individuals with a special interest
by appointment only; loans to members only

Subject coverage
Marine and river police history

Special collections
Manuscripts and books from 1798-1839
Occurrence books, orders from 1839 to date

T3
THAMES SHIP SOCIETY

7 Cranborne Road   Tel: 01707 650958
Potters Bar,
Herts
EN6 3AD

Thanet Branch Archive Office
See East Kent Archive Office

T4
TOPSHAM MUSEUM SOCIETY

25 The Strand   Tel: 01392 873224
Topsham
Exeter EX3 0AX
e-mail: museum@topsham.org
Website: www.devonmuseums.net/topsham

Voluntary organisation/museum with local government
support

Facilities
Enquiries to the Secretary
Information provided by phone, post and e-mail
Open to the public by appointment
Photocopying facilities
Research service available - current charges from £5

Subject coverage
Shipbuilding and shipping on the Exe; Exe salmon
fishing; Captain George Peacock - Panama Canal,
Corinth Canal, inventor of the propeller, the monitor,
antifouling and discoverer and exploiter of South
American nitrate/guano

Special collections
The John Holman Archives
Collections of half models, John Holman & Sons
The Davy Archives

Specific companies and groups
Shipbuilding on the Exe
Memoranda book of Daniel Bishop Davy (1799-1874)
Records of John Holman & Sons (shipbuilding, shipping
and insurance)

T5
TOWER HAMLETS LOCAL HISTORY LIBRARY AND ARCHIVES

Bancroft Library	Tel: 020 8980 4366
277 Bancroft Road	Ext. 129
London E1 4DQ	Fax: 020 8983 4510

Local government organisation

Facilities
Enquiries to the Local History Librarian
Information provided by phone, post and fax
Library open to the public: appointments advisable for
microfilmed (local) newspapers
Opening hours: Tuesdays & Thursdays 0900-2000;
Fridays 0900-1800; Saturdays 0900-1700
Microfilm and microfiche readers; fullsize copies can be
provided; photocopying service

Subject coverage
19th century merchant shipping; Thames-side, especially
Tower Hamlets; shipbuilding and docks; sailing and
steamships

Special collections
Bolt Collection, concerning principally 19th century
shipping - c 3,700 photographs, 25 file boxes of
miscellaneous illustrations and cuttings, loose-leaf
catalogue entries re c7,500 ships, all alphabetically
arranged by name of ship
Glass Collection, general collection regarding 18th-
20th century sailing ships
'Lloyd's Registers of Ships', 1842-1978 with gaps

Town Docks Museum
See Hull Maritime Museum

T6
THE TRANSPORT TRUST

202 Lambeth Road	Tel: 020 7928 6464
London SE1 7JW	Fax: 020 7928 6565

e-mail: hq@thetransporttrust@org.uk
Website: www.thetransporttrust@org.uk

Voluntary organisation

Facilities
Enquiries to the Director General; library open to the
public is located at Ironbridge (see next entry)

Subject coverage
All aspects of the UK's transport heritage

T7
THE TRANSPORT TRUST - LIBRARY AND ARCHIVES

c/o Ironbridge Gorge Museum	Tel: 01952 432141
Telford	Fax: 01952 435937
Shropshire TF8 7DQ	

e-mail: library@ironbridge.org.uk

Voluntary organisation/national charity

Facilities
Enquiries to the Librarian
Information provided by phone
Open to the public, including research students -
appointment essential
Photocopying facilities

Subject coverage
All aspects of UK's transport heritage, on land, sea and
in the air

T8
TYNE AND WEAR ARCHIVES SERVICE

Blandford House	Tel: 0191 232 6789
Blandford Square	Fax: 0191 230 2614
Newcastle-upon-Tyne	
Tyne and Wear NE1 4JA	

e-mail: twas@gateshead.gov.uk
website: www.the northeast.com/archives

Local government organisation

Facilities
Enquiries to the Chief Archivist
Archives open to the public; appointment advised;
specific items by prior appointment

Information given by phone, post, fax and e-mail
Photocopying facilities
Microfilm and microfiche readers
Microcopies and fullsize copies can be provided
Research service available, £15 per hour (minimum charge £30 for initial enquiry. Opening hours: Monday, Wednesday, Thursday, Friday 0900-1715; Tuesday 0900-2030

Subject coverage

Shipbuilding; ship repairing and allied industries; marine engineering and technology; shipping; ship ownership and management; pilotage and navigation; harbour control

Special collections

Trinity House, masters', pilots' and seamen's records, 1421-1965
British Maritime League minutes, 1984-88
Company of Master Mariners of Newcastle-upon-Tyne, apprentices indentures, 1694-1847

Shipbuilding
Armstrong Whitworth and Co. Ltd., Newcastle (including WG Armstrong Mitchell and Co), business papers, 1847-1952, photographs of ships, 1898-1908. In 1927 Armstrongs amalgamated with Vickers Ltd., Elswick (including Armstrong Whitworth and Co. Ltd., Vickers-Armstrong Ltd.). Elswick works photographs, 1857-1935; plans of Elswick and Walker shipyards, 1898-1984
SP Austin and Sons Ltd., Sunderland; ships' contracts, 1904-06 Austin and Pickersgill, Sunderland; business papers, 1962-85; press cuttings, 19th-20th centuries
Bartram and Sons Ltd, Sunderland; business papers, 1865-1969; ships' plans, 19th-20th centuries
DE and A Black, ships photographs, c1905; invitations to Armstrong Mitchell/Armstrong Whitworth launches, 1885-1914
Brigham and Cowan Ltd., South Shields; foreman shipwrights' work journals, 1919-1939
Clelands Shipbuilding Co. Ltd., Willington Quay; photographs and plans, c1935f
John Crown and Sons Ltd., Sunderland; business papers, 1903-55; ships' dimensions book, 1880-1925; ships' photographs, 1946-61; ships' plans, 1908-1922
William Dobson and Co., Wincomblee, Walker; photographs, 1895-1941
William Doxford and Sons Ltd., Sunderland; business papers, 1891-1969; ships' specifications, 1944-65; ships' particulars books, 1871-1942; general arrangement plans, c1907-65; photographs, 1840-1969
GW and WJ Hall, Sunderland; papers, 1858-1912
Sir James Laing and Sons Ltd., Sunderland; business papers, 1818-1967; ships' particulars books, 1794-1962; photographs, 1889-c1971
Palmers' Shipbuilding and Iron Co. Ltd., Jarrow; papers, 1840-1908
Readheads, South Shields; business papers, 1872-1966; engine sketch books, 1883-1940; ships' plans, 1881-1967; photographs, 1878-1966

Lord Stuart Rendel; correspondence, 1874-1912
J Rennoldson, South Shields; subscription by workmen to Newcastle Infirmary
Short Brothers, Sunderland; business papers, 1870-1924
R Stephenson and Co. Ltd., Hebburn; specification of steamer, 1907
Sunderland Shipbuilders Ltd., Sunderland, 1971-76; photographs, c1970-81
Swan Hunter and Wigham Richardson Ltd., Wallsend; papers, 1873-1950; Neptune yard ship plans, c1860f
JL Thompson and Sons Ltd, Sunderland; business papers, 1871-1969; plans, 1941-1945; photographs, 1930-1960s
Robert Thompson, Sunderland; ships built, 1855-1933
Wallsend Slipway and Engineering Co. Ltd.; trials book, 1875-1887; graving dock registers, 1895-1969

Marine Engineering
George Clark Ltd., Southwick Engine Works; business papers, 1883-1937; plans, 1896-1927; photographs, 1887-1960
R and W Hawthorn Leslie and Co. Ltd., Newcastle and Hebburn (including the records of Robert Stephenson and Hawthorn Ltd.) business papers, 1829-1962; list of ships, 1854-1944
North Eastern Marine Engineering Co. Ltd., Wallsend and Sunderland; business papers, 1865-1924
Parsons Marine Steam Turbine Co. Ltd., Wallsend; plans of steam yacht *Turbinia*, 1893-1904; data sheets, 1905f; photograph HMS *Viper*, 1903
Richardson, Westgarth and Co. Ltd., Wallsend; business papers, 1939-1946
Shields Engineering and Dry Dock Co. Ltd.; papers, 1899
Sunderland Engineering Equipment Co. Ltd.; papers, 1959-1973
Sunderland Forge and Engineering Co. Ltd.; papers, 1954-1959
Sunderland Magnetic Ltd.; papers, 1962
Sunderland Shipbuilding, Dry Docks & Engineering Co. Ltd.; business papers, 1954-1976,
Wear Winch & Foundry Co. Ltd.; papers, 1956

Ships outfitting
Robert Farrow and Co. Ltd., Sunderland; business papers, 1881-1964; photographs, 1890-1940
R and W Hutchinson, Sunderland; papers, 1846
Linkleter's Patent Ships Fitting Co., South Shields; business papers, 1907-1952; photographs, 1900-1940
JW MacDonald, 1866-1942 & J MacGregor, 1883-1967; papers
George Parker, Sunderland; letter book, 1891-1929
Isaac Taylor, Newcastle; printed advertisement, c1834

Ship registration
The shipping registers date from 1786 and were originally held by H.M. Customs and Excise Port of: Newcastle-upon-Tyne (includes entries for the whole river to 1848); registers, 1786-1872; transaction books, 1855-1931
Shields; registers, 1848-1866; transaction books, 1855-1857
North Shields; registers, 1866-1931; transaction books,

1863-1891; registers of fishing boats, 1869-1949; index of ships, c1917-1947

South Shields; registers, 1859-1891; transaction books, 1869-1900; ship registration files, 1860-1961

Sunderland; registers, 1786-1915; transaction books, 1855-1900; register of sea fishing boats, 1903-1932

Ship repairing
Greenwell's Dry Dock Co, Sunderland; business papers, 1902-1973
Law Brothers, South Shields; day book, 1958-1965
Tyne Dock Engineering Co Ltd, South Shields; business papers, 1882-1977

Shipping
Argosy Steamship Co. Ltd, Sunderland; journal, 1882-1922
Cambay and Carlton Steamship Companies; business papers, 1892-1924
Chapman and Willan (also Chapman and Miller, R Chapman and Son, and Chapman and Son), Newcastle; business papers, 1830-1968
Common Bros, Newcastle; business papers, 1906-1975
RS Dalgleish Ltd (Dalgleish Steam Ship Co.Ltd), Newcastle; business papers, 1917-1980
Free Trade Wharf Co. Ltd, London; business papers, 1866-1901
Granta Steamship Co. Ltd., Newcastle; business papers and journal, 1926-1958
Hall Bros., Newcastle; business papers, 1883-1971
John George Hill Steamship Co. Ltd., Newcastle; business papers and journal, 1866-1953
J Nicholson, Newcastle; papers, 1868-1881
Prince Line (1895) Ltd., Newcastle and South Shields; papers, 1895-1899
Scholefield Steam Shipping Co. Ltd., Newcastle; business papers, 1911-13
Sharp Steamship Co. Ltd., Newcastle; business papers, 1912-1949
Steamer *Snowdon Range* of Sunderland and Captain EJ Dickenson papers, photographs and press cuttings, 1913-1925
Souter, Hamlet and Co., Newcastle; ledgers, log books and journals, 1920-73
Stag Line Ltd., North Shields; business papers, 1885-1970 and journals, 1933-1970
Stephenson Clarke Shipping Ltd., Newcastle; ship launch photographs, 1943-58
Stott, Mann and Co., Newcastle; business papers, 1921-1976
Sunniside Steamship Co. Ltd., Newcastle; business papers, 1895-1907
Tanner and Beckwith, Newcastle; ledgers, 1819-1825
Turret Steam Shipping Co. Ltd., Sunderland; business papers, 1892-1904; photographs, 1892-1908
Tyne and Blyth Steamship Owning Co. Ltd., Newcastle; business papers, 1912-15
Tyne Tees Steam Shipping Co. Ltd., Newcastle (formerly Tyne Steam Shipping Co. Ltd.); business papers, 1865-1952; scrapbook, 1864-1955
J Westoll and J Westoll Ltd, Sunderland; business

papers, 1879-1940-, crew lists, 1890-1937
Westwick Steamship Co. Ltd., Sunderland; papers, 1916-1951
Andrew and John White, Sunderland; notebooks, 1813-1850
Witherington and Everett, Newcastle; business papers, 1898-1968; journals, 1899-1952; photographs, 1903-1958
North of England Shipowners' Association; business papers and press cuttings, 1860-1965

Publications
User Guide 5: 'Shipbuilding, Outfitting, Registration and Repair'
User Guide 6: 'Maritime Trade and Navigation'
All user guides accessible through website

T9
TYNE AND WEAR MUSEUMS

Blandford House	Tel: 0191 232 6789
Blandford Square	Fax: 0191 230 2614
Newcastle-upon-Tyne	
Tyne and Wear NE1 4JA	

e-mail: ian.whitehead@twmuseums.org.uk
website: twmuseums.org.uk

Local government organisation

Facilities
Enquiries to the Keeper of Maritime History
Open to bona fide students of maritime history, by prior appointment
Information given by phone, post or fax
Fullsize copies can be provided

Subject coverage
Leisure and sailing craft; shipbuilding in wood, and iron; ship management; maritime law and insurance; navigation; trade publications

Special collections
Shipping department library
Chapman Library collection
Turbine launch *Turbinia*
Models of east coast ships

Ulster-American Folk Park
See Centre for Migration Studies

U1
THE ULSTER FOLK AND TRANSPORT MUSEUM

Cultra	Tel: 028 9042 8428
Holywood	Fax: 028 9042 8728
Co. Down	
N. Ireland BT18 0EU	

Museum, local government organisation

Facilities
Enquiries to the Librarian
Information provided by phone, post and fax; loans to members only
Library open to the public: Mondays-Fridays 0930-1300 and 1400-1630
Photocopying facilities
Microfilm and microfiche readers; fullsize copies can be provided
Research service not provided

Subject coverage
Irish maritime history; Irish vernacular boat types; Ulster shipbuilding; Irish fisheries; Irish maritime ethnology

Special collections
'Lloyd's Register of Ships'
Harland and Wolff photographic collection
Harland and Wolff plan collection

Publications
Titanic, education pack
'Titanic', M McCaughan, 1982
'Steel Ships and Iron Men' M McCaughan

U2
UNITED KINGDOM FORTIFICATIONS CLUB

12 Castle Close   Tel: 01553 675053
Reffley Estate
Kings Lynn
Norfolk PE30 3EP

Voluntary association

Facilities
Enquiries to the Hon. Secretary
Information provided by post to all
Library open to members only
Books and other materials loaned to members only

Subject coverage
Sea forts of the UK and Dominions; WD fleet (1885-1945); Martello towers

---

U3
UNITED KINGDOM HYDROGRAPHIC OFFICE

Admiralty Way   Tel: 01823 337900 Ext. 3451
Taunton   Fax: 01823 352561
Somerset TA1 2DN
e-mail: research@ukho.gov.uk
Website: www.ukho.gov.uk

Government agency

Facilities
Enquiries to the Research Manager
Information provided by post, fax (£1.50 per page) or e-mail
Open to the general public by appointment only
Opening hours: Mondays-Fridays 0900-1700
Photocopying facilities
Research service provided. Rates: £24 per hour for private individuals; £70 per hour for commercial organisations, plus VAT, where applicable

Subject coverage
Copies of BA navigational and miscellaneous charts; published annual chart catalogues; record copies of old cancelled charts; hydrographic surveys; reports and geodetic data; associated chronological and geographical catalogues; graphical indexes; views; hydrographic survey field data; ocean sounding sheets; foreign charts and published chart catalogues; maps (mainly UK); aerial photoplots; geographical indexes; atlases; Notices to Mariners; textual hydrographic information held in several hundred thousand files; letter books and minute books from c1800

Special collections
Letter books, minute books, correspondence, surveys and business records from c1800
Records of the Royal Navy Surveying Service

Databases
Some classes of manuscripts and printed charts have been catalogued. Modern bathymetric and associated hydrographical information is available, but more information is available on request

Publications
Professional Paper 13: 'A summary of selected manuscript documents of historic importance preserved in the Archives of the Department' (London, Hydrographic Department, Admiralty, 1950)

U4
UNIVERSITY COLLEGE LONDON – LIBRARY SERVICES

Gower Street   Tel: 020 7679 7050
London WC1E 6BT   Fax: 020 7679 7373
e-mail: library@ucl.ac.uk
Website: www.ucl.ac.uk/library

University library

Enquiries to the Librarian
Information provided by phone and e-mail
Library open to members only; public can pay to be a member for either reference or borrowing
Opening hours: Mondays-Thursdays 0845-2230; Fridays 0845-1900; Saturdays 0930-1630;
Sundays 1100-1700. Vacations: Mondays-Fridays 0845-1900

Photocopying facilities; microfilm and microfiche readers available; charge for regular long term use
Research facilities not provided

Subject coverage
Shipbuilding; naval architecture; British maritime history of the 19th century

Special collections
Archives of the Royal Mail Steam Packet Co, 1840-1949
Rare pamphlet issued in 1838 re Pacific Steam Navigation Co.
Papers of the British Maritime Law Association, c1947-1971
Ms paper of James Cook giving sailing directions in Newfoundland, 1760?
Photocopy of paper of 'Whaling voyages around the world' by Captain Thomas Melvil 1791-96 (original is in the Dixon Library Sydney, Australia)

U5
UNIVERSITY OF ESSEX, ALBERT SLOMAN LIBRARY,

P.O.Box 24	Tel: 01206 873172
Colchester	Fax: 01206 872289
Essex CO4 3UA	

e-mail: nigelc@essex.ac.uk
Website: libwww.essex.ac.uk

University library

Facilities
Enquiries to the Deputy Librarian
Limited information provided by post and e-mail
Library open to members of the University, and to the general public by appointment in writing well in advance of intended visit
Opening hours: Special Collections' Reading Room Mondays - Fridays 0900-1700, throughout the year, except public holidays
Photocopying facilities
Research service not provided

Special collections
Rowhedge Collection: the records of the former Rowhedge Ironworks Company, local shipyard, 1904-1964, an almost complete business archive, including 2,000 major items

Publications
See the Website http://libwww.essex.ac.uk/speccol.htm for listing of all special collections in the library

---

University of Hull
See Brynmor Jones Library

University of London School of Oriental and African Studies
See School of Oriental and African Studies

W1
WARWICKSHIRE COUNTY RECORD OFFICE

Priory Park	Tel: 01926 738959
Cape Road	Fax: 01926 738969
Warwick CV34 4JS	

e-mail: recordoffice@warwickshire.gov.uk
Website: www.warwickshire.gov.uk/countyrecordoffice

Local government organisation

Facilities
Enquiries to the County Record Office
Information provided by phone, post, fax and e-mail
Open to the public: Tuesday-Thursday 0900-1730, Friday 0900-1700 and Saturday 0900-1230
Photocopying facilities
Research service available

Subject coverage
Boats; boatmen; shipping; careers in the navy; defences, diaries; log books; marines; mutinies (deserters); naval personnel; suppliers of ships stores and sails

Special collections
Accounts of Sir Fulke Greville as Treasurer of Marine Causes, 1599-1603
Records of Admiral Lord Hugh Seymour, 1759-1801
Records of Sir George P Seymour, 1787-1870

Publications
Many catalogues are available on the Access to Archives (A2A) website

---

W2
WARWICK UNIVERSITY LIBRARY - MODERN RECORDS' CENTRE

Warwick University	Tel: 024 7652 4219
Coventry CV4 7AL	Fax: 024 7652 4211

e-mail: archives@warwick.ac.uk
Website: modernrecords.warwick.ac.uk

University department

Facilities
Enquiries to the Archivist
Information provided by phone, post, fax or e-mail
Open to the public: Mondays, Tuesdays 0900-1700;
Wednesdays, Thursdays 0900-1900; Fridays 0900-1600
Photocopying facilities
Research service not provided

Subject coverage
Labour organisation in shipping and shipbuilding industries

Special collections
Archives of:
National Union of Seamen
International Transport Workers' Federation
Federation of Sailmakers
Confederation of Shipbuilding and Engineering Unions

Publications
See website

W3
THE WATERWAYS MUSEUM

Dutch River Side   Tel: 01405 768730
Goole   Fax: 01405 769868
East Yorkshire DN14 5TB
e-mail: waterwaysmuseum@btinternet.com
www.waterwaysmuseumandadventurecentre.co.uk

Museum

Facilities
Enquiries to the Museum Officer
Information provided by phone, post, e-mail and visit
Museum open to the public: Monday-Friday 0930-1630,
and Sundays from end of April to end of September.
Appointment necessary for library
Photocopying facilities
Research by arrangement with the Museum Officer

Subject coverage
Transport history: the Aire and Calder Navigation and
associated waterways and organisations
Social history of canal and river workers of Yorkshire
and their families
Growth and development of the port of Goole
History of shipping in the Goole area
Industrial archaeology of Goole port
Ship and boatbuilding in Yorkshire

Special collections
History of 'Tom Puddings', coal-carrying system and
boat hoists
Life and work of WH Bartholomew, Chief Engineer for
the Aire and Calder Navigation, 1853-1919
Ship models
Cabin of Sheffield-size keel, 1910
Wheldale, 1959 diesel tug

Specific companies and groups
Aire and Calder Navigation
Goole Shipbuilding and Repair yard

Specific databases
Archive of 5,000 photographic images
Goole-built ships (under development)

Publications
'Railway on the Water: a history of the Tom Puddings',
Harold Crabtree and Mike Clarke
'The Aire and Calder Navigation', Mike Clarke

W4
THE WATERWAYS TRUST - THE
BOAT MUSEUM

South Pier Road   Tel: 0151 355 5017
Ellesmere Port   Fax: 0151 355 4079
CH65 4FW
e-mail: boatmuseum@easynet.co.uk
Website: www.boatmuseum.org.uk

Museum

Facilities
Enquiries to the Archive and Resources Officer
Information provided by phone, post, fax and e-mail
Open to the public (please ring for appointment):
Monday-Friday 1000-1600
Photocopying facilities
Research service not provided

Subject coverage
Canals and rivers in the UK, plus some information on
canals in the rest of the world, including documents,
photographs, plans and maps, books, periodicals and
oral history tapes

Special collections
Charles Hadfield World Canals Collection
Michael Ware Photograph and Postcard Collection
Robert Aickman Photograph and Correspondence
Collection
De Mare Photographic Collection

Specific companies and groups
IWA Correspondence Collection
Weaver Navigation Company Records
Shropshire Union Minute Books

Specific databases
Photograph, book, periodical, oral history database can
be searched for researchers by members of staff

Publications
Some catalogues can be viewed in Reading Room

See also **Canal Museum**

Welsh Industrial and Maritime Museum

This museum closed on its site in Cardiff Bay in 1998,
but will be re-incarnated as the **National
Waterfront Museum** in Swansea (comprising the
former Swansea Maritime and Industrial Museum) in
the spring of 2005. It will be one of the constituent
museums of the National Museums and Galleries of
Wales. In the meantime, the collections are still
available for consultation by appointment:
phone: 029 2057 3560; fax: 029 2057 3561;
email: industry@nmgw.ac.uk

W5
WEST DUNBARTONSHIRE LIBRARIES - CLYDEBANK

Clydebank Central Library	Tel: 0141 952 1416
Dumbarton Road	Fax: 0141 951 8275
Clydebank G81 1XH	

e-mail: clydebank.local.history@west-dunbarton.gov.uk
Website: www.west-dunbarton.gov.uk

Local government organisation and public library

Facilities
Enquiries to the Information Services Librarian
Information provided by phone, post, fax and e-mail
Open to the public - Monday-Thursday 0930-2000,
Friday 0930-1700 and Saturday 1000-1700
Please phone for an appointment if making more than
a routine enquiry
Photocopying facilities
General enquiries answered - prolonged research not
carried out

Subject coverage
Shipbuilding in Clydebank area

Special collections
J & G Thomson, shipbuilders
John Brown & Co., shipbuilders
William Beardmore & Co., shipbuilders

Publications
'Beardmore Built: The Rise & Fall of a Clyde Shipyard',
Ian Johnston, 1993
'Ships for a Nation: John Brown & Company,
Clydebank', Ian Johnston, 2000

W6
WEST DUNBARTONSHIRE LIBRARIES - DUMBARTON

Strathleven Place	Tel: 01389 733273
Dumbarton G82 1BD	Fax: 01389 607302

e-mail: dunbarton.local.history@west-dunbarton.gov.uk
Website: www.west-dunbarton.gov.uk

Local government organisation

Facilities
Enquiries to the Information Services Librarian
Information provided by phone, post, fax and e-mail
Open to the public: Monday-Thursday 0930-2000,
Friday 0930-1700 and Saturday 1000-1700
Photocopying facilities and microform printouts
Research service available - no charge for quick
reference enquiries, otherwise £10 per hour (up to 5
hours)

Subject coverage
The history of shipbuilding, boatbuilding, marine
engineering and ancillary manufacturing industries
within the western part of West Dunbartonshire, i.e.
Dumbarton, the Vale of Leven and part of Loch
Lomond, and of the passenger boat service on Loch
Lomond
Local newspapers, 1851 to date

Special collections
Collection of books on local shipbuilding and
engineering
Large collection of photographs of Denny, MacMillan,
Scotts of Bowling ships, and other ships with a local
connection
Small collection of the archives of William Denny and
Brothers Ltd., shipbuilders, the majority with the
National Maritime Museum, Glasgow University
Archives, and the Scottish Maritime Museum's Denny
Experimental Tank in Dumbarton
Scott & Linton shipbuilders, 1860s, *Cutty Sark* material,
memo of agreement to build, early ships' logs,
correspondence, sale and catalogue of yard.
Dumbarton Steamboat Company minute books, 1815-1852
Loch Lomond Steamboat Company, minute book
1845-1868
Clyde and Leven Steam Packet Company, minute book
1846-1852.
Dennystown Forge Company archives
Newspapers, 1851-date

W7
WESTERN APPROACHES MUSEUM

1-3 Rumford Street	Tel: 0151 227 2008
Liverpool L2 3SZ	

Museum consisting of the underground command
headquarters for the Battle of the Atlantic.
Opening times vary.

W8
WEST GLAMORGAN ARCHIVE SERVICE

County Hall	Tel: 01792 636589
Oystermouth Road	Fax: 01792 637130
Swansea SA1 3SN	

e-mail: westglam.archives@swansea.gov.uk
Website: www.swansea.gov.uk/archives

Record office

Facilities
Enquiries to the County Archivist
Information provided by phone, post, fax and e-mail
Open to the public: Monday-Thursday 0900-1700 and
Monday evenings 1730-1930 by appointment
Photocopying facilities
Research service available - £15 per hour

Subject coverage
Shipping and harbour records for the ports of West

Glamorgan

Special collections
Crew agreements
Ships' logbooks
Registers of shipping
Registration papers for the ports of Swansea and Port Talbot

Specific companies and groups
Shipping records of Poingdestre & Mesnier & Cie
Shipping records of Stone & Rolfe Ltd. and Thomas Stone & Co. Ltd.
Records of Associated British Ports plc (Swansea and Port Talbot)

Publications
Guide to Collections (1998) - also available on website

W9
CITY OF WESTMINSTER ARCHIVES CENTRE

10 St Ann's Street   Tel: 020 7641 5180
London SW1P 2DE   Fax: 020 7641 5179
                    Minicom: 020 7641 4879
e-mail: archives@westminster.gov.uk
Website: www.westminster.gov.uk/archives

Local government organisation

Facilities
Enquiries to the City Archivist
Information provided by phone, post, fax and e-mail
Open to the public: Monday, Friday-Saturday 0930-1700 and Tuesday-Thursday 0930-1900
Photocopying facilities
Research service is available by written request for those unable to visit Archives Centre. Searches will be in the records available at the City of Westminster Archives Centre at a cost of £20 per hour (although building history research charges vary). Please see Westminster Research Service and/or Archives Centre information leaflets for additional details

Subject coverage
Local history sources: books; pamphlets; newspaper cuttings; prints and photographs of the River Thames and local canals

Special collections
Records of canal boats in Paddington Registration District, registers of boats 1900-32, Inspector's journal 1928-56 and complaint form, certificate book 1947-52
Prospectus for boats on Grand Junction Canal, 1802

Publications
Guide to collections on website

W10
WEST SUSSEX RECORD OFFICE

County Hall   Tel: 01243 753600
Chichester   Fax: 01243 533959
West Sussex PO19 1RN
e-mail: records.office@westsussex.gov.uk
Website: www.westsussex.gov.uk/ro/

Local government organisation

Facilities
Enquiries to the County Archivist
Information provided by phone, post, fax and e-mail
Open to the public: Monday-Friday 0915-1645, Saturday 0915-1230 and 1330-1630
Photocopying facilities
Research service available - £20 per hour

Subject coverage
Church records; diocesan records; family and estate records; local government records; school records; maps and plans; prints and drawings; cine films and videos; local newspapers; records of individuals; antiquarian collections; manorial records

Special collections
Goodwood Archives
Richard Cobden Papers
Hawkins Papers
Maxse Papers
Cowdray Archives
Royal Sussex Regiment Archives
South East Film and Video Archive

Special companies or groups
Harbour commissioners
Inland navigation companies
Turnpike trusts
Solicitors' collections
Local company and business records

Specific databases
West Sussex poor law and photographic databases created by WSRO
1881 census on CD-Rom
Soldiers died on CD-Rom
Microfiche indexes of GRO Records 1837-1997
Census Records for West Sussex, 1841-1901
National Probate Records, 1858-1943
International Genealogical Index, 1538-1875

Publications
Catalogues, guides, leaflets and handlists are available: see website

---

W11
WEST YORKSHIRE ARCHIVE SERVICE - WAKEFIELD HQ

Registry of Deeds   Tel: 01924 305980
Newstead Road   Fax: 01924 305983
Wakefield
West Yorkshire WF1 2DE
e-mail: wakefield@wyjs.org.uk
Website: www.wakefield@wyjs.org.uk

Local government organisation

Facilities
Enquiries to the Principal Archivist
Information provided by phone, post and e-mail
Open to the public by appointment only: Monday 0930-1300 and 1400-2000, Tuesday, Thursday 0930-1200 and 1400-1700 and second Saturday in each month 0930-1230
Photocopying facilities
Research service available - £34 per hour, no limitation on length

Subject coverage
Local government; diocesan; non-conformist; quarter sessions; magistrates; coroners'; societies; schools; police; business

Publications
Accessions database on website

W12
WHITBY LITERARY AND PHILOSOPHICAL SOCIETY LIBRARY

Whitby Museum   Tel: 01947 602908
Pannett Park
Whitby
North Yorkshire YO21 1RE
Website: www.durain.demon.co.uk

Museum

Facilities
Enquiries to the Hon. Librarian and Archivist
Information provided by phone and post
Open to the public and members
Open to non-members: Mondays-Fridays 0930-noon (May-September); Tuesdays-Fridays 1000-noon (October-April)
Photocopying facilities available
Research facilities available (by volunteer staff); time is charged

Subject coverage
Local history, especially maritime, i.e., fishing, shipping and shipbuilding; local topography

Special collections
Some ships' logbooks, diaries

Records of specific companies/groups
Seamen's Hospital Mission muster rolls
Thomas Turnbull & Sons, shipbuilders, including some ship plans

---

W13
WILLIAMSON ART GALLERY AND MUSEUM

Slatey Road   Tel: 0151 652 4177
Birkenhead CH43 4UE   Fax: 0151 670 0253
e-mail: wag@museum-service.freeserve.co.uk
Website: www.wirral.gov.uk

Museum

Facilities
Enquiries to the Curator
Information provided by phone, post, fax and e-mail
Open to the public: Tuesday-Sunday 1000-1700 (closed Monday)
Photocopying facilities

Subject coverage
Shipbuilding; ferries

Specific companies and groups
Cammell Laird collection

W14
WINDERMERE STEAMBOATS AND MUSEUM

Rayrigg Road   Tel: 015394 45565
Windermere   Fax: 015394 48769
Cumbria LA23 1BN
e-mail: steamboat@ecosse.net
Website: www.steamboat.co.uk

Museum

Facilities
Enquiries to the Museum Manager
Information provided by phone, post, fax and e-mail
Open to the public and user groups
Photocopying facilities
Research service not provided

Subject coverage
Steamboats, nautical memorabilia

Special collections
Vast collection of photographic slides and prints of the nautical history of Lake Windermere

Specific databases
Windermere History Society

Publications
Museum Guide

W15
WIRRAL ARCHIVES SERVICE
Wirral Museum   Tel: 0151 666 3903
Hamilton Square   Fax: 0151 666 3965
Birkenhead
Wirral CH41 5BR
e-mail: archives@wirral-libraries.net
Website: www.wirral-libraries.net/archives/

Local government organisation and museum

Facilities
Enquiries to the Archivist or Curator
Information provided by phone, post, fax and e-mail,
plus personal visit
Open to the public (appointments necessary for use of
microform readers and identification required):
Thursday-Friday 1000-1700 and Saturday 1000-1300
Photocopying facilities
Basic free research service available

Subject coverage
Local authority records; public records; local
newspapers; local businesses and institutions

Special collections
Archives of Cammell Laird Shipbuilders Ltd.,
Birkenhead, 1848-1993
Museum collections include models and paintings of
vessels
Henry B. Hornby Ltd., boatbuilders of Wallasey c.1927-
1996 (mainly photographic collection).

Publications
Brief guide to collections via website (please see
above)
Cammell Laird catalogue accessible via Access to
Archives website: www.a2a.pro.gov.uk/

W16
WORCESTERSHIRE RECORD OFFICE
County Hall   Tel: 01905 766351
Spetchley Road   Fax: 01905 763000
Worcester WR5 2NP
e-mail: recordoffice@worcestershire.gov.uk
Website: www.worcestershire.gov.uk/records

Local government organisation

Facilities
Enquiries to the County Archivist
Information provided by phone, post, fax, e-mail and
visit
Open to the public: Monday and Friday 0930-1900,

Tuesday, Wednesday and Thursday 0930-1730 and
Saturday 0930-1600
Reader's ticket required for library
Photocopying facilities
Fee-charging research service available through panel
of researchers. Current charges are £16 per hour
(£20 for corporate clients) with minimum of 1 hour.
Photocopying, p&p, travel costs extra.

Subject coverage
Naval history, canals, rivers

Special collections
Clarendon papers - some navy accounts
Lechmere papers - naval careers of family members
Valentine papers - World War II merchant seaman
(papers and taped interviews)

Specific records
Lower Avon Navigation Trust

W17
WORLD DATA CENTRE FOR GLACIOLOGY, CAMBRIDGE
Scott Polar Research Institute   Tel: 01223 336565
University of Cambridge   Fax: 01223 336549
Lensfield Road
Cambridge CB2 1ER
e-mail: ss10003@cus.cam.ac.uk
Website: www.spri.cam.ac.uk/wdcc/home.htm

University department; data centre co-ordinated by the
International Council of Scientific Unions' Panel of
World Data Centres

Facilities
Enquiries to the Manager
Information provided by phone, post, fax and e-mail
Open to the public
Photocopying facilities; microfiche reader
Research service not provided

Subject coverage
Sea ice, all aspects

Databases
SPRILIB Ice and Snow

W18
THE WORLD SHIP SOCIETY LTD
PO Box 706
Gravesend
Kent DA12 5UB
Website: www.worldshipsociety.org

International voluntary association and research
organisation, with headquarters in the UK

Facilities
Information provided by post, and by personal visits to the Society's library and archive in Kent
Prints available from the Society's collection of some 50,000 negatives
Books loaned to members
Research services available to members
Regular branch meetings at over 50 centres, and annual meetings on naval matters and research
Facilities are available strictly to members only
Enquiries about membership to the General Secretary

Subject coverage
Merchant and naval ships, 1800 to date; shipping company histories and fleet lists; flags and funnels; shipyard histories; war losses; convoys; shipbreaking

Special collections
Complete set of 'Lloyd's Register of Ships' from 1850.
Extensive holdings of 'Mercantile Navy Lists'
Holdings of 'Lloyd's Confidential Indexes'
'Lloyds Lists' (incomplete)
'Lloyds Shipping Indexes' (incomplete)
Extensive holdings of shipping books, journals, manuscripts and non-UK registers
Bonsor collection
Flags and funnels database
Fleet lists of shipping companies
Yard lists
Extensive photographic library comprising separate negative, print and colour slide collections

Publications
Marine News a 64-page illustrated monthly magazine, distributed free to members, containing details of merchant shipping and naval news; details of launches, sales, casualties and demolitions; articles by members; book reviews; news of Society activities, meetings and publications.
Warships, quarterly research journal.
Starke/Schell Registers giving details of all ships over a certain size built in a given year published for many years between 1890 and 1984
The Society is a major publisher of fleet lists and histories of shipping companies, and books on warships and naval operations, with well over 150 titles so far published, although some are out of print. See website.

W19
WORLDSCALE ASSOCIATION (LONDON) LTD

Copenhagen House   Tel: 0207 456 6600
5-10 Bury Street   Fax: 0207 456 6601
London EC3A 5AT
e-mail: wscale@worldscale.co.uk
Website: www.worldscale.co.uk

Consultancy

Facilities
Enquiries to the General Manager or Managing Director.
Information provided by phone, post, fax and website
Access to information only through subscription service
Research service not provided

Subject coverage
Oil tanker nominal freight scale applying to the carriage of oil in bulk

---

W20
THE WORSHIPFUL COMPANY OF SHIPWRIGHTS

Ironmongers' Hall   Tel: 020 7606 2376
Barbican   Fax: 020 7600 3519
London EC2Y 8AA
e-mail: clerk@shipwrights.co.uk

Voluntary organisation

Facilities
Enquiries to the Clerk
Information provided by phone, post, fax and e-mail
Library open to members only
Research service not provided

Subject coverage
The company's archives pre-1920 are held at Guildhall Library in the City of London; papers 1920-1941 were destroyed in 1941

Y1
YACHT CHARTER ASSOCIATION (YCA)

Deacons Boatyard   Tel 023 8040 7075
Bridge Road   Fax 023 8040 7076
Bursledon
Southampton SO31 8AZ
Email charter@yca.co.uk
Web http://www.yca.co.uk

Consultancy and voluntary organisation (non-profit making)

Facilities
Enquiries to the Secretary
Library open to members only
Information given by phone, post and fax to all
Assistance given in finding a reputable charter operator and helping people set up in business.

Subject coverage
Safety standards

Publications
'Guide to Charter'
'List of Charter Operators and their Fleets' (annual)

Y2
YACHT DESIGNERS AND SURVEYORS ASSOCIATION (YDSA)
ASSOCIATION OF BROKERS AND YACHT AGENTS (ABYA)

Wheel House   Tel: 0845 0900162
Petersfield Road   Fax: 0845 0900163
Whitehill
Bordon
Hants GU35 9BU
e-mail: info@ybdsa.co.uk
Website: www.ybdsa.co.uk

Professional association

Facilities
Information provided by phone, post, fax, e-mail and website
Open to all
Photocopying facilities
Research service not available

Subject coverage
Library of marine-related books dating back to origins of the Association in 1912

Specific companies and groups
Members of YDSA
Members of ABYA
Subscribers (including the Professional Charter Association (PCA))

Specific databases
Membership
Certifying Authority for MCA Code vessels

Publications
Training Pack - £75
Sample Report Pack - £10
Key Requirements of a Survey - free
Sale and Purchase Agreement for brokers

Y3
YACHT HARBOUR ASSOCIATION

Evegate Park Barn   Tel: 01303 814434
Smeeth   Fax: 02303 814364
Ashford
Kent TN25 6SX
e-mail: suelambert.tyha.1@virgin.net
Website: www.yachtharbourassociation.com

Trade association

Facilities
Enquiries to the Secretary
Information provided by phone, post, fax and e-mail
Open to the public

No photocopying facilities
Research service available

Publications
Code of practice for the construction and operation of inland and coastal marinas

Z1
ZETLAND LIFEBOAT MUSEUM

5 King Street   Tel: 01642 485370
Redcar
Cleveland TS10 3PF

Voluntary organisation (affiliated to RNLI) and museum

Facilities
Enquiries to the Rota Secretary
Information provided by post
Open to the public
No photocopying facilities

Subject coverage
History of lifeboats; fishing; Redcar memorabilia

Special collections
The *Zetland* - the world's oldest surviving lifeboat
Collection of Redcar crested china

Publications
'Story of the Zetland'

APPENDIX 1. RECORDS OF MERCHANT SEAMEN, CREW AGREEMENTS AND LOG BOOKS
Information supplied by the Registry of Shipping and Seamen

This is a guide to the library of seaman's and ship's records held at the Registry of Shipping and Seamen (RSS), PO Box 420, Cardiff, CF24 5JW; tel: 029 20 44 88 00; e-mail RSS@mcga.gov.uk. It also identifies records transferred to other locations.

To obtain copies of any records held at RSS submit a written application to the Records Officer at the above address. The application should include as many details as possible together with the fee, as shown against each category of record below.

MERCHANT NAVY SEAMAN'S SEA SERVICE RECORDS

1999 to 2003
The Registry of Shipping and Seamen can provide details of a merchant seaman's service for the above years. This information is taken from the official logbooks and crew agreements for the ship on which the seaman sailed. There is a charge of £11.00 per logbook to extract this information, the details of which are then included on a Certificate of Sea Service for the seaman. Further charges are made for additional information and these are listed below.

1973 to 1999
The Registry of Shipping and Seamen is unable to supply details of the sea service of merchant seamen from 1973 to 1999. After 1973 the Registrar General was not required to keep such records.

1941 to 1972 Fifth Register of Merchant Seaman's Service
These records are held by the National Archives (formerly the Public Record Office) in class *BT382: The Fifth Register of Seaman's Service 1941 to 1972.*

Records of individual merchant seamen's sea service details are held in alphabetical order of surname. Details include name of seaman, date and place of birth, discharge book number, rank, and details of the ships on which he served (name of ship and official number), date of engagement (joining ship), date of discharge (leaving ship), whether ship was a foreign-going or home-trade vessel, and in some cases National Insurance contributions. Details shown in these records are similar to those in an individual seaman's discharge book.

1913 to 1940 Fourth Register of Merchant Seaman's Service.
These records are available in the National Archives and are held on microfiche in the following classes: *BT348: Register of Seamen, Central Index, Numerical Series (CR2); BT 349: Register of Seamen, Central Index, Alphabetical Series (CR1); and BT350: Register of Seamen, Special index, Alphabetical Series (CR10).* These three classes have been combined into class *BT 364: Register of Seaman,*

Combined Numerical Index (CR1, CR2 and CR10).

The original records for the above classes are now held at Southampton Archives, Southampton City Council, South Block Civic Centre, Southampton S014 7LY. This office is open Tuesdays to Fridays 0930 to 1630, with one late evening opening each month. There is no charge for a personal visit, but there are charges for enquiries by post, e-mail or fax.

1913 to 1940 Merchant Seaman's Pouches
The pouches were a central repository for the many documents that a seaman would submit to the Registry of Shipping over his career and of copies of documents issued to him. The latter would include applications for discharge books (including photographs of the seaman), sea service records, and records of certificates issued. Some pouches include records cards extracted from the Fourth Register of Seaman's Service.

These records are held in the National Archives under class *BT372: Central Register of Seaman's Records ('Pouches').* They are filed in numerical order of the individual seaman's discharge book number.

1854 to 1856 Third Register of Merchant Seaman's Service
This was opened in 1854. It is arranged in alphabetical order and contains details of the seaman's age, place of birth, and voyage including name of ship and port of departure. In 1856 it was considered that the obligation to maintain a register of seaman was satisfied by the crew list and the Third Register was closed. It is held in the National Archives under class *BT116: Register of Seamen Series III.*

1845 to 1854 Second Register of Merchant Seaman's Service
The Merchant Shipping Act 1844 stipulated that every British seaman should have a register ticket. Details given when applying for a ticket were name, date and place of birth, date and capacity of first going to sea, subsequent capacity, any service in a Royal Navy ship and capacity, present employment at sea, and home address. The records are held in the National Archives under classes *BT113: Registers of Seaman's Tickets. (1845-1853* (in certificate number order), *BT114: Alphabetical Index to Registers of Seaman's Tickets and BT115: Alphabetical Register of Masters Tickets.*

1835 to 1844 First Register of Merchant Seaman's Service
Registration of seamen was introduced by the Merchant Shipping Act 1835. These records are held in the National Archives under classes *BT120: Register of Seamen Series I. (1835-1836)* (arranged alphabetically), *BT112: Register of Seamen Series II. (1835-1844), BT119 Alphabetical Index to Seamen* (this gives the registration number of the seaman).

LOGBOOKS AND CREW AGREEMENTS

Logbooks

Logbooks record a period in the life of a vessel, usually 12 to 18 months. The logbook is divided into tabular and narrative sections. The tabular section includes a record of all the ports which the vessel visited, and other information including births and deaths on board. Entries in the narrative section concern events that occur on the voyage, mainly details of disciplinary matters, illness and accidents amongst the crew.

Fees for photocopies of logbooks

There is a charge of £11 to extract a logbook from the records of the Registry of Shipping and Seamen and additional photocopying charges. Blank pages are not photocopied.

Crew agreements

The crew agreement document is a legal agreement between the crew of a vessel and the owners. It lists all the crew by name, includes their signatures and the name of the last ship on which they sailed. When a copy of a logbook is requested the attached crew agreement is also photocopied.

Logbooks and crew agreements 2000 to 2002

All these records are held at the Registry of Shipping and Seamen, from whom a certificate of sea service may be obtained for individual seamen. No official logbooks and crew agreements have been retained from the period 1996 to 1999.

Logbooks and crew agreements 1977 to 1995

A 10% sample of all logbooks for this period is held in the National Archives under class *BT99: Agreements and Crew Lists, Series II.*

Logbooks and crew agreements 1951 to 1976

A 10% sample of all logbooks from this period is held in the National Archives under class *BT99 Agreements and Crew Lists, Series II.* Some 80% of records for this period are now held by the Maritime History Archive, Memorial University of Newfoundland, St. John's, Newfoundland, Canada A1C 5S7. The National Maritime Museum, Greenwich, London, SE10 9NE keeps the remaining 10% of these logbooks and crew agreements for years ending in the figure 5, i.e. 1955, 1965, 1975.

Logbooks and crew agreements 1947 to 1950

The National Archives holds all surviving logbooks and crew agreements for 1947 to 1950, including merchant and fishing vessels, under class *BT99: Agreements and Crew Lists, Series II.*

Logbooks and crew agreements 1939 to 1946

These are held in the National Archives under class *BT381: WW2 Logbooks and Crew Agreements.* The logbooks and crew agreements are held in order of the ship's official number, so it is vital to know this number. It can be found, along with the dates the logbooks were opened and closed, from *BT385: Index Cards for Ship's Official Logbooks and Crew Agreements.* This index is in alphabetical order of ship's name, and covers all the official logbooks and crew agreements from the Second World War in class *BT381.*

A guide to researching logbooks and crew agreements for the Second World War is available from the Registry of Shipping and Seamen.

Allied crew lists 1939 to 1945

The following documents concerning Allied vessels are held in the National Archives in alphabetical order of ship's name:

> *Return of British Members of the crew of a Foreign Ship that has been Requisitioned or Chartered by, or on behalf of, HM Government and Account of Changes in the Crew of a Foreign-going Ship.*
> *Agreement and List of the Crew of a Foreign-going Ship.*

The records also include details of British crew members of Allied vessels who were lost at sea. A record was kept of the British seamen who served on Dutch and Norwegian ships; these being filed in alphabetical order of ship's names. Some official logbooks of these vessels are also held, but only in rare cases were logbooks attached to the crew lists. These records are held in the National Archives under class *BT387: Allied Crew Lists from WW 2.*

Ships logbooks and crew lists 1861 to 1938

A 10% sample of logbooks and crew agreements for the above period are held in the National Archives under class *BT99: Agreements and Crew Lists, Series II.* A further 80% of the records are held at the Maritime History Archive, Canada. Most of the remaining logbooks, for years which end in the figure 5, are held at the National Maritime Museum, Greenwich. The logbooks and crew agreements for the years 1861 to 1913 not held by the above organisations have been deposited in local records offices, a list of which can be supplied by the Registry of Shipping.

Ships logbooks and crew lists 1835-1860

From 1835 onwards the masters of foreign-going British ships over 80 tons were required to carry on board a written agreement with every seaman employed. These included wage rate, the capacity in which the seaman served, and the nature of the voyage. The agreements are held in the National Archives under class *BT98: Agreement and Crew Lists: Series I.* Records prior to 1854 are arranged by the port of registry numbers; later records are held in order of the ship's official number. From 1852 onwards the official logbook of the vessel was filed with the agreement and crew list.

Ships logbooks and crew lists 1747 to 1851

From 1747 to 1851 masters or owners of merchant ships were obliged to keep muster rolls for each voyage. These include names of the seamen employed on the ship, their home address, when they joined ship and the name of the last ship on which they had served. These are held in the National Archives under class *BT98: Agreements and Crew Lists: Series 1.*

Logbooks and crew lists for special ships 1861 onwards

A selection of logbooks and crew agreements from famous ships, for example the *Titanic* and the *Great Britain*, are held in the National Archives under class *BT100: Agreements and Crew Lists Series III.*

Logbooks and crew lists for fishing vessels 1884 to 1919

A 10% sample for fishing vessels of less than 80 tons for the period 1884 to 1919 are held in the National Archives under class *BT 144: Agreements and Crew Lists Series IV.* Later records of fishing vessel are included in BT99 (see above).

First World War logbooks and crew agreements

Logbooks and crew agreements for the period 1914 to 1918 are held in the National Archives under class *BT165: Agreements and Crew Lists.*

Logbooks containing entries of births and deaths at sea 1902-1938

Logbooks containing information concerning births and deaths at sea were segregated. Those for the years 1902 to 1938 are held in the National Archives under class *BT165: Ship's Official Log Books.*

Copyright

Anyone planning to include a reproduction of a logbook or crew agreement or any part of these documents in a publication must obtain written permission from the Registry of Shipping and Seamen. The Registry of Shipping and Seamen should be acknowledged and the full address included on the same page as the document is reproduced.

APPENDIX 2: SHIP REGISTRATION DOCUMENTS
An overview of their origin, content and usefulness by Roy Fenton

Until recently, the owner of every British ship was required to provide up-to-date details to a designated official in his home port, the registrar. A series of registration documents were given to the owner, kept in the local registrar's office, and forwarded to a central authority. This basic system was in place for some 200 years, and the majority of the documentation this generated has survived. For researchers, the registration documents are an invaluable source of precise data on the ownership, build, dimensions and fate of all British merchant ships since the late 18th century.

How the registration system operated
Registration of a ship involved the owners declaring details of themselves, their ship and its master to the registrar. The owner was given a certificate of registration, which was to be kept on board the ship to provide evidence of its British nationality and its tonnage. The details were copied on to a register form kept in the port. These forms were numbered consecutively so the vessel could be identified by its port number, e.g. Glasgow No. 14 of 1872. A copy of the register form, called a transcript, was sent to a central body. This was originally the Customs House in London, but later the Registrar General of Shipping and Seamen was appointed to oversee registration and keep the records centrally. The term 'Customs register' is often used to refer to registration documents, because of the involvement of the Customs House and because the registrar was commonly a customs official.

The owner was required to notify the registrar of any changes in the ship's details. The registrar noted these changes on the certificate and on the office copy of the register form. He also passed details to the central registration body on another form called a transaction. Researchers should be aware of the distinction between a transcript (simply a copy) and a transaction, which notified changes.

When a ship was sold to an owner in another custom's port, its registration was usually cancelled, and the ship re-registered in the new port. The registrar recorded on the old certificate the date and reason it was cancelled or 'closed'. The port and port number of the new registration was added, making it possible to trace a ship's British career from one registration document to another. Registration was also closed when a vessel became a total loss, was hulked or broken up, or sold abroad. Again, the reason was noted on the certificate.

Prior to 1889, ships were often re-registered at the same port if they were altered in some way, such as receiving a different rig or new machinery.

Development of registration documents
The amount of information recorded in registration documents increased over the years, in line with changes in legislation and developments in the technology of ships.

17th century
Registration of British ships began, but few registration papers survive from before 1786.

1786-1825
Registration was compulsory for all British ships of over 15 tons with a deck. The details listed on the register included: ship's name; date and place of registration plus port number, owner's name, occupation and address; master's name; place and date of build; number of decks and masts; length, breadth and depth of hold; tonnage; whether the ship had a figurehead. Changes in ownership were recorded on the certificate of registration issued to the ship.

1825-1854
Ownership of all vessels had to be held in sixty-fourth shares, although it was possible for a single share to be in joint ownership. The registrar had to be notified of any changes in ownership, even of a single share, and of changes of master.

1854-1889
From 1856 each ship was allocated an official number, which remained constant throughout its life as a British ship, even if the ship was sold or renamed.

New registration documents were introduced, which recorded additional details of the ship, including the name of the builder and, for steamships, engine details. A transcript of the form was sent to the central body (now the Registrar General of Shipping and Seamen). Any changes of ownership had to be recorded on the registration form held in the port. They were also reported on a transaction form, which was sent to the Registrar General.

The transcripts and the transactions for this period were filed separately by the Registrar General's office, and they remain separate today in the National Archives. Each transaction was numbered, and the number written on the transcript. The transaction can be traced once the transcript is found, but examining all the transactions for a given ship can be very time consuming. As transactions are bound in the order in which they were received by the Registrar General's office, individual transactions for one vessel may be scattered through many files, which have to be ordered separately. It is not uncommon for a single ship to have 20 or more transactions over a period of as little as ten years, as a transaction was generated by even a minor change such as the transfer of one 64th share.

1890-1955
From 1890 the transcripts and transactions were filed together by the Registrar General of Shipping and Seamen, even if a ship was renamed, or registered at another port. They remain together in the National Archives (Class BT110), along with any surviving registration certificates carried by the ship. The bundling

of the transcripts, transactions and certificates in this way makes research on ships of this period particularly simple for those who are able to visit the National Archives.

1955-date

Only a few of the registration papers for this period have found their way from the Registry of Shipping and Seamen to the National Archives.

Information recorded in registration documents

Although the amount of information recorded on registration documents has fluctuated over the last two centuries, the researcher can expect to find most of the following details on registration forms from the mid-19th century onwards.

Official number

Ship's name. Any previous names are listed, including a foreign name for ships previously owned abroad. Changes of name are recorded on transaction forms, with the date the change was registered.

Port of registry, date of registration and port number. The port numbers were allocated in sequence each year, and are a unique identifier for the ship.

Previous registration, with port, year and port number.

Hull details. Where, in which year and by whom the hull was built.

Rig, material and build

Details of the machinery, including type, number of cylinders, builders of engines and boilers, dates, horsepower, and speed.

Hull dimensions and **tonnage measurements,** showing calculation of the ship's net and gross tonnages, including deductions for machinery and crew spaces. Alterations in dimensions and tonnages, for example as a result of modifications, changes in legislation or because of a new survey were recorded, with dates.

Master's name at date of registration. Details of changes of master were not routinely recorded on the registration forms kept by the registrar or filed centrally, as such changes could take place at any port at which the ship called. However, changes were recorded on the registration certificate carried by the ship. In most cases where this certificate survived (if the ship was lost the certificate was often lost with it), it was returned to the registrar who forwarded it for filing centrally. For the period 1890 to 1955, the surviving certificates are to be found with the transactions and transcripts.

Name, address and occupation of the owner(s) and number of 64th shares held. Changes of

ownership and mortgages taken out on the ship were recorded on separate transaction sheets. These indicate the precise date when the change took place, and the time and date when it was entered in the registration documents. Even the transfer of a single share was recorded. A further form also gave a summary of ownership.

Details of when and why the registry was closed are recorded on the registration documents. When a ship was registered anew, in the same or a different port, details of the new port number were recorded. In cases where the ship was lost, the date and place of the incident is usually noted, but where the ship is sold abroad the only details recorded are the nationality of the buyers. When a ship is broken up or hulked no details of names of breakers or dates of sale are given.

Location of registration documents

Central holdings

The majority of the transcript and transaction forms from 1786 to 1955 are in the National Archives under the class numbers listed below. Catalogues of these files are kept at the National Archives and can also be viewed on their website.

BT107

Transcripts and transactions received between 1786 and 1854.

This series is not complete for ports except London, because many copies were destroyed in a fire in 1814.

BT108

Transcripts for the period 1855 to 1889.

These are bound by year and by port of registry, in order of port number.

BT109

Transactions for the period 1855 to 1889.

These are filed yearly, under the ship's official number. The transactions are numbered, the numbers being recorded on the transcripts in class BT108.

BT110

Transcripts and transactions for the period 1890 to 1955.

For a given ship, all registration documents from 1890 to 1955 are bound together. Thus, the complete history of a British ship between these dates can be traced by looking through just one file

The registration papers are filed in batches of approximately ten years according to the date the ship's register was closed and the name of the ship at that time. To find a given ship's registration papers, it is therefore vital to know when it left the British register and the final name it carried in British ownership. These details are best found from *Lloyd's Register* or the *Mercantile Navy List.*

Ships registered in British and colonial ports are filed in separate series within the BT110 class.

BT111

Indexes to the transcripts received between 1786 and 1854.

CUST 130

The London Customs Registers from 1818 to 1926.

Local holdings

Registration documents kept at the registry ports were bound into books in order of port number. When all the registers in a book had been closed, they were of no further interest to the local registrar, and many have been donated to local libraries, museums and record offices. The entries in this Guide list many such local sources of registration documents.

Researchers should be aware that even very old ledgers remained with the local registration authorities if ships in them were still registered. This may have happened because the owner never bothered to inform the registrar of what became of his ship. It is therefore important to check that the registers for the years required are indeed held by the library, museum or record office listed.

When local registration of ships ceased in the 1990s, the registration documents held by local registrars were transferred to the Registry of Shipping and Seamen. It is understood that these registration documents are in the process of being donated to local libraries, museums and record offices willing to house them.

APPENDIX 3: MARITIME INFORMATION ON INTERNET
Mike Macdonald

Much maritime information, written maritime history and archive and topical material, is stored in digital form on Internet. The availability and ready accessibility of this huge store of information means that an enquirer or maritime researcher is not restricted to manuscript or printed documents held in libraries and archives. Moreover, Internet offers access to sources of maritime information outside the British Isles; in Australia, Canada, New Zealand and the United States of America, for example, and in languages, other than English, of major seafaring nations like Germany, the Netherlands and Norway.

Enquiries on Internet can be started by typing simple terms or keywords into an Internet search engine (e.g. AltaVista, Copernic, Google, Yahoo). These keywords (indicated here by quotation marks; "...") can either be the names of ships, or types of ship, or the names of naval battles or campaigns, or the names of maritime personalities, or terms like "emigrant ships", or "passenger lists". The search engines will display a list of maritime websites which include the keywords in their titles or in the description of their contents.

General information about maritime history on Internet.

As a starting point, try any of the following websites by keying in the terms: "Maritime History on the Internet", "Maritime History & Naval Heritage", "(United States) Department of The Navy - Naval Historical Center" or "Maritime History Virtual Archives". "Maritime History on the Internet" includes pages on researching a ship, researching a person, (maritime) libraries and databases and a webliography of maritime history sources on Internet.

Names of ships.

There are numerous histories of famous ships on Internet: *Arandora Star, Prince of Wales, Rawalpindi*, emigrant ships *Circassia, Conte Rosso,* the barque *Dunedin.* Simply type in the name of the ship, plus a term such as "ship", "liner", "troopship". The websites include descriptions of the ships, their careers and fates, and digital pictures. Some of these websites, e.g., the "Strathallan" site, include descriptions by passengers of life aboard ship. Enquiries by one ship name will often produce a list of websites containing more general maritime history; e.g., links to "Australian Merchant Navy Website", "German Raiders on the Australian Coast", "Liners sunk around the British Isles, 1900-2000", "The Norwegian Merchant Fleet in WWII".

Major maritime incidents/disasters.

Type in the names of the ships involved; e.g. "*Andrea Doria* and/or *Stockholm*" or "*Queen Mary* and/or *Curaçao*" plus "collision" or "accident". Other "disaster" websites include, for example, the "*Fort Stikine*" and "*Mont Blanc*" explosions, and the "*Princess Victoria*" sinking.

Ship types.

Mainly naval or naval auxiliary types; e.g. "Aircraft Carrier", "Armed Merchant Cruiser", "Battleship", "Commerce Raider", "Isles-class Trawler", "Troopships". Websites usually include lists of ships of the class or type, descriptions, careers (including naval actions) and digital pictures. There are websites dedicated to merchant ship types: "World War I standard ships", "T2 tankers", which include full lists of ships of the type and digital pictures.

Naval operations or battles.

Access to these sites can be simply by name of ship; "*Bismarck*", "*Prince of Wales*", or by name or type of operation; e.g., "Destroyers and anti-submarine warfare", "Rheinübung", "Torch", or by name of campaign; e.g., "Arctic Convoys", "Battle of the Atlantic", or by way of the "Campaign Summaries, WW2" website, plus name of the campaign; e.g., "Balkans, Greece & Crete, 1939-1945". There are also websites about naval "personalities"; e.g., "Felix Graf von Luckner", "Werner Hartenstein", "Captain F J (Johnnie) Walker".

Emigrant ships and passenger lists.

Good starting points are either "Passenger Lists on Internet" or the "ShipsList Homepage"; the latter site includes fleet lists, passenger lists, and pages on marriage at sea and diaries and journals of emigrants. "Online Sourcing of Australian Passenger Lists" is arranged by colony, and gives name of ship, arrival date, port of arrival and list of immigrants. There are websites dealing, *inter alia,* with German, Irish and Italian emigration to Australasia and North America.

"East India Company Ships"

It is worth mentioning this website, as it is in a class of its own as an archive website, with a wealth of detail about the East India Company, its seafarers and ships and their voyages.

Websites with archive photographs of ships in digital format.

It is impossible to list them all; simply type in "ship photographs". There are both public archives; e.g. "State Library of Victoria" and "United States Naval Institute" and shipbuilders' archives; "Vickers Photo Archive". There are also contemporary builders' websites; e.g., "Conoship International", "J J Sietas". The latter are promotional sites, advertising the builder's current range of ship types, and usually include digital images, general arrangement drawings and full technical descriptions of the ships. British and European commercial shipping companies have similar sites, advertising their services and the availability of their ships for future trading; these sites are useful for their current fleet lists, and some include potted histories of the company.

Maritime safety.

The "Marine Accident Investigation Branch" and the "Maritime & Coastguard Agency" publish regular reports on maritime safety on Internet. The M&CA website publishes details of recent maritime accidents, and vessels detained by Port State Control in the United Kingdom.

Access to these websites costs no more than a local telephone call to an Internet service provider. Commercial/subscription websites are another matter.

Maritime websites represent "research completed", and they usually contain sufficient information to satisfy a casual enquiry. So much more maritime history research remains to be done, however, that Internet will never entirely supplant maritime archives and libraries as repositories of primary research material.

APPENDIX 4: PASSENGER RECORDS
Debbie Beavis

The only officially compiled documents recording names of passengers travelling in or out of the United Kingdom are held at the National Archives (formerly the Public Record Office) in Kew, Surrey. The largest series of passenger lists dates from 1878. Inbound records dating from earlier years are generally not strictly speaking passenger lists but instead are indexes and returns of the arrival of aliens into Britain, some of whom may have been in transit to overseas destinations. Earlier departure records relate primarily to emigrants from Britain to the New World, many of which have been published.

Early Series

Inbound Records

FO83/21-22	Aliens arriving at British ports between August 1810 and May 1811.
HO5/25-32	Index of Aliens' Certificates of Arrival 1826 to 1849 (the original certificates were destroyed in the 19th Century).
ADM30/35	Passenger lists of HM Steam Packets travelling between Britain and the Mediterranean or between certain ports within the Mediterranean, 1831 to 1834
HO2/	Aliens' Certificates of Arrival, 1836 to 1852.
HO3/	Returns of Aliens compiled by Ship Masters from July 1836 to January 1861 and January 1866 to December 1869.

Outbound Records

E157	Registers of Licences to Pass Beyond the Seas: 1634-1639, (and one for 1677), now published as *Original Lists of Persons Emigrating to America, 1600-1700* [Hotten, London 1874].
CO1	Passengers bound for America, 1630s, found in America and West Indies Colonial Papers.
T47/9-12	Treasury Register of emigrants from Britain to the New World, 1773 to 1776; names and other details of emigrants from England and Wales have been extracted into a card index. This short series also includes some passengers bound for European ports.
ADM30/35	Passenger lists of HM Steam Packets travelling between Britain and the Mediterranean or between certain ports within the Mediterranean, 1831 to 1834.
CO208/269-272	Registers of Cabin Passengers held in New Zealand [shipping] Company Original Correspondence from 1839 - 1850.
CO208/273-274	Applications for Free Passage, 1839 to 1850 also indexed in CO208/275

Board of Trade passenger lists

The largest series of ship passenger lists are those compiled for the Statistical Department of the Board of Trade. It covers the period from 1878 to 1960 by which time the upsurge in air travel (for which no official records were maintained) had rendered the system pointless.

The collection originally contained much earlier material but was severely weeded at the turn of the 19th century and most of the earliest records no longer exist. The exception is a very small number of lists dating from 1878 to 1888 for ships arriving in Queenstown (Cobh) from the United States. The survival rate for lists from 1890, when the main series begins, is excellent and very few lists are missing. It is important however to understand that these records do not contain an exhaustive list of every single passenger who arrived or left on every single ship, and it is important to understand the limitations of the documents.

Inbound

BT26/1	Passenger Lists, Inwards, 1878-1888 and 1890-1960 give the names of all passengers arriving in the UK where the ship's voyage began at a port outside Europe and the Mediterranean Sea. Names of passengers who boarded these ships at European ports and disembarked in the UK should be included in these lists. Passenger lists for ships whose voyages both began and ended within Europe (including the UK and the Mediterranean Sea) are not included.

Outbound

BT27/1	Passenger Lists, Outwards, 1890-1960 give the names of all passengers leaving the UK where the ship's eventual destination was a port outside Europe and the Mediterranean Sea. Names of passengers who disembarked at European ports from these ships should be included in these lists. Passenger lists for ships whose voyages both began and ended within Europe (including the UK and the Mediterranean Sea) are not included. Lists earlier than 1890 have not survived.

Registers of Passenger Lists 1906-1951. (BT32/1-15) These registers recording the date at which passenger lists were received at the Board of Trade and are held at the National Archives as Class BT 32/1-15. It is important to note that no destinations are shown for any ship and, for most of the class, the date of departure or arrival is not shown. The coverage is not complete, the series begins in 1906 with entries for a few ports only, and ends in 1951, far short of the span covered by the main class to which they refer. These records may only be useful if the name of the ship and a rough date is already known.

British lists have not been micro-filmed. Many are in a fragile condition and searching them is time consuming. The information given varies considerably over the period, but can include age, occupation, last address in the UK, (outbound, after 1920) and proposed country of destination. Inbound lists after 1920 will usually include the proposed address in the UK but they do not show a passenger's last address prior to joining the ship. Some lists show the name of the steamship company which brought transmigrants to the UK, and in the case of aliens, by 1907 the lists note the country of which the traveller was a national. In many cases, it will be easier to trace them arriving at their destination than leaving the UK and, due to the time-consuming nature of the British records, enquiries should always first be made in the country of destination, where arrival records may have been indexed or transcribed.

Passenger lists not available

In general, passenger lists do not exist for the following:

Ships travelling between ports in Ireland, Scotland, Wales and England.

Ferries including those on the English Channel, North Sea and Irish Sea.

Feeder ships carrying passengers across the North Sea for onward passage by transatlantic steamers.

Ships sailing between Britain and all European ports, or those which lie on the shores of the Mediterranean Sea, including all islands in the Mediterranean such as Malta unless the ship's voyage started or ended outside that area.

Cruise ships.

Troop ships - although there are some 20th century records for civilian passengers on troop transports.

Ships bound for Britain but which sank before they reached their port. (This means there is no arrival list for the *Lusitania's* last voyage, nor for any other ship which did not arrive at its British destination for whatever reason).

Debbie Beavis, a freelance maritime researcher, can be contacted at marine@beavis.co.uk

INDEX

The index includes subjects referred to in the entries and appendices, and the names of all organizations referred to, including their main entries. Names of ships are in italics, as are titles of publications. Entries are referred to by the alphabetical identifiers (e.g. A.11, C.3) or, for appendices, App.1 to App.4

Index compiled by Elizabeth Wiggans
(elwiggans@onetel.net.uk)